Prentice Hall Brief Review

The Living Environment

John Bartsch / Mary P. Colvard

Ordering Information

Send orders to:
  Pearson
  PO Box 6820
  Chandler, AZ 85246

or call toll free:
  1-800-848-9500
  (8:00 A.M.–6:00 P.M. EST)

School orders:
  k12oasis.pearson.com

Individual orders:
  pearsonschool.com/nybriefreviews

About the Authors

John Bartsch and **Mary Colvard** each have taught high school biology for over 30 years. Their many professional activities include working for the New York State Education Department as Education Specialists and serving the Science Teachers Association of New York State (STANYS) as officers, on the Board of Directors, and on various committees. They were also coordinating biology mentors for the Biology and Chemistry Mentor Network.

Mr. Bartsch has written a chemical safety manual, worked on several writing projects for Pearson, attended and worked as a consultant/instructor for the Cornell Institute for Biology Teachers (CIBT) program, and is a long-time member of both the National Association of Biology Teachers (NABT) and the National Science Teachers Association (NSTA).

Ms. Colvard has developed activities for CIBT, the Howard Hughes Medical Institute Holiday Lectures, and the Cold Spring Harbor Dolan DNA Learning Center. She has also served on the Board of Directors for NABT and on several National Research Council Committees.

Teacher Reviewers and Contributors

Anthony (Bud) Bertino
Canandaigua Academy
Canandaigua, New York

Patricia L. Nolan
Scotia-Glenville High School
Scotia, New York

Elise Russo, Ed.D.
Administrator for Secondary Curriculum
Amityville Union Free School District
Amityville, New York

Content Reviewer

Jerry Sanders

Acknowledgments begin on page I-4 and constitute an extension of this copyright page.

ISBN-13: 978-1-4182-9216-4
ISBN-10:   1-4182-9216-8

Brief Review in
The Living Environment

New York Standards

Standard Key Idea

4.2.1

Performance Indicator

4.1 Intro	4.1.2d	4.1.2h
4.1.2a	4.1.2e	4.1.2i
4.1.2b	4.1.2f	4.1.2j
4.1.2c	4.1.2g	4.1.3a

4.1.2c	4.5.1f	4.5.2g
4.1.2d	4.5.1g	4.5.2h
4.5 Intro	4.5.2a	4.5.2i
4.5.1a	4.5.2b	4.5.2j
4.5.1b	4.5.2c	4.5.3a
4.5.1c	4.5.2d	4.5.3b
4.5.1d	4.5.2e	
4.5.1e	4.5.2f	

4.2 Intro	4.2.1g	4.2.2c
4.2.1a	4.2.1h	4.2.2d
4.2.1b	4.2.1i	4.2.2e
4.2.1c	4.2.1j	4.3.1c
4.2.1d	4.2.1k	4.3.1d
4.2.1e	4.2.2a	
4.2.1f	4.2.2b	

4.4 Intro	4.4.1e
4.4.1a	4.4.1f
4.4.1b	4.4.1g
4.4.1c	4.4.1h
4.4.1d	

4.3 Intro	4.3.1f	4.3.1l
4.3.1a	4.3.1g	
4.3.1b	4.3.1h	
4.3.1c	4.3.1i	
4.3.1d	4.3.1j	
4.3.1e	4.3.1k	

4.1 Intro	4.6 Intro	4.6.1g
4.1.1a	4.6.1a	4.6.2a
4.1.1b	4.6.1b	4.6.2b
4.1.1c	4.6.1c	4.6.3a
4.1.1d	4.6.1d	4.6.3b
4.1.1e	4.6.1e	4.6.3c
4.1.1f	4.6.1f	

New York Standards

4.7 Intro	4.7.2b
4.7.1a	4.7.2c
4.7.1b	4.7.3a
4.7.1c	4.7.3b
4.7.2a	

1.1.1a	1.2.1	1.3.2
1.1.1b	1.2.2a	1.3.3
1.1.1c	1.2.3a	1.3.4a
1.1.2a	1.2.3b	1.3.4b
1.1.2b	1.2.3c	1.3.4c
1.1.3a	1.2.4	1.3.5a
1.1.3b	1.3.1a	1.3.5b
1.1.4a		

Appendix A: Bullets 5, 9–17

Appendix A: Bullets 1–8

Separate Teacher Answer Key Contents:

Teacher Strategies/Explanations of Topic Openers

Diagnostic Tests with Answers

Topic Quizzes with Answers

Answers to Review Questions

Answers to Regents Exam Practice Questions

About This Book

This book is designed to enhance review of the concepts, skills, and applications of The Living Environment Core Curriculum that may be tested on the Living Environment Regents Examination. For nearly all students, passing this examination will be a requirement for graduation from high school.

Features

Content Review

The Regents Examination will be based entirely on the content and understandings specifically addressed by The Living Environment Core Curriculum. **For the most part, any material *not* addressed in the core curriculum is not included in this book.**

Vocabulary Many exam questions require an understanding of the language of biology.

Bold Words Bold-type terms listed at the beginning of a topic are defined within. These terms are likely to appear on the exam.

Underlined Words Underlined terms are either words that appear as bold in other topics or that describe basic biological concepts, or are words commonly used in discussions of science concepts.

Real-world Examples Many real-world examples are included to reinforce content understandings. Use these examples or others of your choosing to answer questions on the exam. The examples you choose demonstrate your understanding of the content as well as your ability to apply these understandings to the real world.

Sidebars

Memory Jogger Recalls relevant information covered elsewhere in this book or previous science courses.

Digging Deeper Goes beyond what you need to know to help you better understand the required material.

Review Questions Questions similar to those on the exam, totaling more than 400, appear throughout each topic to clarify and reinforce understanding.

Practice Questions for the New York Regents Exam

A total of more than 300 practice questions are written and organized for each topic in the format of the exam.

Part A Multiple-choice questions test knowledge of concepts.

Part B Both multiple-choice and constructed-response questions test understandings and skills.

Part C These questions often require extended constructed responses with more detailed answers supported by applications or examples. Each question is worth one point as indicated by the [1] at the end of each item or bullet.

Reference and Support

Strategies for Answering Test Questions Support to help you interpret and answer the range of exam questions.

Appendix *NY State Required Laboratory Activities* Information regarding the skills, content, and types of questions you can expect to find on Part D of the Regents Examination.

Glossary Defines all bold vocabulary words and underlined words appearing in the topics.

Index Cross-references concepts in the topics.

Regents Examinations

The most recent released Regents Examinations are reproduced at the end of this book to provide practice in taking actual Regents Examinations.

Answer Key with Diagnostic Tests   A separate Answer Key includes all answers to the Review and Practice Questions plus topic-by-topic Diagnostic Tests to help determine which concepts require more intense review and Topic Quizzes for quick assessment with different questions.

Strategies for
Answering Test Questions

This section provides strategies to help you answer various types of questions on The Living Environment Regents Examination. Strategies are provided for answering multiple-choice and constructed-response questions as well as for questions based on diagrams, data tables, and graphs. For each type of question, practice questions are provided to show you how to apply the strategies to answer specific questions.

Strategies for Multiple-Choice Questions

Multiple-choice questions account for more than 50 percent of The Living Environment Regents Examination. Part A is totally made up of multiple-choice questions, and Parts B and D include some. Therefore, it is important to be good at deciphering multiple-choice questions. Here are a few helpful strategies. For any one question, not all strategies will need to be used. The numbers are provided for reference, not to specify an order (except for Strategies 1 and 2).

1. Always read the entire question, but wait to read the choices. (See Strategy 4.)

2. Carefully examine any data tables, diagrams, or photographs associated with the question.

3. Underline key words and phrases in the question that signal what you should be looking for in the answer. This will make you read the question more carefully. This strategy applies mostly to questions with a long introduction.

4. Try to think of an answer to the question before looking at the choices given. If you think you know the answer, write it on a separate piece of paper before reading the choices. Next, read all of the choices and compare them to your answer before making a decision. Do not select the first answer that seems correct. If your answer matches one of the choices, and you are quite sure of your response, you are probably correct. Even if your answer matches one of the choices, carefully consider all of the answers, because the

obvious choice is not always the correct one. If there are no exact matches, re-read the question and look for the choice that is most similar to your answer.

5. Eliminate any choices that you know are incorrect. Lightly cross out the numbers for those choices on the exam paper. Each choice you can eliminate increases your chances of selecting the correct answer.

6. If the question makes no sense after reading through it several times, leave it for later. After completing the rest of the exam, return to the question. Something you read on the other parts of the exam may give you some ideas about how to answer this question. If you are still unsure, go with your best guess. There is no penalty for guessing, but answers left blank will be counted as wrong. If you employ your best test-taking strategies, you just may select the correct answer.

Practice Questions

1. Most of the oxygen that enters the atmosphere results from the process of

   (1) respiration   (3) excretion
   (2) photosynthesis   (4) digestion

Explanation of Answer Use strategy 5. Eliminating choices 3 and 4 may be easy, but think about the other two choices carefully before choosing your final answer. Be sure that you are not confusing respiration with photosynthesis. The correct answer is choice (2), photosynthesis.

2. Cellular respiration in humans occurs in

   (1) red blood cells, only
   (2) the cells of the lungs, only
   (3) the cells of the digestive system, only
   (4) all the cells of the body

Explanation of Answer Use strategy 4. Note that the question is asking where cell respiration occurs in humans. Your answer before reading the choices should say that respiration occurs in all of the cells of the body or that respiration occurs in the mitochondria. All of the choices are different types of cells. Think about what cell respiration is, and why cells respire. Lung cells and red blood cells help obtain and carry oxygen, but cell respiration is a process that releases energy in *all* cells. Therefore, the correct answer is choice (4), all the cells of the body.

---

3. A number of white potato plants are grown by placing pieces of one potato in the ground. This method of reproduction is most similar to

(1) sexual reproduction
(2) cloning
(3) genetic engineering
(4) zygote formation

Explanation of Answer Use strategy 5. You should be able to eliminate choices 1 and 4, since both are related to the same form of reproduction. The fusion of sex cells (during sexual reproduction) results in the formation of a zygote. Since there can be only one correct answer, these will not work. Genetic engineering refers to the manipulation of genes leading to the development of new combinations of traits and new varieties of organisms. Since only one parent (potato) is involved, the genetic makeup of the new potato plants will be the same as the original plant. Therefore, cutting up a potato and planting the pieces is most like choice (2), cloning. This is a form of asexual reproduction in which all offspring are genetic copies.

---

4. Overexposure of animals to X-rays is dangerous, because X-rays are known to damage DNA. A direct result of this damage is cells with

(1) unusually thick cell membranes
(2) no organelles located in the cytoplasm
(3) abnormally large chloroplasts
(4) changes in chromosome structure

Explanation of Answer Use strategy 3. As you read this question, underline key words: Overexposure of <u>animals</u> to <u>X-rays</u> is dangerous, because X-rays are known to <u>damage</u> <u>DNA</u>. A <u>direct</u> <u>result</u> of this damage is cells with (4) changes in chromosome structure. You should know that chromosomes are composed of DNA molecules and that X-rays can cause mutations, which are changes in DNA and/or chromosome

structure. Choices 1, 2, and 3 can be eliminated, since even if they could occur, it would not be a *direct* *result* of the <u>DNA</u> being <u>damaged</u>.

Strategies for Constructed–Response Questions

Some questions in Parts B and D, and all questions in Part C of The Living Environment Regents Examination require a constructed response. Some of these questions require you to write one or two words, while others require much more. Students who use complete sentences when appropriate tend to have more organized answers. As a result, they usually get higher scores. Remember, someone other than your teacher will be reading your answers and scoring your paper. Make your answers clear!

No matter which type of answer is requested, the following strategies will help you write constructed responses.

1. Always read through the entire question.

2. Underline key words and phrases in the question that signal what you should be looking for in the answer. This will make you read the question more carefully.

3. Write a few notes to yourself, about what should be included in the answer.

4. Pay attention to key words that indicate how to answer the question and what you need to say in your answer. Several of these words are very common. For example, you might be asked to identify, describe, explain, state, compare, contrast, or design. The table on the next page lists key words and directions for your answers.

5. When you write your answer, don't be so general that you are not really saying anything. Be very specific. You should use the correct terms and clearly explain the processes and relationships. Be sure to provide details, such as the names of processes, names of structures, and, if it is appropriate, how they are related. If only one example or term is required, do not give two or more. If one is correct and the other is wrong, your answer will be marked wrong.

Using Key Words to Direct Your Answers	
Key Word	**What Direction Your Answers Should Take**
Analyze	• Break the idea, concept, or situation into parts, and explain how they relate. • Carefully explain relationships, such as cause and effect.
Compare	• Relate two or more topics with an emphasis on how they are alike. • State the similarities between two or more examples.
Contrast	• Relate two or more topics with an emphasis on how they are different. • State the differences between two or more examples.
Define	• State the exact meaning of a topic or word. • Explain what something is or what it means.
Describe	• Illustrate the subject using words. • Provide a thorough account of the topic. • Give complete answers.
Discuss	• Make observations about the topic or situation using facts. • Thoroughly write about various aspects of the topic or situation.
Design	• Plan an experiment or component of an experiment. Map out your proposal, being sure to provide information about all of the required parts.
Explain	• Clarify the topic of the question by spelling it out completely. • Make the topic understandable. • Provide reasons for the outcome.
State	• Express in words. • Explain or describe using at least one fact, term, or relationship.

6. If a question has two or three parts, answer each part in a separate paragraph or bullet. This will help the person scoring your paper find all of the information. Don't risk losing credit for one part of the question by spending too much time on another part. Check to be sure you have an answer for *each* of the questions!

7. Whenever it is appropriate, answer in complete sentences. A sentence should always have a subject and a verb, and not start with the word *because*. Note that you will not lose points for incorrect grammar, spelling, punctuation, or poor penmanship. However, such errors and poor penmanship could impair your ability to make your answer clear to the person scoring your paper. If that person cannot understand what you are trying to say, you will not receive credit for the question.

Practice Questions

5. State one safety precaution that a student should use when heating liquid in a test tube. [1]

Sample Answer When heating liquid in a test tube, the student should wear safety goggles.

6. The diagram below shows the setup of an experiment.

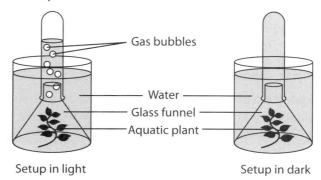

Setup in light　　　　　　Setup in dark

State a problem that could be investigated using this experimental setup. [1]

Sample Answer Is light needed for photosynthesis?

Tip Note that "State a problem" here really means to state a question. You are not expected to describe a problem (fault) with this setup.

7. The diagram below shows two ways in which grains, such as wheat or corn, can provide food for humans.

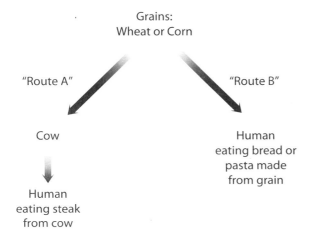

Grains:
Wheat or Corn

"Route A"   "Route B"

Cow   Human
                   eating bread or
                   pasta made
                   from grain

Human
eating steak
from cow

Select which "Route ," A or B, involves the least energy loss and explain why this is true. [1]

Hint You should have underlined the words "Select which Route" and "explain why", to be clear on what your answer must include. If you do not identify the route, you could lose credit for the question, even though you correctly explained why.

Scoring Guide Teachers are provided with Scoring Guides and Sample Answers to use when rating your answers. Often there are several correct answers to a question. Here is an example of what teachers would use to score question 7:
[1] Allow 1 credit for Route B and explaining why this is true. Acceptable responses include, but are not limited to:
• Route B involves the least energy loss because some energy is lost at each step on a food chain.
• Route B because the energy goes directly from the corn to the human, so less is lost. That is not the case with Route A.

8. Provide two reasons why it is important to preserve biodiversity. [1]

Scoring Guide and Sample Answers Allow 1 credit for *two* correct reasons. Acceptable responses include, but are not limited to:
• Biodiversity ensures the availability of a variety of genetic material.
• Biodiversity may allow us to find plants or animals that could be used as new medicines.
• Biodiversity helps an ecosystem remain stable.
• A lot of tropical plants may contain chemicals people can use to cure cancer or HIV.
• Loss of species from an ecosystem could disrupt the food web.

Hint Very few questions will ask for a two part answer like this one, but if you get one, be sure to give two reasons, or you will not receive credit.

Base your answers to questions 9 through12 on the information and paragraph below and on your knowledge of biology.

It is possible to collect human sperm and to use this sperm later to fertilize eggs in a process called *artificial insemination*. The collected sperm samples are frozen and stored in a sperm bank until needed. When a woman makes use of a sperm bank, she requests sperm from a donor with the physical features she wants for her baby. The name of the donor is not revealed. The artificial insemination process involves placing the sperm in the woman's body and allowing fertilization to occur in the normal manner.

9. A woman whose husband cannot produce sperm becomes pregnant through artificial insemination. Explain how the baby's DNA will compare to the DNA of the woman and her husband. [1]

10. If a woman were given sperm from the same donor for three different pregnancies, and she had three daughters, would the three girls look alike, or would they be different? Support your answer. [1]

11. A developing embryo must be protected from harmful environmental factors. Identify one way a pregnant woman could avoid exposing the developing embryo to environmental risks. [1]

12. Artificial insemination is also used on animals. State one benefit farmers or animal breeders gain from using artificial insemination. [1]

Scoring Guide For questions 9 through 12:

9. Allow one credit. Acceptable responses include, but are not limited to:

- The baby received DNA from the mother, but none from the mother's husband.

- The baby's DNA sequence would have much (one half) in common with the mother's DNA sequence, but it would have no specific resemblance to the DNA of the woman's husband.

10. Allow 1 credit for stating that the girls would not look alike and explaining why they would not look alike. Acceptable responses include, but are not limited to: ·

- The girls would look different from each other, since they came from different eggs and sperm, each containing unique DNA information.

11. Allow 1 credit. Acceptable responses include, but are not limited to:

- Do not drink alcohol/do drugs.

- Do not smoke.

- Do not eat an unhealthy diet.

12. Allow one credit. Acceptable responses include, but are not limited to:

- They could breed animals that live far apart without transporting them to the same location.

- It would be cheaper than buying an animal to breed with other animals on the farm.

- One animal could produce hundreds of off-spring with desired traits in many different locations in a short period of time.

Strategies for Questions Based on Diagrams

Both multiple-choice and constructed-response questions frequently include diagrams or pictures. Usually the diagrams provide information needed to answer the question. The diagrams may be realistic, or they may be a representation of how parts interact or show a sequence of events that occurs in a system.

Practice Questions

Base your answer to questions 13 and 14 on the diagram below and on your knowledge of biology.

The diagram illustrates one possible pattern in the evolution of several groups of animals.

- **First, study the diagram.** Ask yourself what the diagram is about and what it shows you. Read the title or description provided, if there is one.

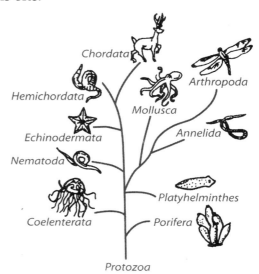

You are told that the diagram represents a possible sequence of events in the evolution of a number of organisms. Based on the illustration, you see that *Protozoa* are the common ancestor of all the other animals shown. It also indicates that *Porifera, Platyhelminthes, Nematoda,* and *Coelenterata* existed before *Echinodermata, Hemichordata, Chordata, Arthropoda, Annelida,* and *Mollusca.* The diagram also shows that *Platyhelminthes* and *Nematoda* are very closely related, as are *Arthropoda, Annelida,* and *Mollusca.*

You need to know that the closer the point of branching, the more closely related the organisms. The farther apart the point of branching, the more distant the relationship.

- **Second, read the question.**

13. Which inference does the diagram best support?

(For this type of question, it is difficult to try to anticipate what the correct answer might be. Carefully read each of the choices, one at a time, and see if they make sense by looking back at the diagram. As you do this, eliminate any choices you can.)

(1) Members of the animal kingdom are more complex than members of the plant kingdom.
(2) Members of the animal kingdom and members of the plant kingdom share common ancestry.
(3) Chordates are more closely related to arthropods than to echinoderms.
(4) Members of the group *Echinodermata* and the group *Annelida* share a common ancestor.

Explanation of Answer There is no information provided about plants by the diagram; you can eliminate choices 1 and 2 based on what you see here or even on what you have learned during the year.

According to the diagram, chordates are more closely related to *Echinodermata* than they are to *Arthropoda*—the opposite of what choice (3) states—because *Echinodermata* branches off the same line that chordates are on. Arthropod ancestors branched before that.

The correct answer is (4), Members of the group *Echinodermata* and the group *Annelida* share a common ancestor. All of the animals on this evolutionary diagram share a common ancestor—*Protozoa.*

14. Which two groups of organisms in the diagram are shown to be the most closely related?

(Before reading the choices provided, think about how you could tell which organisms are most closely related (by two organisms being close together on one branch). Then apply this to eliminate obviously wrong choices. Do not select the first answer that seems correct.)

(1) Porifera and Echinodermata
(2) Chordata and Platyhelminthes
(3) Mollusca and Annelida
(4) Arthropoda and Coelenterata

Explanation of Answer Choices 1, 2, and 4 have separate branches and are widely separated. Therefore, these choices can be eliminated. *Mollusca* and *Annelida* are the only two groups that share a common side branch on the diagram. Therefore, the correct answer is (3), *Mollusca* and *Annelida.*

- **First, study the diagram for Question 15.** This illustration shows a rabbit and a plant giving off CO_2 and taking in O_2 from the environment. This analysis of the illustration indicates that materials are being cycled through the environment.

- **Second, read the question.**

15. Which ecological principle is best illustrated by the following diagram?

(Before reading the choices provided, think about the diagram and what the question is asking. It seems that the ecological principle illustrated here has something to do with cycles in the environment. As you read the choices, eliminate any choices that you can.)

(1) In an ecosystem, material is cycled among the organisms and their environment
(2) In ecosystems the number of producers and consumers is always equal.
(3) Competition within a species results in natural selection.
(4) An ecosystem requires a constant source of energy.

Explanation of Answer Ecosystems normally contain more producers than consumers but this varies. The number of each is not "always" equal so choice 2 is incorrect. Choices 3 and 4 are not addressed by the illustration. It does not show competition within the rabbit species. There is no energy source shown in the diagram, nor is the ecosystem requirement for a constant energy source illustrated. Therefore, you would probably select the correct answer as being choice (1), In an ecosystem, material is cycled among the organisms and their environment.

- **First, study the diagram for Question 16.** Ask yourself what the diagram is about and what it shows you. It shows CO_2 and H_2O entering, and sugar and O_2 leaving. The illustration seems to have something to do with photosynthesis, since CO_2 and H_2O are raw materials and sugar and O_2 are products.

- **Second, read the question.**

16. The diagram represents some events that take place in a plant cell. With which organelle would these events be most closely associated?

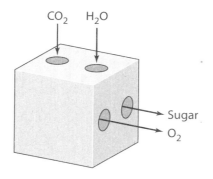

(Before reading the choices provided, write what you think the answer should be on a separate piece of paper. Then compare your answer to the choices provided.)

(1) mitochondrion   (3) ribosome
(2) chloroplast   (4) vacuole

Explanation of Answer Mitochondria are associated with cellular respiration, ribosomes with protein synthesis, and vacuoles with storage. Since this diagram illustrates photosynthesis, which occurs in chloroplasts in plant cells, the correct answer is choice (2).

Note: If you realized that the process was either photosynthesis or respiration but weren't sure which one, you at least could narrow your choices to 1 and 2 and improve your chances of guessing the right one.

Base your answers to questions 17 and 18 on the information below, and on your knowledge of biology.

The map was drawn by an ecologist. It represents the vegetation around a small pond in a forest located in New York State.

KEY Open water   Forest
      Shallow water containing Wet area with grass
      pond plants   and cattails

- **First, study the diagram.** Think about what the diagram shows you. Did you read the information at the top of the illustration?

If you were approaching the pond from the forest, you would walk through trees, then wet areas with tall plants, such as cattails and grasses. The ground would be wet and squishy. Next, you would enter shallow water in which many rooted plants grow. From this point, open water would be visible. The water would be much deeper, and you would probably not be able to walk but would need to swim or use a boat. There are many different questions you could be asked about this diagram.

- **Second, read the questions.**

17. Describe one specific way this environment would be likely to change if it were left undisturbed by humans for 100 years. [1]

Sample Answers The pond environment will probably fill in, leaving mostly forest.

OR

The species present in the nonforest communities will disappear, and forest plants and animals will replace them.

Explanation of Answers Both answers relate to the idea of ecological succession. All ecosystems progress through a series of changes during which one community modifies the environment, making it more suitable for another community. The organic matter from decaying vegetation will gradually fill the pond.

---

18. Identify two organisms in this ecosystem that are producers. [1]

Sample Answers and Scoring Guide Allow 1 credit for correctly identifying *two* organisms in this ecosystem that are producers. Acceptable responses include, but are not limited to:

- cattails and grass
- trees and pond plants

Explanation of Answer Producers are organisms that are capable of taking inorganic raw materials from the environment and synthesizing their own food. Plants are producers. *Be sure you only identify plants from this ecosystem, not just any producer organism.*

Strategies for Questions Based on Data Tables

Most data tables contain information that summarizes a topic. A table uses rows and columns to condense information and to present it in an organized way. Rows are the horizontal divisions going from left to right across the table, while columns are vertical divisions going from top to bottom. Column headings name the type of information included in a table. Sometimes different categories of information are listed down the left-hand column of the table.

Examine the sample data table below. It provides information collected during an old study of the death rates of policy holders of a large life insurance company.

Before attempting to answer any questions based on the data, go through the following steps:

Deaths as a Result of Disease		
Cause of Death	Deaths per 100,000 People	
	1911	1957
Tuberculosis	224.6	6.7
Communicable disease	58.9	0.1
Cancer	69.3	136.2
Heart disease	156.4	256.2

1. Find the title of the table. It is usually located across the top. What is the title of the sample table? (Answer: Deaths as a Result of Disease)

2. Determine the number of columns in the table and their purpose. Do this for the sample table. (Answer: There are three columns. They show the causes of death and deaths per 100,000 people during the years of 1911 and 1957.)

3. Determine the number of rows and their purpose. Do this for the sample table. (Answer: There are four rows. The rows provide you with the number of deaths due to tuberculosis, communicable diseases, cancer, and heart disease.)

4. Read across the rows and down the columns to determine what the relationships are. Do this for the table shown. Notice how the numbers of deaths changed for each disease between 1911 and 1957. Some decreased and some increased.

Now you are ready to read the question with the sample data table and answer it.

19. The study most clearly indicated that during the time period examined

(1) cancer of the lungs was increasing
(2) people were living longer
(3) children were safer from communicable diseases
(4) better housing reduced deaths from tuberculosis

Explanation of Answer Choice 1 doesn't work because even though cancer death rates increased from 69.3 to 136.2 per 100,000, there is no way to tell what type or types of cancer caused the difference. Choice 2 is not correct because you have no information about how long people were living in either 1911 or 1957. Choice 4 is not correct because no information is provided about what caused the decrease in deaths due to tuberculosis. You only know that the death rate decreased from 224.6 in 1911 to 6.7 per 100,000 in 1957. The correct answer is choice (3), children were safer from communicable diseases. The number of those deaths decreased from 58.9 per 100,000 in 1911 to 0.1 per 100,000 in 1957.

Practice Questions

Base your answers to questions 20 and 21 on the information below and on your knowledge of biology.

A dog was placed in a special room free of unrelated stimuli. On repeated trials, a tone was sounded for 5 seconds; approximately 2 seconds later, the dog was given food. Trials 1, 10, 20, 30, 40, and 50 were test trials; that is, the tone was sounded for 30 seconds and no food was given. The following data were collected:

Data Table		
Test Trial Number	Drops of Saliva Secreted	Number of Seconds Between Onset of the Tone and Salivation
1	0	—
10	6	18
20	20	9
30	60	2
40	62	1
50	59	2

20. The greatest increase in the number of drops of saliva secreted occurred between test trials

(1) 1 and 10   (3) 20 and 30
(2) 10 and 20   (4) 30 and 40

Explanation of Answer The increase for choice 1 amounted to 6 drops, since it increased from 0 drops to 6 drops between Test Trial Numbers 1 to 10. Choice 2 resulted in an increase of 14 drops, since Test Trial Number 10 resulted in 6 drops, while Test Trial Number 20 resulted in 20 drops. The difference is 14 drops. Choice (4) only resulted in an increase of 2 drops. The correct answer is choice (3), 20 to 30. The number of drops of saliva secreted increased from 20 in Test Trial 20 to 60 in Test Trial 30, for an increase of 40 drops of saliva.

21. At test trial 60, the number of drops of saliva secreted would probably be closest to

(1) 75   (2) 55   (3) 35   (4) 25

Explanation of Answer Choice 1 is wrong, since it shows a large increase. Choices 3 and 4 are incorrect, because the decrease in number of drops is very large. These numbers do not fit the trend shown in the data table. The correct answer is choice 2, because the number of drops of saliva secreted between trials 30 and 50 has been changing slowly and at trial 50 has started to go down.

Strategies for Questions Based on Graphs

Graphs represent relationships in a visual form that is easy to read. Three different types of graphs commonly used on science Regents examinations are line graphs, bar graphs, and circle graphs. Line graphs are the most common, and they show the relationship between two changing quantities, or variables. When a question is based on any of the three types of graphs, the information you need to correctly answer the question can usually be found on the graph.

When answering a question that includes a graph, first ask yourself these questions:

- What information does the graph provide?
- What are the variables?
- What seems to happen to one variable as the other changes?

After a careful analysis of the graph, use these strategies along with the other strategies you have learned:

- Read the question.
- Read each of the possible answers and consider which is the correct choice by referring to the graph.

Practice Questions

Use the graph below to answer questions 22 and 23.

Genetic Diversity in Corn and Wheat Varieties

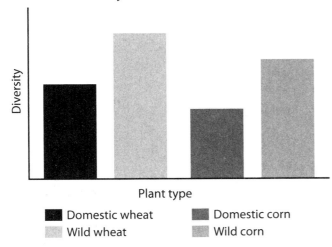

Plant type

- ■ Domestic wheat
- ■ Domestic corn
- ▨ Wild wheat
- ▨ Wild corn

22. Which types of plants represented on the graph have the greatest diversity?

(1) wild wheat and wild corn
(2) wild wheat and domestic corn
(3) domestic wheat and wild corn
(4) domestic wheat and domestic corn

Explanation of Answer Choices 2, 3, and 4 do not work, because they each contain one or more of the domestic plant types that do not extend as high on the diversity scale. The correct choice is (1), wild wheat and wild corn. The bars for wild wheat and corn extend higher on the diversity scale than the others.

23. If the environment were to change dramatically or a new plant disease affecting both corn and wheat were to strike, which of the plant types would be most likely to survive?

(1) wild wheat   (3) wild corn
(2) domestic wheat   (4) domestic corn

Explanation of Answer To be able to answer this question correctly, you need to know two things. First, biodiversity increases the stability of an ecosystem. Second, the diversity of species increases the chance that some will survive in the face of environmental changes. Therefore, the bar representing the plant with the greatest diversity would be the best choice for an answer. For that reason, the correct answer is choice (1), wild wheat.

24. Which statement best describes the relationship between enzyme action and temperature shown in the graph below?

(Remember to first study the graph in order to determine what it is about and what information it gives you about the variables. Then read the question and analyze the choices by referring to the graph.)

(1) Enzyme synthesis begins at 30°C.
(2) Enzyme activity constantly increases with increasing temperature.
(3) The pH has a greater effect on this enzyme than temperature does.
(4) Enzyme activity increases as the temperature increases from 22°C to 34°C.

Explanation of Answer Choice 1 is not correct since the graph tells you nothing about enzyme synthesis. The graph starts to show data at 30°C, but shows nothing about synthesis. Choice 2 is wrong, because enzyme activity does not continue to increase. It starts to decrease rapidly at about 37°C. Choice 3 is incorrect, since there is no mention of pH anywhere on the graph. The correct answer is choice 4. If you follow the graph line, it does show an increase in relative rate of enzyme activity as the temperature increases from 22°C to 34°C.

Similarities and Differences Among Living Organisms

What do You Think?

Body Systems at Work

Blood vessels in organs of the digestive system pick up nutrients such as glucose, starch, and protein and transport them to cells.

Blood vessels in the respiratory system pick up oxygen and drop off carbon dioxide and water.

Blood vessels in organs of the excretory system drop off wastes from cells and food that was not digested.

Similarities and Differences Among Living Organisms

Vocabulary

active transport	excretion	organelle
amino acids	homeostasis	organic
cell	hormone	receptor molecule
cell membrane	immunity	reproduction
cell respiration	inorganic	respiration
chloroplast	metabolism	ribosome
circulation	mitochondria	simple sugars
cytoplasm	nucleus	synthesis
diffusion	organ	tissue
digestion	organ system	vacuole
enzymes		

Topic Overview

Earth's living environment is made up of millions of diverse organisms, from towering redwood trees, sleek antelope, and mushrooms that grow in huge circles, to microscopic bacteria, one-celled organisms that turn the tides red, and the students in your class.

These living organisms are both similar to and different from each other. They also differ from the nonliving parts of the environment. Although that difference may seem obvious, scientists have not been able to agree upon a simple definition of life.

The Characteristics of Life

Although there is no simple definition of life, most scientists agree that living things share certain characteristics that distinguish them from nonliving things.

- Living things are organized structures. All are made of one or more **cells,** which are the basic units of structure and function. They maintain their cellular organization throughout life.
- Living things use energy to maintain life and to grow and develop. These activities require that the cells carry out various chemical reactions. The combination of all the chemical reactions that occur in an organism is called **metabolism.**
- Living things maintain a fairly stable internal environment even when their external environment changes dramatically. The maintenance of this internal stability is known as **homeostasis.** To maintain homeostasis, organisms must respond and adapt to both their internal and external environments.

- Living things pass hereditary information to new organisms of the same type in the process of **reproduction**.

Only living things share the characteristics of life. Nonliving things have no functioning cells and no metabolic activity; they do not maintain homeostasis, nor do they reproduce.

Diversity Among Living Things

Although living things share the characteristics of life, there are differences among the many kinds of organisms. Throughout history, people have tried to bring order to all the varieties of life on Earth by grouping, or classifying, them. Several classification systems have been popular at different times. As we learn more about the similarities among organisms and how they carry out their life processes, classification systems change. Currently, biologists classify organisms into kingdoms, which are large groups of related organisms.

Similarities Among Living Things

Although living things have many differences, they are also alike in important ways. The first similarity is that they share the characteristics of life. They are made of cells, reproduce, maintain homeostasis, and carry out metabolic activities. They also share similar life processes, chemical composition, and organization.

Life Processes Living things are similar in that they rely on a variety of specific processes to maintain life. Organisms may differ in the way they carry out these processes, however. Some of these life processes include

- obtaining nutrients from the environment and breaking them down for transport
- transporting materials throughout the organism
- breaking nutrients into smaller units to release the chemical energy stored in them through the process known as **cell respiration**
- combining simple substances into complex substances during the process known as **synthesis**
- increasing the size or number of cells through the process of growth
- removing waste products from the organism through the process known as **excretion**
- responding to internal and external stimuli
- reproducing more of their own species

Chemical Composition All living things are made of four main elements—carbon, hydrogen, oxygen, and nitrogen—as well as many other elements in smaller amounts. The elements combine to form molecules.

Organic molecules contain BOTH carbon and hydrogen. Organic molecules include all of the major molecules of life: structural molecules, such as those in cell walls and membranes, as well as biologically active molecules, such as the enzymes that help carry out the chemical reactions of life. DNA, protein, fats, and carbohydrates—such as glucose ($C_6H_{12}O_6$) and starch—are **organic** molecules.

Digging Deeper

Many scientists do not include viruses with living things. The reason is that viruses are not cells. Instead they are made only of protein and genetic material. As a result, viruses do not independently carry out all processes of life. To reproduce, they must invade the cell of a living organism.

Inorganic molecules do *not* contain *both* carbon and hydrogen, but can contain any other combination of elements. Inorganic molecules include salts and minerals, most acids and bases, oxygen (O_2), carbon dioxide (CO_2), and water (H_2O), the most abundant substance in any organism.

Organization The shared organization of specialized structures that work together to accomplish a specific task is another similarity of living things. In other words, organisms share a similar "building plan." The basic structural and functional unit of living things is the cell.

Simple organisms may consist of just one cell; complex organisms may consist of billions of cells. Most cells contain specialized structures called **organelles,** which have specific life maintenance functions.

This organization of cells into increasingly specialized structures is the basis for much of the complex life on Earth. Complex organisms have several advantages over simpler organisms. For example, many complex organisms can explore their environment or gain energy in ways that simpler organisms cannot. In Figure 1-1, notice that the organizational structure of organisms resembles a pyramid with a base of cells.

In multicellular organisms, groups of specialized cells may be grouped into **tissues** to expand how they function. For example, a single muscle cell would not be strong enough to move any organism—not even one as light as a hummingbird. Grouped with other muscle cells, however, muscle tissue can move an elephant.

Different kinds of tissues may be combined to form an **organ** that performs one of the life processes. Several organs may work together as an **organ system** that also performs one of the life processes. For example, the heart is an organ with the function of pumping blood. The organ may be a simple "arch" like the heart of the earthworm, or it may be a complex four-chambered structure like the heart of a monkey. In either case, the organ's function is to pump blood. Each heart is part of an organ system that transports materials throughout the body.

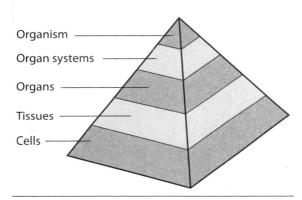

Organism
Organ systems
Organs
Tissues
Cells

Figure 1-1. The structural organization of organisms

Review Questions

Set 1.1

1. State two ways in which a single-celled organism, such as an amoeba, and a human body cell are alike. *Respiration and have organs, in amoebas case organelles.*

2. One characteristic of all living organisms is that they

   (1) make food
   (2) live on land
   (3) maintain homeostasis
   (4) move from place to place

3. Which sequence is listed in order from simplest to most complex?

   (1) tissue → cell → organ system → organ
   (2) cell → tissue → organ → organ system
   (3) cell → tissue → organism → organ
   (4) organism → tissue → organ → organ system

4. A student brings a specimen and claims it is a living organism. Explain how a microscope could be used to determine if the specimen is a living thing.

5. A biologist would most likely study all of the chemical activities of an organism to obtain information about the organism's

(1) number of mutations
(2) reproductive cycle
(3) development
(4) metabolism

6. Cells are to tissues as organs are to

(1) organ systems   (3) genes
(2) cells   (4) organelles

7. The ability of an organism to maintain internal stability is known as

(1) metabolism   (3) circulation
(2) homeostasis   (4) excretion

8. State two ways living and nonliving things differ.

9. Which statement about cells is *not* true?

(1) One or more cells make up all living organisms.
(2) Cells carry on the basic life functions of living organisms.
(3) Cells contain structures that carry on life functions.
(4) Most cells cannot reproduce.

10. Living things are made mostly of these four main elements:

(1) hydrogen, oxygen, nitrogen, and protein
(2) water, protein, carbohydrate, and fat
(3) carbon, hydrogen, oxygen, and nitrogen
(4) glucose, salt, mineral, and base

Cells: The Basic Structure of Life

Many of the world's organisms are made of only one cell, but all organisms—no matter how simple or complex—are made of cells. Each cell contains a jellylike substance surrounded by a thin membrane. Most cells also contain organelles that perform specific tasks for the cell. Despite their seemingly "simple" structure, cells carry out the processes of life and function together in a coordinated manner.

Inside the Cell

The jellylike substance inside the cell is known as the **cytoplasm**. The cytoplasm contains specialized structures, transports materials through the cell, and is the site of many chemical reactions associated with the cell's metabolism.

Organelles Organelles are formed of many different molecules and vary in size, shape, and function. They interact to transport materials, extract energy from nutrients, build proteins, dispose of waste, and store information. Figure 1-2 shows several vital organelles.

Nucleus The **nucleus** is a large structure that controls the cell's metabolism and stores genetic information (DNA in chromosomes). Many people think of the nucleus as the cell's "control center" because it directs the cell's activities.

Vacuoles The storage sacs within the cytoplasm are **vacuoles.** They may contain either wastes or useful materials such as water or food. Some vacuoles are specialized to digest food; others pump excess water out of the cell. Vacuoles in plant cells are usually a lot larger than the vacuoles in animal cells, as shown in Figure 1-2.

Ribosomes The cell contains many tiny structures, called **ribosomes,** that are important to the process of making protein. Some ribosomes are attached to membranes in the cell. Others float in the cytoplasm.

(A) A typical plant cell

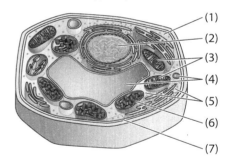

(1)
(2)
(3)
(4)
(5)
(6)
(7)

(B) A typical animal cell

(1)
(2)
(3)
(4)
(5)

(7)

Figure 1-2. Some parts of plant and animal cells: (1) cytoplasm, (2) nucleus, (3) mitochondria, (4) vacuoles, (5) ribosomes, (6) chloroplast, (7) cell membrane.

Memory Jogger

Bacteria cells contain no nucleus; their genetic material simply floats in the cytoplasm as a large chromosome. Some bacteria have smaller loops of DNA as well.

Mitochondria Mitochondria are pod-shaped structures that contain special proteins, known as **enzymes,** used to extract energy from nutrients. Mitochondria are sometimes called the cell's powerhouses because they release most of the cell's energy.

Chloroplasts The green structures found in plants and some one-celled organisms are **chloroplasts.** They contain the green pigment chlorophyll and capture light energy, which is then used to produce food for the plant. Animal cells do not contain chloroplasts.

Review Questions

Set 1.2

11. Which structure is the boundary between a living cell and its environment?

(1) cell membrane
(2) cytoplasm
(3) vacuole
(4) ribosome

12. The structures labeled A, B, C, and D in the diagram below represent

(1) organelles
(2) organs
(3) nuclei
(4) mitochondria

13. The cell nucleus functions

(1) in obtaining energy for the cell
(2) in the storage of digestive enzymes
(3) as the center of control for cell metabolism and reproduction
(4) in the transport of materials throughout the cell

14. The genetic material of an animal cell is found in the

(1) nucleus
(2) cytoplasm
(3) ribosomes
(4) vacuole

15. In the diagram below, structure A is most probably a

(1) mitochondrion   (3) vacuole
(2) ribosome   (4) nucleus

16. Current evidence indicates that ribosomes are most closely associated with

(1) contraction of the cytoplasm
(2) production of DNA
(3) synthesis of protein
(4) regulation of mitosis

17. Mitochondria are organelles that

(1) store digestive enzymes
(2) package cell products
(3) release energy from nutrients
(4) manufacture cell protein

18. Which cell organelles are most closely associated with energy changes in a plant?

(1) mitochondria and chromosomes
(2) chloroplasts and mitochondria
(3) chromosomes and nucleus
(4) chloroplasts and nucleus

19. Which is the most accurate statement concerning protein synthesis in cells?

(1) Proteins are synthesized by mitochondria in all living cells.
(2) Proteins are synthesized at the ribosomes in all living cells.
(3) Proteins are synthesized at the ribosomes in plant cells only.
(4) Proteins are synthesized by nuclei in animal cells only.

The Cell Membrane

The **cell membrane** is a thin structure that surrounds the cell. It is made mainly of fats (lipids), with some proteins embedded throughout. Some of the functions of the cell membrane include

- separating the contents of the cell from the outside environment
- controlling the transport of materials—including waste products—into and out of the cell
- recognizing and responding to chemical signals

Maintaining Separation Cells are organized internally. Without the cell membrane, this organization would be lost.

Unlike animals, plants and most bacteria and fungi have a cell wall outside the cell membrane. This wall of plant cells is made of nonliving material (a carbohydrate called cellulose) that surrounds the cell and gives it strength and rigidity. If the plant gains too much water, its membranes could burst. The cell wall helps prevent this.

Controlling Transport In and Out of the Cell If the cell is to survive, the membrane cannot totally separate the cell from its environment. Some materials, such as water, oxygen, and nutrients, must pass through the membrane and into the cell. Other materials, such as waste products, must pass out of the cell. Molecules can enter or leave a cell through either diffusion or active transport.

Diffusion Molecules are constantly in motion. As they jiggle, they bump into one another, then bounce away like bumper cars at an amusement park. In time, the molecules will have bumped and bounced until they are evenly distributed. The result is that the concentration of molecules in any container remains approximately the same everywhere in the container.

However, when the concentration of molecules is greater in one part of a substance, molecules will spread into areas where their concentration is lower. This movement of molecules from areas of high concentration to areas of low concentration is called **diffusion.** (See Figure 1-4.) Because diffusion results from the normal jiggling of molecules, it requires no outside energy. It is like sledding downhill.

Many molecules diffuse into and out of cells. One of the most important of these molecules is water. The diffusion of water into and out of cells is important to the maintenance of homeostasis. For example, plant cells maintain a stable balance of water and dissolved minerals. This is typically about 98% water and 2% dissolved materials. When salt is spread on roads and walkways, that balance changes. The runoff water from these salted roads may reach concentrations of 5% salt (which means only 95% water). Damage can occur when water in the plant cells diffuses from the higher (98%) concentration in the cell to the lower (95%) concentration outside the cell. Under these conditions, the loss of water places serious stress on the plant. In some cases the plant may die.

Active Transport Moving a molecule from an area of low concentration to an area of high concentration is like pulling a sled uphill. (See Figure 1-5.) It requires energy. Cells must use energy from ATP to transport molecules

Proteins

Fats (lipids)

Figure 1-3. **The cell membrane**

Figure 1-4. **Diffusion:** These molecules are moving from an area of high concentration to an area of low concentration.

Figure 1-5. **Active transport:** These molecules are moving from an area of low concentration to an area of high concentration.

from areas of low concentration through the cell membrane to areas of high concentration. The process is called **active transport.**

Many desert plants use active transport to bring water (which is at low concentrations in the soil) into root cells where the water concentration is higher. Some pond organisms use active transport to "collect" calcium or other minerals that are in very low concentrations in the pond water.

Molecules in Cells Both organic and inorganic substances are dissolved in cells and are involved in the chemical reactions that maintain life. Some organic molecules, such as proteins and starches, are too large and complex to enter the cell. Large molecules must first be broken down into simpler molecules in the process known as **digestion**.

The digestion of proteins results in smaller molecules of **amino acids;** the digestion of starches results in **simple sugars.** Digestion is vital because only small molecules, such as amino acids and simple sugars, can enter blood vessels or cells.

When some nutrients from our food enter a cell, they become the building blocks of compounds necessary for life. This process, called cell synthesis, is like manufacturing. Simple molecules (such as amino acids and sugars) are assembled or reassembled into more complex molecules of proteins, starches, DNA, or other substances necessary for life.

Not all nutrients are used as building blocks. Some nutrients that enter a cell are broken down even more to release the energy stored in their chemical bonds. This is the process of cell respiration. All of these processes will be reviewed in detail in later topics.

Recognizing Signals Scientists have learned that certain protein molecules in the cell membrane can receive chemical messages from other cells. These molecules are called **receptor molecules.**

When cells are part of a larger organism, receptor molecules play an important role in the interactions between cells. As shown in Figures 1–6 and 1–7, chemicals produced in the endocrine glands—**hormones**—and chemicals produced by nerve cells are primarily responsible for communication between cells. If nerve or hormone signals are blocked, cellular communication is interrupted, and the organism's homeostasis may be affected.

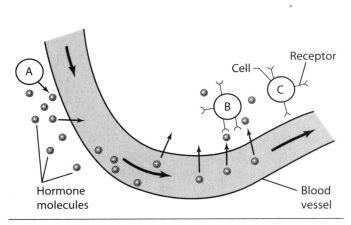

Figure 1-6. Receptor molecules: Specific receptor molecules on the membranes of some cells detect hormones that stimulate the cell to respond. In this case, only cell B (not cell C) will respond to the hormone from cell A.

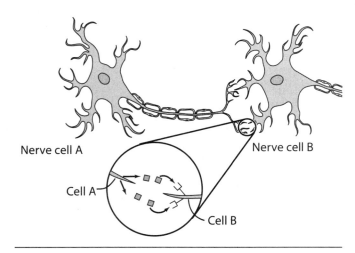

Figure 1-7. Receptor molecules: Nerve cells secrete chemicals that signal adjacent nerve, muscle, or gland cells. These secretions are detected by specific receptor molecules on cell membranes.

20. Defective receptor proteins on a cell membrane have the *least* effect on

(1) homeostasis   (3) nerve signals
(2) muscle activity   (4) diffusion

21. In the following diagram, nerve cell A is communicating with nerve cell B. Identify the structures present on the membranes of nerve cell B that enable it to detect a message from nerve cell A.

22. Which process accomplishes the movement of gases illustrated by the arrows in the diagram?

(1) excretion   (3) active transport
(2) diffusion   (4) chemical digestion

23. In both plant and animal cells, the cell membrane

(1) produces enzymes
(2) controls reproduction
(3) is composed of sugars
(4) regulates diffusion

24. Since the relative concentration of water in the pond in which a paramecium (a single-celled organism) lives is greater than the concentration of water in its cytoplasm, water molecules constantly move from the pond into the paramecium. The best long-term solution to the problem of maintaining a stable internal environment is for the paramecium to

(1) change the water into carbon dioxide and excrete it
(2) store water molecules
(3) incorporate water molecules into its structure
(4) actively transport water molecules out of its cell

25. A biologist diluted a blood sample with distilled water. While observing the sample with a microscope, she noted that the red blood cells had burst. This bursting is most likely the result of which process?

(1) staining   (3) digestion
(2) diffusion   (4) active transport

26. A student using a compound light microscope to study plant cells observed that most of the cells resembled the one shown in the following diagram.

Which diagram best illustrates how the plant cell will appear after being placed in a solution that has a lower water concentration than the cell?

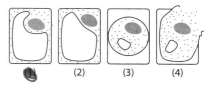

27. Amino acids tend to diffuse from a blood capillary to the adjacent cell because

(1) this is the only direction they can move
(2) the brain directs the movement into cells
(3) the cell needs the amino acids to make protein
(4) the concentration of amino acids is lower in the cell

28. In the following diagram of a plant cell, the small circles represent water molecules.

Which statement *best* describes the behavior of most of these water molecules?

(1) They move from region A to region B.
(2) They move from region B to region A.
(3) They do not move in either direction.
(4) Their overall movement is equal in both directions.

29. Nutrients that are not used as building blocks for the cell may be broken down to release the energy stored in their chemical bonds. This process, which provides cells with energy, is called

(1) chemical synthesis   (3) digestion
(2) cell respiration   (4) homeostasis

30. Cytoplasm in a plant cell will shrink if the cell is

(1) placed in a concentrated salt solution
(2) kept warm and moist and in medium light
(3) placed in distilled water
(4) exposed to a different concentration of nitrogen gas

31. The diagram below represents a cell in water. Formulas of molecules that can move freely across the membrane are shown. Some molecules are located inside the cell and others are in the water outside the cell.

Based on the distribution of molecules, what would most likely happen to these molecules after a few hours?

(1) The concentration of $C_6H_{12}O_6$ will increase inside the cell.
(2) The concentration of CO_2 will increase outside the cell.
(3) The concentration of NH_3 will increase inside the cell.
(4) The concentration of O_2 will increase outside the cell.

32. A cell containing 98% water in its cytoplasm is placed in a 2% salt solution. It should

(1) lose water
(2) gain water
(3) neither lose nor gain water
(4) gain salt because of the high rate of diffusion

33. A cell is placed in distilled water and then transferred to a 5% salt solution. As a result of this procedure, the cell would be likely to

(1) get larger
(2) get smaller
(3) get larger, then smaller
(4) get smaller, then larger

34. A high concentration of calcium salts is normally found within the cytoplasm of a certain protozoan, while the surrounding environment contains a lower concentration of the calcium salts. The higher concentration in the protozoan is most probably the result of

(1) diffusion   (3) active transport
(2) excretion   (4) cellular dehydration

35. A student prepared a normal wet mount slide of an *Elodea* leaf and observed it with a compound microscope. He then made drawing A from his observations. His second drawing, B, shows his observations of the same cell after it was mounted in a 5% salt solution.

The results are most fully explained by

(1) loss of water from the cell
(2) entrance of water into the cell
(3) shrinkage of the cell wall
(4) entrance of salt into the cell

Multicellular Organisms

Multicellular organisms can be highly complex. They require multiple organs and systems to complete their life processes. These systems must interact to maintain the life of the organism.

Human Body Systems

Humans are complex organisms. Their specialized cells must interact to maintain life. Humans require a variety of organs and organ systems to complete the life processes of digestion, respiration, circulation, excretion, movement, coordination, immunity, and reproduction.

Digestion The human digestive system, shown in Figure 1-8, is a one-way passage through the body. This passageway includes the mouth, stomach, and intestines as well as other organs.

Food enters the body through the mouth and is moved slowly through the system by muscular contractions. The food never actually enters the body tissue. Instead, it is broken down both mechanically (by chewing) and chemically. This produces molecules that are small enough to pass through cell membranes and that can be transported to wherever nutrients can be used by the body. Undigested food is eliminated from the body as solid waste.

Respiration The process of **respiration** uses oxygen to break down food molecules to release energy. The function of the respiratory system is the exchange of gases between the blood of the circulatory system and the environment. The system takes in oxygen for cell respiration and transfers it to the blood. It also removes carbon dioxide—a waste of cell respiration—from the bloodstream and releases it from the body. As shown in Figure 1-9, the lungs and nose are parts of the respiratory system.

Circulation **Circulation** involves the movement of materials inside the cell as well as the movement between parts of a multicellular organism. The function of the human circulatory system, shown in Figure 1-10, is to transport materials throughout the body.

The system carries digested food and oxygen to cells. It also carries wastes from the cells to the lungs, kidneys, and the skin for excretion. The blood vessels of the system also carry chemical messengers (hormones) and the proteins that attack foreign substances to give the body immunity (antibodies). The human circulatory system includes the heart, blood vessels, and blood.

Excretion Many people confuse the process of excretion with the removal of the waste products of digestion. **Excretion,** however, is actually the removal of all the waste produced by the cells of the body. The human excretory system, shown in Figure 1-11, includes the lungs and kidneys as well as the sweat glands in the skin.

Movement Movement of the body involves the interaction of muscles and bones. The muscular and skeletal systems, shown in Figure 1-12, work together to provide movement and support for the body. These body systems make it possible for the organism to avoid danger and to find food, mates, and shelter.

Coordination The nervous system and endocrine system, shown in Figure 1-13, control the coordination of many of the body's activities. Together these systems respond to and send messages to cells throughout the body.

The nervous system sends signals along nerves. The glands of the endocrine system produce chemical messengers (hormones) that travel in the bloodstream. The brain and nerves are part of the nervous system. The endocrine system includes several glands—such as the pancreas and ovaries or testes.

Immunity The immune system increases the body's **immunity**—its ability to resist disease. Some white blood cells of the immune system engulf and

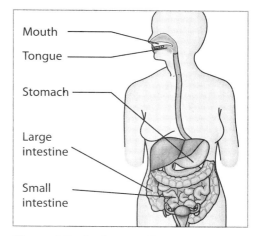
Figure 1-8. The human digestive system

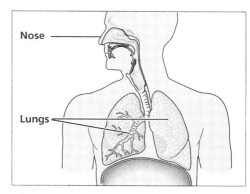
Figure 1-9. The human respiratory system

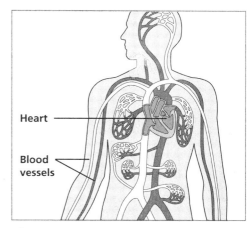
Figure 1-10. The human circulatory system

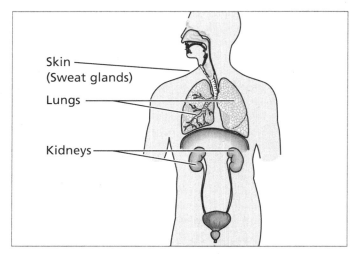

Figure 1-11. The human excretory system

Skin
(Sweat glands)

Lungs

Kidneys

Figure 1-12. The human muscular (A) and skeletal systems (B): The bones provide support; the muscles allow movement.

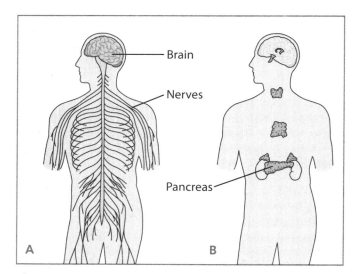

Brain

Nerves

Pancreas

Figure 1-13. The human nervous (A) and endocrine (B) systems

destroy invading bacteria and viruses by digesting them. Others protect the body against specific foreign invaders.

Reproduction The process by which organisms produce new organisms of the same kind is called **reproduction.** The reproductive system releases sex cells and hormones that are critical to the creation of offspring and the regulation of their development. The human reproductive system allows for sexual rather than asexual reproduction. Sexual reproduction makes it possible for two individuals to produce offspring that are of the same species but not exactly like either parent.

Interactions for Life Processes and Regulation

Like all organisms, the human body's systems continually interact to perform life processes. Examples of these interactions may involve several systems.

- Nutrients from the digestive system are transported to cells by the circulatory system.
- The functioning of the reproductive system is regulated by hormones from the endocrine system.
- Body systems also continuously interact to maintain a balanced internal environment (homeostasis). To successfully accomplish this, humans and other complex organisms have a variety of control mechanisms that constantly monitor and correct deviations that could throw the body's internal environment off balance. Examples of these control systems include the regulation of body temperature and blood sugar level.
- When body temperature drops, nerve impulses from the brain signal the muscles to shiver, which generates heat and warms the body.
- Blood sugar level is constantly monitored, and hormones are released as needed to keep it at acceptable levels.

If any organ or organ system does not function properly, the entire organism may fail to maintain homeostasis. The result may be disease or even death. For example, if the heart fails to beat regularly, the circulation of blood will be affected. This may result in a failure of certain materials (oxygen, for example) to flow throughout the body. Without oxygen, cells may stop functioning and death may result.

Comparing Single-celled and Multicellular Organisms

The organelles of single-celled organisms are far less complex than organ systems of multicellular organisms. However, organelles and organ systems are equally capable of completing metabolic activities. For example, the paramecium in Figure 1-15 has a specialized organelle—the food vacuole—that digests food. The human digestive system is more complex and also digests food. The organelle and organ system accomplish the same function: breaking down nutrients so that they can be used by the organism.

Table 1-1 shows examples of life functions that are handled by organelles in single cells and by organ systems in multicellular organisms.

Comparing Humans and Other Organisms

In most biological respects, humans are like other organisms.

- Humans have much the same chemical composition as other organisms. All organisms—from bacteria to tulips to humans—are made of mainly carbon, hydrogen, oxygen, and nitrogen. These elements combine in different ways and amounts to form carbohydrates, proteins, and other essential organic molecules.

- Humans are made up of different kinds of cells that are similar to those found in other animals. For example, human muscles, nerves, and blood cells are similar in structure and function to the muscles, nerves, and blood cells of other complex animals—from geese to gorillas.

- Humans have organ systems and physical characteristics similar to many other complex animals. For example, worms, frogs, and pigs have digestive systems that break down large food molecules. They also have systems that circulate blood. Pig hearts, in fact, are so similar to human hearts that they can be used for transplants.

- Humans reproduce in the same way as many other organisms. For example, fish, amphibians, reptiles, birds, and mammals reproduce sexually; the sperm and egg cell combine, each contributing half of the genetic information to the offspring.

- Humans use the same kind of genetic information as other organisms. Like nearly every living organism—from *E. coli* bacteria and fruit flies to roses and dogs—humans use DNA as their genetic material.

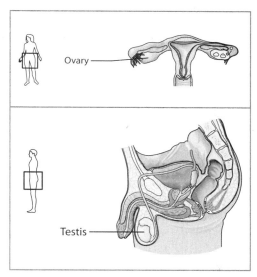

Figure 1-14. The reproductive systems of the human male and female

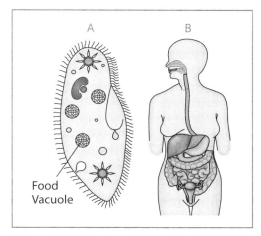

Figure 1-15. Single-celled and multicellular function: The food vacuoles in a one-celled organism (A) are much simpler than the human digestive system (B), but they still digest the organism's food.

Table 1-1. The Function of Organelles in Single Cells and Organ Systems in Multicellular Organisms		
Function	**Single Cell**	**Multicellular Organism**
Gas exchange	Cell membrane	Respiratory system
Transport of substances	Cytoplasm	Circulatory system
Nutrition	Specialized vacuoles	Digestive system
Excretion	Cell membrane	Excretory system

36. Organisms remove metabolic cellular wastes by the process of

(1) excretion
(2) absorption
(3) coordination
(4) digestion

37. A similarity between the nervous system and the hormone-secreting system in humans is that they both

(1) are composed of the same type of cells
(2) are composed of many glands
(3) help to maintain homeostasis
(4) secrete chemicals directly into the blood

38. The diagram below shows an air sac surrounded by the thin-walled blood vessels of a human lung.

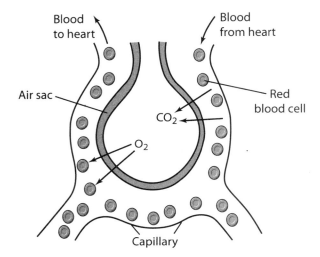

Which two body systems are interacting in the diagram?

(1) respiratory and coordination
(2) respiratory and circulatory
(3) digestive and circulatory
(4) reproductive and coordination

39. Finding shelter, avoiding predators, and obtaining food are most closely related to the ability of an animal to

(1) use structures adapted for movement
(2) increase the rate of mitosis
(3) transport carbon dioxide to cells
(4) excrete waste products of metabolism

40. Which letter in the diagram below indicates a cell structure that functions primarily in the synthesis of protein?

(1) A   (2) B   (3) C   (4) D

41. Inhaling carbon monoxide reduces the ability of red blood cells to carry oxygen. This can lead to brain damage. Which three systems of the body interact in this situation?

(1) digestive, respiratory, and circulatory
(2) immune, circulatory, and digestive
(3) respiratory, circulatory, and nervous
(4) excretory, nervous, and respiratory

42. The activity of all human body systems is coordinated by

(1) the secretion of hormones and the nervous system
(2) the interaction of nerve impulses with the excretory system
(3) the movement of digested food by the circulatory system
(4) the secretion of hormones and the circulatory system

43. Which two systems are most directly involved in providing molecules needed for the synthesis of fats in human cells?

(1) digestive and circulatory
(2) excretory and digestive
(3) immune and muscular
(4) reproductive and circulatory

44. Organ systems of the human body interact to maintain a balanced internal environment. As blood flows through certain organs of the body, the composition of the blood changes because of interactions with those organs. State one change in the composition of the blood as it flows through the respiratory system. [1]

Directions

Review the Test-Taking Strategies section of this book. Then answer the following questions. Read each question carefully and answer with a correct choice or response.

Part A

1 A few bacteria are placed in a nutrient solution. After several hours, thousands of bacteria are present. Which life activities are primarily responsible for this?
   (1) digestion and movement
   (2) digestion and reproduction
   (3) circulation and respiration
   (4) excretion and coordination

2 Mitochondria are organelles that
   (1) are necessary for the process of diffusion to take place
   (2) are found in the nucleus of some cells
   (3) initiate cell division in living cells
   (4) contain respiratory enzymes

3 Most of the enzymes found in the mitochondria are involved in the reactions associated with
   (1) extracting energy from nutrients
   (2) storing energy in nutrients
   (3) DNA production
   (4) protein synthesis

4 Which statement best describes a cell membrane?
   (1) It is found only in animal cells.
   (2) It is a nonliving structure.
   (3) It controls reproduction in a cell.
   (4) It controls the passage of materials into the cell.

5 The transfer of specific molecules through cell membranes is an important factor in the process of
   (1) cytoplasmic flow   (3) homeostasis
   (2) mitotic division   (4) nuclear transfer

6 After a cookie has been eaten and digested, sugar molecules enter the bloodstream by the process of
   (1) active transport   (3) excretion
   (2) diffusion   (4) cellular respiration

7 The concentration of nitrates is often higher in plant roots than it is in the soil around them. Plants maintain this difference in concentration through
   (1) active transport   (3) excretion
   (2) diffusion   (4) coordination

8 In the diagram of root cells below, in which direction would the net flow of water be the greatest as a result of diffusion?
   (1) A to C
   (2) A to B
   (3) B to C
   (4) C to B

Key
○ = Water molecule

9 Diagrams A and B represent two slide preparations of *Elodea* leaves (an aquatic plant).

Elodea leaf mounted in tap water

Elodea leaf mounted in 6% salt solution

The tap water used contained 1 percent salt and 99 percent water, while the salt solution contained 6 percent salt and 94 percent water. *Elodea* cells normally contain 1 percent salt. Ten minutes after the slides were prepared, a microscopic examination of cells in leaves A and B would most likely show evidence that
   (1) water had moved out of the cells of leaf B
   (2) salt had moved out of the cells of leaf B
   (3) water had moved into the cells of leaf A
   (4) salt had moved into the cells of leaf A

10 One reason a fish that lives in the ocean may have trouble living in a freshwater lake is that
   (1) there are more carnivores in freshwater habitats
   (2) salt water holds more dissolved nitrogen than fresh water
   (3) more photosynthesis occurs in fresh water than in salt water
   (4) water concentration in the fish is affected by salt levels in its environment

11 Refer to the diagram below of a beaker with a membrane dividing it into two halves containing two kinds of molecules.

Which process explains the change in the positions of molecules after five hours?
(1) respiration
(2) photosynthesis
(3) diffusion
(4) excretion

12 Most of the reactions by which energy from sugars is released for use by the cell takes place within the
(1) vacuoles
(2) nuclei
(3) ribosomes
(4) mitochondria

13 The diagram below shows how an animal is organized.

Which label is needed to complete the diagram?
(1) atoms   (3) organelles
(2) molecules   (4) tissues

14 Two organs are considered to be a part of the same body system if the organs
(1) are located next to each other
(2) work independently of each other
(3) work together to carry out a life function
(4) are made up of cells with organelles

15 During exercise, the heart beats faster to
(1) carry digestive juices to the small intestine
(2) provide muscles with additional oxygen
(3) lower the blood pressure
(4) digest more food

16 The ability to avoid danger is possible because of the life process of
(1) excretion
(2) reproduction
(3) nutrition
(4) movement

17 The diagram below shows several organs of the human body.

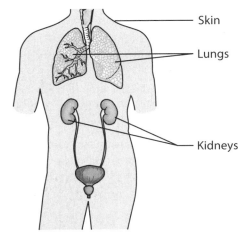

All of these organs interact to help carry out the
(1) removal of waste products
(2) digestion of food
(3) production of hormones
(4) coordination of body movements

18 The circulatory system helps to maintain homeostasis by interacting with the
(1) nervous system and transporting chemicals produced by nerve cells from one cell to another
(2) respiratory system and producing oxygen for gas exchange
(3) digestive system by removing undigested food from the stomach
(4) excretory system in helping to regulate body temperature through sweating

19 In the diagram of the ameba (a single-celled organism), the arrows show the direction of movement of various substances.

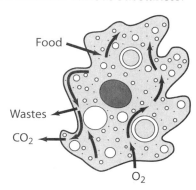

Which of the cell's life activities are represented by the arrows?
(1) digestion, reproduction, and respiration
(2) excretion, transport, and respiration
(3) immunity, digestion, and movement
(4) digestion, coordination, and reproduction

20 All cells are able to continue living because of their ability to
(1) produce food
(2) excrete wastes
(3) produce offspring
(4) produce hormones

21 Which structure in a cell corresponds with the function of the human lungs?
(1) nucleus
(2) vacuole
(3) cell membrane
(4) mitochondria

Part B

22 A scientist wanted to know whether the cells of a particular single-celled green algae could survive without any mitochondria. The scientist removed all of the mitochondria from hundreds of these cells. All of the cells died.

Explain the most likely reason the green algae could not survive without mitochondria. [1]

Base your answers to questions 23 and 24 on the information below and on your knowledge of biology.

Cell communication involves a cell detecting and responding to signals from other cells. Receptor molecules play an important role in these reactions. Human cells have insulin receptors that are needed for the movement of glucose out of the blood.

23 State one way that the shape of the insulin receptor is related to its role in cell communication. [1]

24 A typical human liver cell can have over 90,000 insulin receptors. If a genetic error occurred, resulting in each liver cell in a person having only 1,000 insulin receptors, what specific effect would this have on the liver cells? [1]

25 If vegetables become wilted, they can often be made crisp again by soaking them in water. However, they may lose a few nutrients during this process.

Using the concept of diffusion and concentration, state why some nutrients would leave the plant cell. [1]

26 Describe *one* specific example of diffusion in the human body. In your description be sure to:

• identify the place where your example of diffusion occurs [1]
• identify a substance that diffuses in your example [1]
• state where that substance diffuses from and where it diffuses to, at the place you identified above [1]

Part C

27 A student claims that a dead cell can still carry out diffusion and active transport.

Explain why this claim is not entirely correct. In your answer be sure to explain why a dead cell can or cannot carry on

• diffusion [1]
• active transport [1]

28 Skin cells from a pond animal and skin cells from a land animal were placed in a solution with a 0.85% concentration of salt. When examined later, the cells of the pond animal had swollen and burst, while the cells of the land animal had shrunk.

Explain why the cells responded as they did. In your answer be sure to explain why

- the pond animal cells swelled and burst [1]
- the land animal cells got smaller [1]

29 People sometimes use large quantities of salt to preserve food. The salt kills bacteria that would otherwise cause the food to spoil. Based on your knowledge of diffusion, explain how the salt kills the bacteria. [1]

Base your answers to questions 30 through 33 on the information below and on your knowledge of biology.

The heart of an older person or of someone recovering from a heart attack may become severely weakened or damaged. This sometimes leads to a serious condition called congestive heart failure in which the heart muscle is too weak to pump enough blood throughout the body. As a result, the heart may become exhausted. Sometimes it completely stops.

In a recent study, 2647 patients were given medication called beta-blockers that lowered their risk of death by 34 percent over 15 months (compared to patients who did not take the drugs). Another study reached a similar conclusion.

Although beta-blockers have long been used for treating heart attacks and other medical problems, doctors thought them too dangerous for patients with congestive heart failure. Their reason was that beta-blockers counteract the body's response to adrenaline, a hormone that prepares the body for emergencies by attaching to receptors on heart muscle cells, stimulating the heart to beat faster. Since beta-blockers attach to these adrenaline receptors too, they keep the adrenaline molecules from making contact. This leads to a slowing of the heart, which would appear to cause a problem for a person whose heart is not pumping blood effectively anyway.

The opposite turns out to be the case. When the heart of a person with congestive heart failure is not pumping enough blood, the body responds by releasing more adrenaline to stimulate the heart. As a result, the heart is overstimulated and works even harder—making it more likely to fail. Since beta-blockers interrupt this destructive cycle, the heart stabilizes.

Doctors hope that once more studies are done, proper use of beta-blockers may eventually save many thousands of lives.

30 Describe how adrenaline is involved in the cell-to-cell communication of a person with congestive heart failure. [1]

31 Label the following parts of the illustration of the heart muscle cell below:
1—beta-blocker molecule [1]
2—adrenaline molecule [1]
3—heart cell receptor [1]

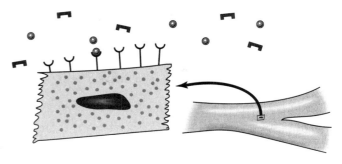

32 Explain how you could tell which objects represent the adrenaline and which represent the beta-blocker in the illustration in question 31. [1]

33 Many drugs have side effects that make them dangerous to some people. For this reason, individuals who take prescription medicine must watch for any unexpected changes in their health.

Based on the information provided in the passage and on your knowledge of biology, describe one possible side effect that might result when people *without* congestive heart failure use beta-blockers. [1]

Homeostasis in Organisms

What do YOU Think?

Respiration and Photosynthesis

Plants don't carry out respiration. They use photosynthesis instead.

At night, plants use oxygen for respiration just like animals, but not during the day.

I think that animals use oxygen and plants use carbon dioxide for the process of respiration.

I think both plants and animals use oxygen for respiration, and they do this day and night.

2 Homeostasis in Organisms

Vocabulary

AIDS	dynamic equilibrium	mitochondria
allergy	enzyme	pancreas
antibiotics	feedback mechanism	parasite
antibodies	fungi	pathogen
antigen	gas exchange	pH
ATP	glucose	photosynthesis
bacteria	guard cells	respiration
biochemical processes	homeostasis	stimuli
catalyst	immune system	synthesis
cellular respiration	insulin	vaccine
chloroplast	microbe	virus
disease		

Topic Overview

All living things—from the simplest single-celled bacteria to the most complex multicellular animals—are organized biological systems. To stay alive, all organisms must keep their biological systems stable even though they live in a changing, and sometimes life-threatening, environment. To maintain this stability, organisms continually monitor and respond to changes in the environment. The internal stability that organisms maintain is known as **homeostasis.**

Homeostasis is the maintenance of internal conditions within a narrow range that varies only slightly over time. For example, your body temperature must stay within a specific temperature range (approximately 98.6°F, or 37°C) for you to survive. If you become too hot or too cold, the biochemical processes that keep you alive will begin to fail.

Digging Deeper

Homeostasis sometimes appears with the words *dynamic equilibrium* or *steady state*. These terms all involve the idea of "a constant balance." To picture this concept, it may help to think of a child learning to balance a bicycle. There may be some wobbling back and forth, but generally the rider remains upright.

Basic Biochemical Processes of Living Organisms

Biochemical processes are the chemical processes that occur in living things. All organisms need both energy and raw materials (atoms and molecules) to carry on the internal biochemical processes that are essential for their survival. Two of these enzyme-controlled biochemical processes are photosynthesis and respiration. **Photosynthesis** is the process by which energy is stored in chemical bonds of organic molecules such as carbohydrates. Plants, algae, and many single-celled organisms carry out photosynthesis. Recall that **respiration** is the process by which chemical energy stored in nutrients is released for use in cells. All living organisms carry out respiration.

Storing Energy: Photosynthesis

The energy for life comes primarily from the sun. In Figure 2-1, notice that photosynthesis is the connection between the energy released by the sun and the energy available to living systems.

The cells of organisms that carry out photosynthesis contain light-capturing molecules. In plant cells, these molecules are located in the **chloroplasts,** which are green-colored organelles where photosynthesis occurs. In Figure 2-2, the chloroplasts are the oval structures. You may have seen these green structures on microscope slides of cells prepared from plant leaves.

All plants, algae, and many one-celled organisms use solar energy to convert inorganic molecules (carbon dioxide and water) into any one of several energy-rich organic compounds. One such organic compound is the sugar **glucose**—a simple carbohydrate.

In the chemical reaction shown in Figure 2-3, notice that water and carbon dioxide from the environment are combined to make glucose. Oxygen gas, which is also formed in the process, is released into the environment.

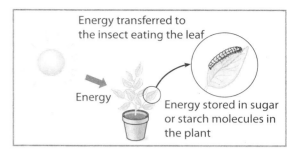

Figure 2-1. Energy transfer: The sun provides energy for most of the life on Earth.

Figure 2-2. Chloroplasts in a typical plant cell: The chloroplasts capture light energy.

light energy + water + carbon dioxide ⟶ glucose + oxygen

light energy + 6 H_2O + 6 CO_2 ⟶ $C_6H_{12}O_6$ + 6 O_2

Figure 2-3. Photosynthesis

What Happens to the Sugar Produced by Photosynthesis? Plant cells use the organic compounds (such as glucose) from photosynthesis in two ways. Their primary use is to generate ATP molecules during **cellular respiration,** which is the process of releasing the energy in chemical bonds. Glucose is also used as a raw material for building more complex molecules, such as those listed in Table 2-1.

Using Glucose to Produce ATP Molecules One way plants (and animals) use glucose is to generate high energy molecules known as **ATP.** This process occurs during cellular respiration. Energy stored in the chemical bonds of ATP molecules is the energy source for almost all life processes from obtaining, transforming, and transporting materials to eliminating wastes. Because cell processes actually "run" on ATP (rather than glucose), the transfer of energy from glucose to ATP is essential to both plants and the

Table 2-1. Complex Molecules and Their Functions	
Molecule	Function
ATP	Supplies energy for cells to run on
DNA	Carries hereditary information
Carbohydrates	Acts as a food reserve molecule
Lipids (fats and oils)	Acts as a food reserve molecule
Protein	Makes up enzymes and many cell parts

organisms that consume them. All organisms—not just plants and animals—use organic food compounds to supply the ATP energy they need to live.

Using Glucose to Build Complex Molecules Cells also use glucose as the starting point for **synthesis** (chemical combining) that forms complex organic compounds. For example, plants store much of the glucose from photosynthesis as starch. Table 2-1 provides some examples of complex molecules and how they are used.

When animals eat plants or other animals, they digest the complex molecules into simpler molecules for their own cells to use. Some of these molecules provide energy for the organism. For example, starches from plants and fats from animals can both be digested and used right away for energy. If they are not all needed for energy, the molecules can be stored as fat to provide a food reserve for the animal.

Table 2-2. Summary of Photosynthesis	
Energy	The energy comes from sunlight as solar energy and ends up in glucose molecules as chemical bond energy.
Materials used	Carbon dioxide gas and water are used; both molecules come from the environment.
Materials produced	Molecules made from the carbon dioxide and water include molecules of the sugar glucose (a simple carbohydrate) and oxygen gas. Oxygen is actually released as a byproduct of photosynthesis.
Time frame	Photosynthesis occurs in plant cells when light is available, which is generally during the daytime.
Location	Photosynthesis occurs in the chloroplasts of plant cells, algae, and some one-celled organisms when they are exposed to light.
Importance of photosynthesis	Organisms either (1) use glucose to synthesize other molecules they need or (2) break down the glucose to release its stored energy.
Relationship to respiration	The energy originally stored in glucose during photosynthesis is transferred to the chemical bonds of ATP. All cells "run" on the energy released from ATP.

Review Questions
Set 2.1

1. In a plant cell, the synthesis of sugar compounds from inorganic raw materials occurs in the
   (1) cell membrane
   (2) mitochondria
   (3) nucleus
   (4) chloroplasts

2. Which word equation represents the process of photosynthesis?
   (1) glucose → alcohol + carbon dioxide
   (2) carbon dioxide + water → glucose + oxygen
   (3) chlorophyll + water → glucose + alcohol
   (4) glucose + oxygen → carbon dioxide + water

3. Which factor *least* influences the rate of photosynthesis?
   (1) atmospheric concentration of carbon dioxide
   (2) time of day
   (3) number of chloroplasts
   (4) concentration of nitrogen in the air

4. The basic raw materials of photosynthesis are
   (1) sugar and carbon dioxide
   (2) oxygen and water
   (3) water and carbon dioxide
   (4) oxygen and sugar

5. Which compound is formed as a common product of the process of photosynthesis?

(1) DNA
(2) sugar ●
(3) chlorophyll
(4) carbon dioxide

6. In the test tube shown, what is produced by the snail that is used by the plant?

(1) oxygen
(2) carbon dioxide ●
(3) food
(4) egg cells

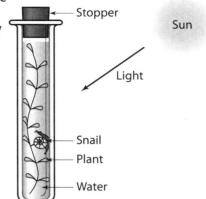

Stopper

Sun

Light

Snail

Plant

Water

7. Which activity occurs during the process of photosynthesis?

(1) Chemical energy from organic molecules is converted into light energy
(2) Organic molecules are absorbed from the environment.
(3) Organic molecules are converted into inorganic food molecules. ●
(4) Light energy is stored as chemical energy in organic molecules.

8. Photosynthesis in plants requires chloroplasts and light energy.
- Identify two raw materials plants also use in this process [1]
- Explain why these two substances are needed [1]

Releasing Energy: Cell Respiration

All living things need energy to stay alive. Before the energy in the bonds of complex carbohydrates, such as starch, can be used, the molecules must be broken down (digested) into simpler ones, such as glucose.

Then, the glucose (or other simple molecules) must be broken down further. This process involves a series of chemical reactions controlled by **enzymes,** which are special proteins that affect the rate of chemical reactions.

In the final step, the chemical bonds of the glucose molecule are broken, and the energy in those bonds is released. This process of releasing the energy in chemical bonds is called cellular respiration.

In many organisms, cellular respiration requires oxygen, which must be brought into the organism from the environment. Obtaining oxygen from the environment and releasing carbon dioxide is called **gas exchange.**

During cellular respiration, cells capture much of the energy that is released from the glucose bonds. The captured energy is then used to form new bonds in high-energy molecules known as ATP. Figure 2-4 shows how ATP temporarily stores energy. Most of the energy that the cell fails to capture to make ATP is lost to the environment as heat.

Memory Jogger

Sometimes people use the term *respiration* when they really mean *breathing.* *Respiration* is the process that involves oxygen and breaks down food molecules to release energy. *Cellular respiration* refers specifically to the transfer of energy from simple organic molecules like glucose to ATP molecules within cells.

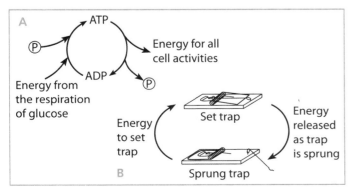

A

ATP

Energy for all cell activities

ADP

Energy from the respiration of glucose

Energy to set trap

Set trap

Energy released as trap is sprung

Sprung trap

B

Figure 2-4. Energy storage in ATP molecules: (A) Chemical energy from the breakdown of glucose molecules is used to attach a phosphate (P) to a molecule of ADP. The result is called ATP. When the cell needs energy, the ATP is broken down into ADP. During that process, the phosphate (P), along with the energy that was stored in its chemical bond, is released. (B) A similar form of temporary energy storage occurs when a mousetrap is set. The mechanical energy that is put into the act of setting the trap is stored in the spring. When the trap is sprung, that energy is released.

Figure 2-5. Cellular respiration in a mitochondrion: Partially broken down glucose molecules and oxygen (O$_2$) enter the organelle and are rearranged, with the help of enzymes. Water (H$_2$O) and carbon dioxide (CO$_2$) are released as waste products. The energy that was stored in the glucose is transferred to ATP molecules.

Cellular respiration in many organisms is completed in organelles called **mitochondria.** (See Figure 2-5.) Mitochondria are common in animal cells. Cells that require more energy contain more mitochondria. For example, muscles require more energy to complete their functions than skin cells do. Muscle cells usually contain mitochondria, which corresponds with their increased energy needs.

As they generate ATP, mitochondria release carbon dioxide and water molecules that come from fragments of molecules that were involved in the reactions. Most cellular processes use ATP as a direct source of energy. Basically, cells "run" on ATP.

Table 2-3. Summary of Cellular Respiration	
Energy	Comes from the chemical bond energy of glucose molecules; ends up in the bonds of ATP where it can be utilized for cell activities
Materials used	Sugar or other energy-rich organic food compounds and oxygen gas from the environment • Food is obtained through photosynthesis in producers and by feeding in consumers. • Oxygen is obtained through gas exchange.
Materials produced	ATP molecules and two waste products— carbon dioxide gas and water. The release of carbon dioxide into the environment is part of the process of gas exchange.
Time frame	Cellular respiration occurs in all cells (including plant cells) 24 hours a day.
Location	Respiration occurs in the cells of all living things. In most organisms, cellular respiration is concluded in mitochondria.
Importance of respiration	All cells "run" on the energy released from ATP. Organisms can use the ATP they make as the source of energy to help them obtain raw materials and nutrients, to transform materials in chemical reactions, to transport materials (for example, active transport), and to eliminate wastes. ATP is essential for metabolic processes. The energy is also used to allow the organism to grow and to move from one place to another.

Digging Deeper

The D in ADP is for **Di**phosphate, or two phosphates. The T in ATP is for **Tri**phosphate, or three phosphates. ADP and ATP are converted back and forth as a phosphate is added or removed.

$$ADP + P = ATP$$
$$ATP - P = ADP$$

Review Questions
Set 2.2

9. Energy for use in cells is stored in the form of
   (1) chemical bond energy
   (2) physical energy
   (3) heat energy
   (4) mechanical energy

10. In which process do organisms transfer the chemical bond energy in organic molecules to ATP molecules?
    (1) excretion   (3) autotrophic nutrition
    (2) cellular respiration (4) photosynthesis

11. Energy released from the cellular respiration of glucose is
    (1) first stored within ATP
    (2) stored in the liver as fat
    (3) turned into fat
    (4) used directly for body activity

12. The process during which energy is released from digested foods is called
    (1) cellular respiration (3) photosynthesis
    (2) chemical digestion   (4) excretion

13. As a direct result of the life process called cellular respiration in humans,

(1) liquid wastes are eliminated from the body
(2) food is digested and absorbed into the blood
(3) energy is released from digested food within the cells
(4) nutrients are transported within the cells

14. Which process involves the transfer of energy from carbohydrates to ATP molecules?

(1) photosynthesis　　(3) digestion
(2) respiration　　　　(4) circulation

15. During respiration, the energy within the bonds of a glucose molecule is released in small amounts in a step-by-step, enzyme-controlled reaction. In this process, the energy released is used to

(1) synthesize ATP
(2) control the process of diffusion
(3) synthesize more glucose
(4) produce oxygen molecules

16. Which statement best describes one of the events taking place in the chemical reaction represented below?

$$H_2O + ATP \xrightarrow{\text{enzymes}} ADP + P + energy$$

(1) Energy is being stored as a result of cellular respiration.
(2) Energy is being released for metabolic processes.
(3) Decomposition is taking place, resulting in the synthesis of ATP.
(4) Photosynthesis is taking place, resulting in the storage of energy.

17. Compare photosynthesis and respiration with regard to each of the following:

- source of energy [1]
- materials used by each process [1]
- location of each process in the cell [1]
- when each process occurs in plants and animals [1]

18. Which statement most accurately describes the process of respiration?

(1) It occurs only in plants during the daylight hours and usually involves the exchange of gases.
(2) It occurs only in plants during the daylight hours and involves the taking in of preformed organic molecules.
(3) It occurs continuously in the cells of all organisms and involves the synthesis of carbohydrate molecules.
(4) It occurs continuously in the cells of all organisms and often involves an exchange of gases.

19. During daylight hours green plants carry out photosynthesis. Do they also carry out respiration at this time? Support your answer. [1]

Base your answers to questions 20 through 22 on the diagram of a mitochondrion below and on your knowledge of biology.

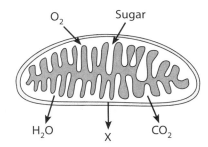

20. The process represented in this diagram is

(1) respiration　　(3) photosynthesis
(2) coordination　　(4) immunity

21. What term would most appropriately be represented by the "X"?

(1) ATP　　　　　(3) antibodies
(2) chlorophyll　　(4) glucose

22. What is present within the mitochondrion that allows the reaction to occur?

(1) enzymes　　　(3) bacteria
(2) chlorophyll　　(4) carbon dioxide

Enzymes

A **catalyst** is any substance that can affect the rate of a chemical reaction without itself being changed or used up during the reaction. Because it is neither changed nor used up, the catalyst is capable of carrying out the same function again and again. Protein catalysts known as enzymes affect the chemical reactions in living things.

The Function of Enzymes Biochemical processes, such as digestion (breakdown), synthesis (building up), cellular respiration (energy release),

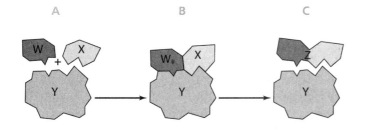

A　　　　B　　　　C

Figure 2-6. Enzymes interact with specific molecules:
Enzyme interactions are determined by molecular shape. After the two molecules W and X collide with enzyme Y (A), the enzyme forms a temporary physical connection with them (B) and then separates after a reaction has occurred (C). As a result, the molecules W and X have chemically bonded for the synthesis of the new molecule Z. If the arrows in the illustration were reversed, the reaction would involve splitting molecule Z into two smaller molecules, W and X. This reverse process is digestion.

and photosynthesis (energy capture), are made possible in living things by enzymes.

All living organisms contain enzymes. Enzymes interact with other molecules when they collide. Chemical reactions in living organisms are regulated by many different enzymes that function best at whatever the normal "body" temperature is for the organism.

Importance of Molecular Shape Enzymes and several other molecules, such as hormones, antibodies, and receptor molecules on cell membranes, have specific shapes that influence both how they function and how they interact with other molecules. Many enzymes will interact with some substances, but not others. The enzyme salivary amylase, for example, acts on starches but not proteins. In Figure 2-6, notice how the shapes of W, X, and Y fit together precisely. If the shape of an enzyme is altered, it will not interact with other molecules the way it must to catalyze a reaction, and its function will be impaired.

Enzyme Reaction Rates

Several conditions, such as shape, temperature, and pH, can either speed up or slow down the rate of enzyme action.

Shape Enzymes are chain-like protein molecules that are folded into precise shapes. Each enzyme must have a specific shape to work correctly, and anything that alters that shape will affect the enzyme's ability to function properly. High temperatures and strong <u>acids</u> or <u>bases</u> can change the enzyme's shape either temporarily or permanently. When this happens, the enzyme cannot function, and the reaction rate will decrease in proportion to the number of enzyme molecules that are altered.

Temperature Most enzymes have an <u>optimum</u> temperature at which they function most efficiently and produce the highest reaction rate. For human enzymes, this temperature is typically 98.6°F (37°C). As the temperature of a cell or organism reaches its optimum level, enzymes and the molecules they are interacting with will move faster and collide more often, causing the reaction rate to increase. Beyond the optimum temperature, the rate falls rapidly because the fragile enzyme molecules begin to change shape or break apart. Trace the rise and fall of an enzyme reaction rate in Figure 2-7.

pH The **pH** of a substance is a measure of whether a substance is <u>acidic</u>, <u>neutral</u>, or <u>basic</u>. Placing enzymes in solutions of varying pH values affects their activity. Many enzymes work best in an optimum pH of about 7, which is neutral. This makes sense, since most body fluids and cells maintain a pH of near 7. However, some parts of organisms have typical pH values that are far from neutral. For example, the human stomach is acidic and has a pH of 2 or 3. The small intestine has a pH around 8. Enzymes in these locations typically have optimum rates that correspond to the pH of their environment, as shown in Figure 2-8.

A pH of about 7 is neutral, the same as pure water. A low pH, such as 1 or 2, indicates a strong acid. A high pH, such as 13 or 14, indicates a strong base. In a typical high school biology laboratory, pH is measured with pH paper treated with various indicator dyes.

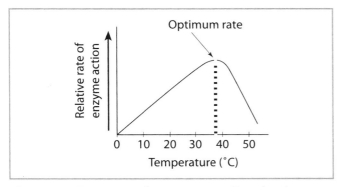

Figure 2-7. Enzymes and temperature: Note that the rate of enzyme action is fastest at about 37°C, which is typical of a human enzyme. The reason the rate declines so quickly beyond the optimum is that the higher temperature alters the shape of the enzyme. In this example, by the time the temperature reaches 55°C, all the enzyme molecules have been altered, and as a result, they no longer function.

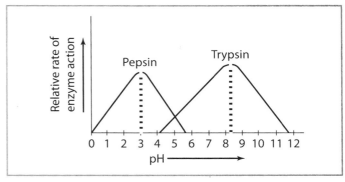

Figure 2-8. Enzymes and pH: Pepsin is found in the human stomach and has a pH that matches the acid environment found there. Trypsin is an enzyme located in the small intestine where the pH is close to 8. Notice that each enzyme is less effective if the pH is either raised or lowered from its optimum point.

Review Questions
Set 2.3

23. Only small amounts of enzymes are required for reactions within cells because enzymes are

   (1) fragile
   (2) reused
   (3) small molecules
   (4) constantly synthesized

24. Which cell organelle indicated in the diagram below controls the synthesis of enzymes?

   (1) A
   (2) B
   (3) C
   (4) D

25. In order to survive, all organisms must carry out

   (1) autotrophic nutrition
   (2) heterotrophic nutrition
   (3) enzyme-controlled reactions
   (4) the process of reproduction

26. Which group of organic compounds includes the enzymes?

   (1) proteins
   (2) carbohydrates
   (3) sugars
   (4) fats

27. Luciferin is a molecule that, when broken down in fireflies, produces heat and light. The rate at which luciferin is broken down in cells is controlled by

   (1) a carbohydrate
   (2) a simple sugar
   (3) an enzyme
   (4) a complex fat

28. At which point on the graph below can the rate of enzyme activity be increased by increasing the concentration of sugar molecules?

(Enzyme concentration constant)

   (1) 1   (3) 3
   (2) 2   (4) either 2, 3, or 4

29. Which statement best describes the relationship between enzyme action and temperature shown in the graph below?

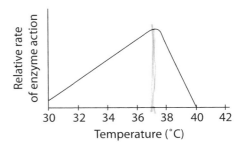

   (1) Enzyme synthesis begins at 30°C.
   (2) Enzyme activity constantly increases with increasing temperature.
   (3) The pH has a greater effect on this enzyme than temperature does.
   (4) Enzyme activity increases as the temperature increases from 32°C to 34°C.

30. The enzyme salivary amylase will act on starch but not on protein. This action illustrates that salivary amylase

(1) contains starch
(2) is chemically specific
(3) is not reusable
(4) lacks protein

31. The graph below shows the effect of temperature on the relative rate of action of enzyme X on a protein.

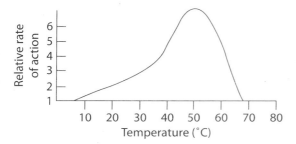

Which change would not affect the relative rate of action of enzyme X?

(1) the addition of cold water when the reaction is at 50°C
(2) an increase in temperature from 70°C to 80°C
(3) the removal of the protein when the reaction is at 30°C
(4) a decrease in temperature from 40°C to 10°C

32. Enzymes influence chemical reactions in living systems by

(1) becoming part of the product after the reactions occur
(2) combining with atmospheric gases to form waste products
(3) affecting the rate at which reactions occur
(4) absorbing water during synthesis and digestion

33. The diagram below represents three steps in the digestion of the sugar sucrose. In this diagram, structure X is most likely

(1) a molecule of oxygen
(2) the end product
(3) an enzyme molecule
(4) the sugar

Base your answers to questions 34 through 36 on the diagram of an enzyme-controlled reaction and on your knowledge of biology.

34. Explain what is happening during Steps 1-3 in the following diagram. Use the labels—A, B, C, D, and E—to help you with your explanation. As part of your answer, indicate which molecules represent the enzyme and the product.

35. Is this reaction an illustration of synthesis or digestion? Support your answer. [1]

36. Explain why heating these molecules might *slow* the rate at which this reaction occurs? [1]

Base your answers to questions 37 through 41 on the diagram and data table below and on your knowledge of biology.

A student is studying the effect of temperature on the action of a protein-digesting enzyme that is contained in stomach fluid. An investigation is set up using five identical test tubes. Each test tube contains 40 milliliters of stomach fluid as well as a 20-millimeter glass tube filled with cooked egg white, as shown in the diagram. After 48 hours, the amount of egg white digested in each tube was measured. The data collected are shown in the following table.

40 mL of gastric fluid

Glass tube containing egg white

Digestion at Different Temperatures		
Tube	Temperature (°C)	Amount of Digestion After 48 Hours
1	4	0.0 mm
2	8	2.5 mm
3	21	4.0 mm
4	37	7.5 mm
5	100	0.0 mm

37. Identify the independent variable in this investigation.

(1) gastric fluid
(2) length of glass tubing
(3) temperature
(4) time

38. State the amount of digestion (in mm) that might be expected after 48 hours in a test tube that is identical to the other 5 test tubes, but at a temperature of 15°C.

    (1) less than 2.5 mm
    (2) between 2.5 and 4 mm
    (3) between 4.0 and 7.5 mm
    (4) more than 7.5 mm

39. The best graph of the results of this investigation would be made by plotting the data on which set of axes?

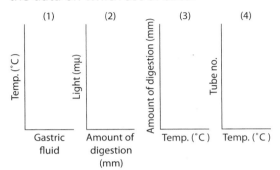

40. The student repeated this same experiment using a glass tube containing potato instead of egg white. After 48 hours, he found no evidence of any digestion.

Explain why no digestion occurred. [1]

41. During the winter, many fish eat very little. Some students thought this might be because less oxygen is dissolved in the cold winter water than in the same water during the warm summer months. The students tested the water and found that cold water holds more dissolved oxygen than warm water. They also discovered that the fish have nearly as much food available during the winter as in the summer.

Explain why the fish eat very little during the winter. [1]

Feedback and Homeostasis

Because an organism's external and internal environment is constantly changing, its homeostasis is constantly threatened. As a result, living things must monitor and respond to changes in the environment. Stability (homeostasis) results when the organism detects <u>deviations</u> (changes) in the environment and responds with an appropriate corrective action that returns the organism's systems to normal. If an organism's monitoring systems or control mechanisms fail, disease or even death can result.

As you go about your daily tasks, your body temperature readjusts, your heart and breathing rates alter slightly, and your blood flow increases or decreases. If your monitoring were to fail, these small adjustments would not be made. Soon, your body's homeostasis would begin to deteriorate. Under extreme conditions, you could become quite ill or even die. However, simple corrective actions usually take care of problems with your homeostasis and life goes on. Some examples of responses organisms have to changes they encounter are shown in Table 2-4.

Dynamic Equilibrium

Organisms have a variety of mechanisms that maintain the physical and chemical aspects of the internal environment within the narrow limits that are favorable for cell activities. The stability that results from these responses is called homeostasis or a "steady state." To many biologists, the phrase *steady state* suggests an

Table 2-4. Responses to Environmental Change

Organism	Change (stimulus)	Response
Species of bacterium	Temperature falls below a certain point.	Bacterium produces a chemical that acts as an antifreeze.
Many plants	Air is hot and dry.	Leaf pores close to conserve water.
Monarch butterflies	Seasons change.	Butterflies migrate.
Human	Person hears a loud noise.	The person becomes alert; heart rate increases for "fight or flight."

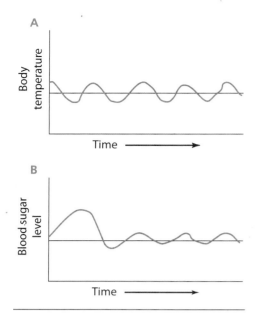

Figure 2-9. Dynamic equilibrium: (A) Temperature: Our body temperature shows a regular pattern of slight changes around a "normal" temperature of about 98.6°F (37°C). The graph represents the slight differences in temperature that are part of a daily cycle. Mechanisms such as shivering and sweating help maintain this range. **(B)** Blood sugar: Normal blood sugar levels show a rise in blood sugar after a meal, but blood sugar level is quickly restored to equilibrium as the hormone insulin prompts glucose to move from the blood to body cells.

unchanging condition. They prefer to use the term **dynamic equilibrium** to describe the constant small corrections that normally keep the internal environment within the limits needed for survival.

In Figure 2-9, notice that these small corrections include a normal range of variations. Certain microorganisms or diseases can interfere with dynamic equilibrium, and therefore with homeostasis. Organisms, including humans, have mechanisms to deal with such interference and restore the normal state. Homeostatic adjustments have their limits. They can operate only within certain set ranges.

Feedback Mechanisms

A **feedback mechanism** involves a cycle in which the output of a system "feeds back" to either modify or reinforce the action taken by the system. A variety of feedback mechanisms have evolved for helping organisms detect and respond to **stimuli** (changes in the environment). Multi-celled organisms detect and respond to change both at the cellular level and at the organism level. Their systems detect deviations from the normal state and take corrective actions to restore homeostasis.

Feedback responses can be simple or complex. A simple feedback response might involve a hormone that regulates a particular chemical process in a cell. A complex feedback response might be an elaborate behavior, such as bird migration.

Positive Feedback Feedback mechanisms can be either positive or negative. In positive feedback systems, a change prompts a response, which leads to a greater change and a greater response. Childbirth is an example of a positive feedback system. The first contractions push the baby's head against the base of the uterus, which causes stronger contractions in the muscles surrounding the uterus. This increases the pressure of the baby's head against the base of the uterus, which causes stronger contractions and so on. Eventually the baby is born, and the feedback cycle ends.

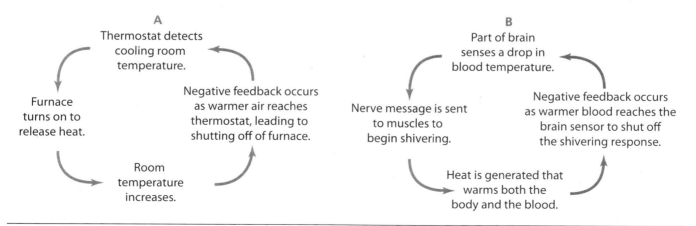

Figure 2-10. Negative feedback systems: (A) The furnace and thermostat in most houses are part of a negative feedback system. **(B)** Like the household heating system, the regulation of body temperature is a negative feedback system.

Negative Feedback Negative feedback systems are the most common. In this case, a change in the environment can prompt system 1 to send a message (often a hormone) to system 2, which responds by attempting to restore homeostasis. When system 1 detects that system 2 has acted, it stops signaling for further action.

A typical house heating system is an example of negative feedback. The furnace has a thermostat that is set to a specific temperature called the set point. When the room cools below the set point, the thermostat sends a message to turn on the furnace. When the room temperature rises above the set point, the thermostat stops sending the message, and the furnace shuts down. (See Figure 2-10.)

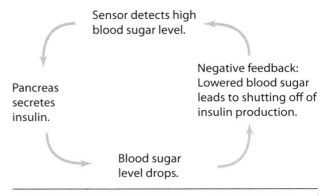

Figure 2-11. **Negative feedback involving blood sugar level**

Regulating human body temperature uses a similar system. A structure in the brain detects that the temperature of the blood is too low. This brain structure then sends a signal to muscles, causing them to contract and relax in rapid cycles. The result is shivering, which generates body heat. When shivering has sufficiently warmed the body and blood, sensors in the brain detect the change, and the signal to shiver stops.

Negative Feedback and Cell/Organ System Interaction

Maintaining dynamic equilibrium often involves interactions between cells and body organs or systems. For example, certain cells in the body monitor the level of glucose in the blood. When the glucose level is above normal limits, an endocrine organ called the **pancreas** secretes insulin. **Insulin** is a hormone that prompts glucose to move from the blood into body cells, resulting in a lower glucose level in the blood. Another hormone secreted by the pancreas works in the opposite way. When the glucose level in the blood is too low, this hormone prompts the release of glucose stored in the liver. The negative feedback process involving insulin is shown in Figure 2-11.

Other examples of cell/organ feedback interactions include:

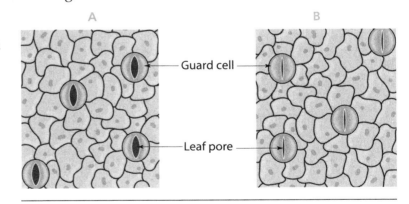

- Increased muscle activity is often accompanied by an increase in heart rate and breathing rate. If this did not occur, the muscles would not receive the increase in blood flow and oxygen they need to continue working.
- When plant leaves detect a shortage of water, **guard cells**—specialized cells that surround pores on the surface of the leaf—change shape to close the pores and reduce evaporation. The process is shown in Figure 2-12.

Figure 2-12. **Guard cell activity on the surface of a leaf:** (A) The guard cells have opened the pores in the leaf, allowing gas exchange between the leaf and the environment. Water can exit from the leaf, and CO_2 can enter. This situation commonly exists when the sun is shining, the air is warm, and water is available from the soil. (B) The guard cells have nearly closed the pores in the leaf, thus protecting the leaf from drying out. Under these conditions, gas exchange is limited. Photosynthesis slows down because little CO_2 is available. This situation commonly exists when the sun is shining, the air is hot and dry, and little water is available from the soil.

42. Some plants respond to light with a sudden enlargement of their leaf pores. This response is important because it enables the plant to increase its intake of

(1) carbon dioxide   (3) oxygen
(2) soil   (4) nitrogen

43. An increase in the blood's level of a thyroid gland hormone decreases the release of thyroid-stimulating hormone. This mechanism illustrates

(1) negative feedback
(2) enzyme action
(3) immune response
(4) positive feedback

44. Maintenance of the pH of human blood within a certain range is an example of

(1) chemical digestion
(2) synthesis
(3) respiration
(4) dynamic equilibrium

45. Homeostasis is illustrated in the human body by the effects of insulin on the amount of

(1) proteins digested
(2) amino acids absorbed into the blood
(3) oxygen transport to the lungs
(4) glucose in the blood

46. The chart below shows the amount of oxygen and carbon dioxide exchanged through the skin and lungs of a frog for a period of one year.

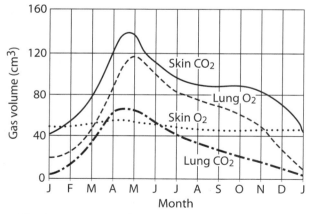

The lowest rate of gas exchange is most likely the result of

(1) increased mating activity
(2) elevated body temperature
(3) environmental conditions
(4) competition with other species

47. A student is frightened by a loud noise, which results in a hormone being released into the blood. The hormone causes the student's heart to beat rapidly. The two systems that work together to cause this reaction are the endocrine system that secretes the hormone and the

(1) nervous system   (3) excretory system
(2) reproductive system   (4) digestive system

48. Which important human process is represented in the diagram below?

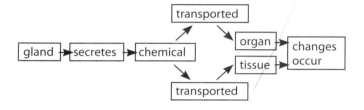

(1) coordination   (3) excretion
(2) digestion   (4) cell respiration

49. Describe what normally happens to a person's blood sugar level soon after he or she eats a meal that contains carbohydrates. [1]

50. Describe the role of insulin in regulating blood sugar levels. [1]

51. On a sheet of graph paper, mark an X and a Y-axis, then draw a line representing the relative blood sugar levels for two individuals (Person A and Person B) over a 5-hour period after a meal. Both people ate the same foods. Person A produces a normal amount of insulin, and Person B does not.

Explain any differences in the lines representing Persons A and B. [1]

52. During hot weather and vigorous exercise, people sweat. As the water on their skin evaporates, the water molecules absorb heat energy.

Explain why this process is important to the individual. [1]

53. Many different feedback mechanisms have evolved over time. These mechanisms allow an organism to respond to changes in both its internal and external environment.

Select an organism from those you have learned about and describe how a specific feedback process works within that organism. Include how the feedback specifically helps the organism maintain homeostasis. [1]

Disease as a Failure of Homeostasis

Disease is any condition that prevents the body from working as it should. As a result, the body may fail to maintain homeostasis. Diseases in humans may result from foreign invader organisms, called **pathogens,** or from abnormal cells in the body that lead to cancer. Disease may also result from toxic substances, poor nutrition, organ malfunction, an inherited disorder, or risky personal behavior. All can lead to a disruption of the body's ability to function normally—that is, to maintain homeostasis.

Sometimes the onset of a disease becomes apparent right away, as in the case of some birth defects or poisoning. Sometimes, however, the disease may not show up for many years, as is the case with lung cancer caused by exposure to tobacco smoke. Some examples of these kinds of diseases are noted in Table 2-5.

Pathogens There are many potentially dangerous disease-causing organisms in the air, water, and food we take in every day. A variety of pathogens—viruses, bacteria, fungi, and other parasites—can interfere with our normal functioning and make us seriously ill. Plants and other animals can also be infected by these and similar organisms. Some examples of pathogens and the diseases they cause are shown in Table 2-6.

Cancer Certain genetic mutations in a cell can result in uncontrolled cell division called cancer. Exposing cells to certain chemicals and radiation increases mutations and thus increases the chance of cancer. In this disease, genes that control and coordinate a cell's normal cycle of growth and division are altered by mutation. As a result, the cell begins to divide abnormally and uncontrollably. The result is a mass of abnormal cells referred to as a tumor.

Table 2-5. Causes of Disease

Cause of Disease	Examples
Inherited disorders	Down syndrome, cystic fibrosis, sickle cell disease
Exposure to toxins	Lead poisoning, radiation poisoning
Poor nutrition	Scurvy (vitamin C deficiency), goiter (iodine deficiency)
Organ malfunction	Heart attack, diabetes
High-risk behaviors	Lung cancer, drug addiction, skin cancer

Table 2-6. Pathogens and Disease

Pathogen	Description of Pathogen	Examples of Disease
Virus	**Viruses** are particles composed of nucleic acid and protein. They reproduce when they invade living cells.	Examples include the common cold, influenza, AIDS, and chicken pox. Immunizations have been developed to combat many viral diseases.
Bacterium	**Bacteria** are one-celled organisms.	Bacterial illnesses include strep throat, syphilis, and food poisoning. **Antibiotics,** drugs like penicillin that we get from microorganisms, are used to treat many bacterial diseases.
Fungus	**Fungi** are organisms made of either one or many cells. They include yeasts and molds. They eat by absorbing organic substances.	Examples include athlete's foot and ringworm. Fungicides and antibiotics are used to fight fungal diseases.
Parasites	Some animals and one-celled organisms are **parasites** that survive by living and feeding on other organisms.	Parasites include leeches and tapeworms. Malaria is a disease caused by a one-celled organism. It is transmitted to humans by mosquitoes. Heartworm is a parasitic worm that lives in dogs and cats. Medicines are available to treat some parasitic diseases. Avoiding exposure to the parasite is also effective.

Once they are identified, often by abnormal proteins on their surfaces, cancer cells may be attacked by the immune system and destroyed. If the immune system is unable to destroy the cancer cells, the disease may become life-threatening.

The Immune System

Humans have many ways of protecting themselves from danger and disease. For example:

- Our eyes, ears, and sense of smell help us detect danger.
- We release hormones that stimulate emergency responses to danger.
- Our muscles allow us to fight off some threats and to flee from others.
- Our skin—when unbroken—keeps out many foreign organisms that could be harmful.
- Our tears, saliva, and other body secretions trap and/or destroy invaders that come into contact with them.
- Our nervous system provides rapid coordination of many of our responses to danger.

Once invaded, however, the body needs an effective way to combat invaders or body cells that malfunction. The **immune system** is the body's primary defense against disease-causing pathogens.

Pathogens, foreign substances, or cancer cells that threaten our homeostasis can usually be identified by molecules on their outer surfaces or membranes. These molecules, called **antigens,** trigger a response from the immune system. Toxins, the poisonous wastes of certain pathogens, can also act as antigens.

All cells have potential antigens on their surfaces. However, the immune system can usually tell the difference between the molecules of "self" cells, which belong to the body, and "non-self" (foreign) cells, which come from outside the body. When cells of our immune system recognize foreign antigens, specialized white blood cells and antibodies attack them and the cells that display them.

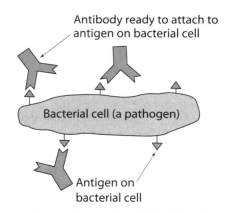

Antibody ready to attach to antigen on bacterial cell

Bacterial cell (a pathogen)

Antigen on bacterial cell

Figure 2-13. Certain white blood cells produce Y-shaped antibodies: The antibodies match the shape of certain antigens on pathogens or abnormal proteins on cancer cells. Note that the antibodies and antigens are not drawn to scale. They would be MUCH smaller than the pathogen cell.

White Blood Cells and Antibodies Some white blood cells are specialized to surround and engulf invading pathogens that are recognized as a threat. Others produce **antibodies**—proteins that either attack the invaders or mark them for killing. The marked invaders may then be destroyed by other white blood cells. In Figure 2-13, notice the Y-shaped antibodies that match the shape of antigens.

Most of the antibodies and white blood cells that attack an invader break down soon after they have defended the body. However, some specialized white blood cells will remain. These cells are capable of quickly dividing and producing more antibodies of the same kind to fight off later invasions of the same **microbes** (microscopic organisms). Antibodies are effective even against microbes that appear years later.

Vaccinations Scientists have discovered that weakened microbes (pathogens) or even parts of microbes can stimulate the immune system to react. The antigens found on the live pathogens are usually present on the weakened or killed ones, too. As shown in Figure 2-14, **vaccines** are made using these weakened, killed, or parts of microbes (pathogens). When vaccines are injected into the body, the immune system responds just as if it had been invaded by a live pathogen. It produces antibodies. These antibodies can attack and destroy any of that pathogen that is still present in the body.

After a vaccination, the immune system "remembers" specific pathogens by leaving behind white blood cells that protect the body for years. The vaccinated body reacts as if it has already defeated the specific pathogen and responds faster in the future than it did when attacked the first time. The second response is so rapid that in most cases the disease will not even have time to develop before the immune system wipes it out.

Damage to the Immune System A person's immune system may weaken with age or other factors. Stress and fatigue, for example, can lower our resistance and make us more vulnerable to disease. Some viral diseases, such as **AIDS,** result from an attack on the immune system. Damage from the disease may leave the person with AIDS unable to deal with infections and cancerous cells. Their weakened immune system is one reason people with AIDS often die of infections that a healthy immune system would easily destroy.

Problems Associated with the Immune Response Although our immune system is essential for our survival, it creates problems for some people. These people have an **allergy**—a rapid immune system reaction to environmental substances that are normally harmless. Examples of such substances include certain foods, pollen, and chemicals from insect bites.

In people with allergies, the immune system reacts by releasing histamines. This leads to anything from a runny nose and sneezing to a rash and swelling. It is the swelling that makes some allergies dangerous: Occasionally, the throat swells, interfering with the victim's ability to breathe. People with allergies often use antihistamines to reduce the effects of the histamines and the symptoms they cause.

Sometimes the immune system fails to recognize the "self" molecules and attacks the body's own cells. For example, in some cases, the immune system attacks and destroys the pancreas cells that produce insulin. The result is one type of diabetes.

Since transplanted organs come from another person, they have foreign antigens on their cells. As a result, the immune system recognizes transplants as "invaders" and attacks them. To avoid "rejection" of their new organ, transplant patients receive injections of special drugs to reduce the effectiveness of their immune system. Of course, because the immune system's ability to protect the transplant patient from normal pathogens is reduced, the patient may become ill from a pathogen that normally would be no threat.

Remember germs? At one time *germ* was the word of choice for people who were talking about the tiny living things that cause disease. *Germ*, however, had two meanings in science, so the term *microbe* became the more accurate word choice. You still need to know that a microbe is any microscopic organism, but scientists now usually use the term *pathogen*. The reason is that the meaning of pathogen also includes viruses, those tiny "almost-organisms" that don't quite fit the description of a living thing.

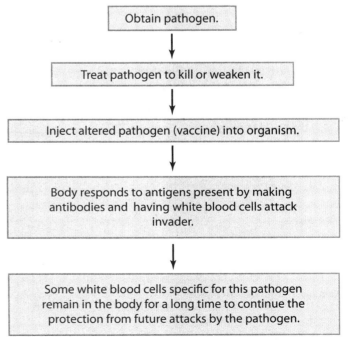

Figure 2-14. Preparation and use of a vaccine

Research and Progress Against Disease Biological research of diseases and their causes has generated a vast amount of knowledge that is used to find ways of diagnosing, preventing, controlling, or curing diseases of plants and animals. Some examples of how medical knowledge has developed are shown in Table 2-7.

Table 2-7. Biological Research of Diseases

Category of Research	Methods Developed
Diagnosing disease	• Culturing (growing) bacteria from the infected person to determine what specific pathogen is responsible for the illness • Using X-rays, CAT scans, ultrasound, blood pressure monitoring devices, and other methods to determine the cause or extent of the illness • Detecting genetic abnormalities that may be present in cells
Preventing and controlling disease	• Promoting improved sanitation measures, including frequent hand washing, safe garbage disposal, and sewage treatment • Sterilizing surgical instruments and treating wounds with antiseptics and other chemicals • Controlling populations of rats, flies, mosquitoes, and other disease-carrying organisms with pesticides or sanitation measures • Treating water, milk, and other foods to reduce the presence of pathogens • Vaccinating to promote the body's immune response to pathogens • Identifying the dangers of risky behaviors such as tobacco use
Treating and curing disease	• Developing antibiotics and other drugs to kill pathogens • Developing medical procedures, including surgical operations and laser techniques, to remove damaged or diseased tissue from the body

Review Questions

Set 2.5

54. When a person is suffering from an infection, such as strep throat or chicken pox, his blood usually shows a significant increase in the number of

(1) enzymes   (3) hormones
(2) antibodies   (4) sugars

55. When microscope slides are stained to show blood cells, the small red blood cells that appear on the slides are much more numerous than the large white blood cells. This supports the concept that

(1) the body's need for white blood cells is less than its need for red blood cells
(2) red cells are more numerous because they are smaller than white blood cells
(3) the nuclei of the white blood cells help them work more efficiently than the red blood cells, which lack nuclei
(4) each kind of cell is present in the numbers best suited to meet the needs of the body

56. Which response usually occurs after an individual receives a vaccination for the influenza virus?

(1) Hormones in the blood stop reproduction of the virus.
(2) Pathogens from the vaccine deactivate the virus.
(3) Enzymes released from antigens digest the virus.
(4) Antibodies against the virus are found in the blood.

57. A patient has just received an organ transplant. Which treatment would be most effective in preventing the patient's body from rejecting the organ?

(1) Treat the patient with medications that decrease the immune system's response.
(2) Treat the patient with antibiotics to fight off a possible viral infection.
(3) Restrict the patient's salt intake.
(4) Give the patient blood transfusions.

58. The body makes chemicals that can help to destroy harmful viruses and bacteria. These chemicals are called

(1) antibodies
(2) vaccines
(3) hormones
(4) antibiotics

59. A vaccine can protect you against a disease because it

(1) destroys toxic substances from bacteria before they can make you sick
(2) stimulates your immune system against the pathogen
(3) kills any pathogenic bacteria in your body
(4) changes pathogenic bacteria into harmless bacteria

60. The body is protected against harmful flu viruses by

(1) red blood cells and hormones
(2) white blood cells and antibodies
(3) white blood cells and enzymes
(4) red blood cells and antibodies

61. In some people, substances such as peanuts, eggs, and milk cause an immune response. This response to usually harmless substances is most similar to the

(1) action of the heart as the intensity of exercise increases
(2) mechanism that regulates the activity of guard cells
(3) action of white blood cells when certain bacteria enter the body
(4) mechanism that maintains the proper level of antibiotics in the blood

62. Parasitic strains of *E. coli* may produce poisonous chemicals that attack living tissue and cause disease in humans. These chemicals are called

(1) antibodies
(2) toxins
(3) viruses
(4) antibiotics

63. Uncontrolled cell division is known as

(1) meiosis
(2) cancer
(3) antibody production
(4) sexual reproduction

64. The resistance of the body to a pathogen is called

(1) immunity
(2) antigen
(3) cancer
(4) infection

65. Diseases can be caused by inherited disorders, exposure to toxic substances, organ malfunction and certain personal behaviors.

Choose *two* of the above causes and *for each one* give a specific example of an associated disease. [1]

66. Our immune system normally helps us resist infection and disease. Sometimes, however, it may actually work against us by attacking certain tissues or organs in the body.

State one example of the immune system attacking the body and explain how we try to counteract the problem. [1]

67. Vaccinations play a major role in medicine today. Explain the role of vaccines in the prevention of disease. Your answer must include at least:

- a description of the contents of a vaccine [1]
- a description of how a vaccine protects the body from disease [1]
- one specific reason certain vaccinations are required for students to attend public schools. [1]

Base your answer to question 68–70 on the information below and on your knowledge of biology.

Stem cells present in an embryo are responsible for the formation of various tissues and organs. Recent research suggests that it may be possible to replicate stem cells from sections of skin taken from adult mice, rather than having to use stem cells from the embryos of mice.

In the future, human stem cells may be used to replace human tissue damaged by diseases such as Parkinson's disease and multiple sclerosis.

68–70. Discuss why the use of stem cells taken from a patient to replace damaged tissues and organs may decrease the potential risk to a patient. In your answer, be sure to:

- identify the major problem that may occur when tissues and organs donated by another individual are used [1]
- explain why this problem may occur [1]
- explain why this problem will not occur if tissues and organs produced by stem cells from the patient are used [1]

Directions
Review the Test-Taking Strategies section of this book. Then answer the following questions. Read each question carefully and answer with a correct choice or response.

Part A

1 Most of the oxygen in our atmosphere comes from processes carried out
(1) in the soil
(2) by animals
(3) in factories
(4) by plants

2 Which organism releases oxygen into the atmosphere?
(1) mold
(2) bird
(3) fish
(4) tree

3 Plants provide food for animals through the process of
(1) respiration
(2) digestion
(3) photosynthesis
(4) excretion

4 Which word equation represents the process of photosynthesis?
(1) starch → many glucose molecules
(2) glucose + oxygen → carbon dioxide + water + energy
(3) carbon dioxide + water → glucose + oxygen
(4) fats → sugar molecules

5 Which statement correctly relates the two organisms in the illustration below?

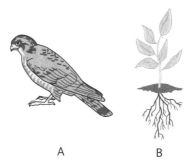

A   B

(1) A carries out cell division, but B does not.
(2) B transports needed organic materials, but A does not.
(3) Both A and B carry out cellular respiration to release energy from organic molecules.
(4) Neither A nor B is able to use energy to combine carbon dioxide and water to make organic compounds.

6 A plant cell that lacks chloroplasts will not
(1) give off oxygen
(2) take in food
(3) give off carbon dioxide
(4) take in water

7 Which process removes carbon dioxide from the atmosphere rather than adding it?
(1) cellular respiration
(2) combustion of gasoline
(3) photosynthesis
(4) deforestation

8 Which process in plants produces carbon dioxide?
(1) respiration
(2) photosynthesis
(3) coordination
(4) digestion

9 The size of the openings in a leaf through which gases move in and out is controlled by the
(1) root cells
(2) chloroplasts
(3) chromosomes
(4) guard cells

10 What process does the word equation below represent?

$$\text{glucose} + \text{oxygen} \xrightarrow{\text{enzymes}} \text{carbon dioxide} + \text{water} + \text{energy}$$

(1) photosynthesis
(2) breathing
(3) transport
(4) respiration

11 The major source of weight gain in a growing plant is
(1) sunlight
(2) carbon dioxide
(3) oxygen
(4) soil

12 Green plants do not release large amounts of CO_2 all the time because they use CO_2 in the process of
(1) photosynthesis
(2) respiration
(3) reproduction
(4) evolution

13 The diagram below represents some events that take place in a plant cell. With which organelle would these events be most closely associated?

CO_2 H_2O

Sugar

O_2

(1) mitochondrion
(2) chloroplast
(3) ribosome
(4) vacuole

14 An enzyme that digests starch will not act upon the sugar sucrose. This fact is an indication that enzymes are
(1) specific
(2) synthetic
(3) starches
(4) generalized

15 Which statement best describes the enzyme represented in the graphs below?

(1) This enzyme works best at a temperature of 37°C and a pH of 8.
(2) This enzyme works best at a temperature of 55°C and a pH of 12.
(3) Temperature and pH have no effect on the action of this enzyme.
(4) This enzyme works best at a temperature near freezing and a pH above 4.

16 The body usually responds to foreign material by forming
(1) hormones   (3) vaccines
(2) antibodies   (4) antigens

17 A sudden increase in the number of white blood cells in a human may be an indication of
(1) growth
(2) color blindness
(3) mental retardation
(4) an infection

Part B

Base your answers to questions 18 and 19 on the equation below and on your knowledge of biology.

$$C_6H_{12}O_6 + 6\,O_2 \rightarrow H_2O + 6\,CO_2 + 36\,ATP$$

(glucose) + (oxygen) → (water) + (carbon dioxide) + ATP

18 The equation represents the process of
(1) excretion   (3) respiration
(2) photosynthesis   (4) coordination

19 Explain the energy connection between the glucose and the formation of ATP in this process. [1]

_____

Base your answers to questions 20 through 23 on the summary equations of two processes below and on your knowledge of biology.

Photosynthesis

water + carbon dioxide $\xrightarrow{\text{enzymes}}$ glucose + oxygen + water

Respiration

glucose + oxygen $\xrightarrow{\text{enzymes}}$ water + carbon dioxide

20 Choose one of the processes and identify the source of the energy in the process you chose. [1]

21 Identify where the energy ends up at the completion of that process. [1]

22 State one reason the processes of photosynthesis is important for living things.[1]

23 State one reason the processes of respiration is important for living things. [1]

Base your answers to questions 24 through 28 on the information and data table below and on your knowledge of biology.

The results of blood tests for two individuals are shown in the data table below. The blood glucose level before breakfast is normally 80–90 mg/100 mL of blood. A blood glucose level above 110 mg/100 mL of blood indicates a failure in a feedback mechanism.

Injection of chemical X, a chemical normally produced in the body, may be required to correct this problem.

Time	Blood Glucose (mg/100 mL)	
	Individual 1	Individual 2
7:00 a.m.	90	150
7:30 a.m.	120	180
8:00 a.m.	140	220
8:30 a.m.	110	250
9:00 a.m.	90	240
9:30 a.m.	85	230
10:00 a.m.	90	210
10:30 a.m.	85	190
11:00 a.m.	90	170

Data Table

Directions (39–40): Using the information in the data table, construct a line graph on the grid below, following the directions below.

24 Mark an appropriate scale, without any breaks in the data, on each labeled axis. [1]

25 Plot the blood glucose levels for the individual who will most likely need injections of chemical X. Connect the points and surround each point with a small circle.

Example:

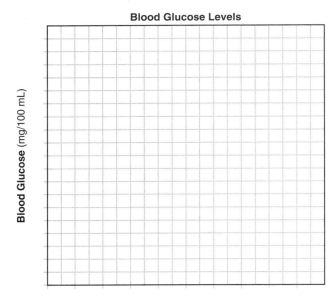

Blood Glucose Levels

26 Identify chemical X. [1]

27 State one reason for the change in blood glucose level between 7:00 a.m. and 8:00 a.m. [1]

28 What term refers to the relatively constant level of blood glucose of individual 1 between 9:00 a.m. and 11:00 a.m.? [1]

30 Select one of the paired items below and describe how the first item in the pair regulates the second item for the maintenance of homeostasis. [1]

- insulin—blood sugar level
- CO_2 in blood—breathing rate

Base your answers to questions 31 through 34 on the passage below and on your knowledge of biology.

Lyme Disease

Since 1980, the number of reported cases of Lyme disease in New York State has been increasing. The vector (carrier) of Lyme disease is the black-legged tick, *Ixodes scapularis*. The disease is spread from infected animals to ticks that bite these animals. Humans bitten by these ticks may then become infected.

The symptoms of Lyme disease do not always occur immediately after a tick bite. An individual may develop a skin rash several days to weeks after being bitten by a tick. Flu-like symptoms, such as headaches, muscle aches, joint pain, and fever, may also develop. Generally, these symptoms clear up even if the individual does not seek medical help. In some cases, there may be no symptoms other than a sudden onset of arthritis. However, in a small number of cases, if the infection is not treated, it may lead to chronic arthritis, disorders of the heart and nervous system, or in a few cases, death. A blood test can help to confirm a diagnosis, and antibiotics are effective in treating the infection.

People may take preventive action by frequently checking themselves and their pets for ticks, tucking their pant legs into socks when walking through woods or high grass, wearing light-colored clothing to aid in spotting a tick, and using insect repellent.

31 Describe how Lyme disease is transmitted. [1]

32 State one way people might protect themselves from Lyme disease. [1]

33 State two symptoms that may occur if a person has Lyme disease. [2]

34 State one danger of ignoring any symptoms that may develop after a tick bite. [1]

Base your answers to questions 35 through 37 on the information and data table below and on your knowledge of biology.

Twenty-five geranium plants were placed in each of four closed containers and then exposed to the light conditions shown in the data table. All other environmental conditions were held constant for a period of two days. At the beginning of the investigation, the quantity of carbon dioxide (CO_2) present in each container was 250 cm^3 (cubic centimeters). The data table shows the amount of CO_2 remaining in each container at the end of two days.

Changes in CO_2 Levels			
Container	Color of Light	CO_2 (cm^3) at Start	CO_2 (cm^3) After 2 Days
1	blue	250	50
2	red	250	75
3	green	250	200
4	orange	250	150

35 The independent variable in this investigation was the
(1) type of plant
(2) color of light
(3) amount of CO_2 in each container at the beginning of the investigation
(4) number of days needed to complete the investigation

36 State the problem being investigated in this experiment. [1]

37 Identify the source of the carbon used in photosynthesis. [1]

Part C

Base your answers to questions 38 through 40 on the information below and on your knowledge of biology.

An investigation was performed to determine the effects of enzyme X on three different disaccharides (double sugars) at 37°C. Three test tubes were set up as shown in the diagram below.

At the end of 5 minutes, the solution in each test tube was tested for the presence of disaccharides (double sugars) and monosaccharides (simple sugars). The results of these tests are shown in the table below.

Result of Sugar Test			
	Test Tube 1	Test Tube 2	Test Tube 3
Monosaccharide	not present	not present	present
Disaccharide	present	present	not present

38 What can be concluded about the activity of enzyme X from the data table? [1]

39 With only the materials list supplied below and common laboratory equipment, design an investigation that would show how a change in pH would affect the activity of enzyme X. Your design must include a *detailed procedure* and a *data table*. [3]

> *Materials*
> Enzyme X
> Sugar C Solution
> Indicators
> Substances of various pH values —
> > vinegar (acidic)
> > water (neutral)
> > baking soda (basic)

40 State one safety precaution that should be used during the investigation. [1]

41 Enzyme molecules are affected by changes in conditions within organisms. Explain how a prolonged, excessively high body temperature during an illness could be fatal to humans. your answer must include:
- the role of enzymes in a human [1]
- the effect of this high body temperature on enzyme activity [1]
- the reason this high body temperature can result in death [1]

Base your answer to question 42–44 on the information below and on your knowledge of biology.

42–44 In order to enroll in most schools, students must be vaccinated against certain viral diseases, such as mumps. Even with these vaccinations, many students still suffer from other diseases. Discuss how a vaccination works and why some students still become infected with other diseases. In your answer, be sure to:
- identify what is present in a vaccine that stimulates an immune response [1]
- describe how a vaccine protects against disease [1]
- state why a student vaccinated against mumps can still be infected by the pathogens that cause other diseases, such as chicken pox [1]

45 State one way guard cells of a leaf help to maintain homeostasis in the plant? [1]

Genetic Continuity

What do You Think?

Genes in Cells

The genes in my brain cells are different from the genes in my liver cells.

The genes in all of my cells are the same and all of them are turned on and making proteins.

The genes that are turned on in my brain are not the same genes as the ones turned on in my liver.

3 Genetic Continuity

Vocabulary

asexual reproduction	egg	replicate
biotechnology	expressed	selective breeding
body cell	genes	sexual reproduction
bond	genetic engineering	sperm
chromosome	genetic recombination	subunit
clone	heredity	template
DNA	mutation	traits

Topic Overview

When two organisms reproduce, their offspring receive genetic instructions, called **genes**, from each parent. The genes determine which **traits**—or characteristics—each offspring will have. All organisms—whether they are animals, plants, or members of one of the other kingdoms—pass their genetic characteristics along in this manner. Because of this transfer of genetic information, offspring tend to resemble their parents.

Heredity and Genes

Heredity is the passing of genetic information from one generation to the next through reproduction. The hereditary information (**DNA**) is organized in the form of genes located in the **chromosomes** of each cell. Recall that chromosomes, which are found in the cell nuclei, contain the DNA molecules. (See Figure 3-1.) It is the DNA molecules that carry the genetic information of the cell.

A human cell contains many thousands of genes in its nucleus, and each gene carries a separate piece of coded information. The traits inherited by an individual can be determined by one pair of genes or by several pairs of genes. It is also true that a single gene pair can sometimes influence more than one trait. Table 3-1 shows several examples of these variations.

Chromosome

Unwinding

DNA

Figure 3-1. Chromosomes contain DNA: Notice that the chromosome contains one very long double strand of DNA.

Some traits that an organism inherits are readily observable. These include traits such as hair color, leaf shape, flower scent, and wing structure. The overall structure of the body is also an observable trait that is inherited from the parents. Some children, for example, inherit long, slender toes or large ear lobes.

Other traits are not so obvious. Less obvious traits may involve a defective heart, a single kidney, or

Table 3-1. Human Traits Inherited with Different Numbers of Genes

Trait	Number of Gene Pairs Needed to Affect Trait
Cystic fibrosis	Single gene pair
Skin color	Multiple gene pairs
Sickle cell disease	Single gene pair affecting multiple traits

how some of the body's chemicals function. Examples include the ability to produce insulin, the types of receptors present on a cell membrane, and whether an individual can make a particular respiratory enzyme.

Methods of Reproduction

There are two common methods of reproduction: asexual and sexual. The major difference between these two methods is whether one or two parents are involved in producing the offspring. **Asexual reproduction** involves one parent or individual (often a single-celled organism); **sexual reproduction** involves two parents.

Asexual Reproduction In organisms that reproduce asexually, all the genetic instructions (genes) come from one individual or parent. Since the genes are all from one parent, offspring are usually identical to the parent.

Because the coded instructions in their cells are the same as the instructions in their parent's cells, asexually produced offspring are genetically identical to their parents. Identical genetic copies are known as **clones.** Because they are asexually produced, entire populations of bacteria—perhaps millions of cells—may be genetically identical clones.

Sexual Reproduction In organisms that reproduce sexually, two parents are required to produce offspring. Each parent produces sex cells. **Sperm** are the sex cells produced by the male; the **egg** is the sex cell produced by the female. Recall that genes in **body cells**—cells other than sex cells—occur in pairs, but each sex cell contains only one gene from each pair. The offspring that results from sexual reproduction therefore receives half of its genetic information from the female parent (via the egg) and half from the male parent (via the sperm).

Genetic Recombination When a sperm and egg combine to form a new cell with a complete set of genetic instructions, a unique combination of genes results. The term for this is **genetic recombination.** This unique combination of thousands of genes produces an offspring that may resemble either or both parents in many ways but will not be identical to either of them.

Review Questions

Set 3.1

1. A cell is represented in the diagram below.

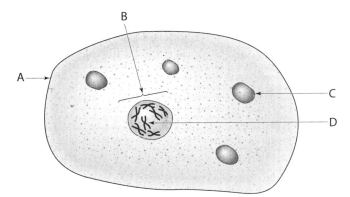

Which statement about the cell is correct?

(1) Structure A synthesizes and secretes cellular products.

(2) Structure B contains chromosomes involved in transmitting genetic information.

(3) Structure C utilizes DNA in the process of photosynthesis.

(4) Structure D is the site of protein synthesis.

2. Which materials are composed of DNA?

(1) proteins   (3) nerve secretions

(2) genes   (4) fluid in vacuoles

3. In an animal cell, DNA is found in the greatest concentration in the

(1) vacuole (3) nucleus
(2) ribosome (4) cytoplasm

4. Cystic fibrosis is a genetic disease. Examine the illustration below.

Father with cystic fibrosis
Father has two abnormal genes for the trait

Mother who does not have cystic fibrosis
Mother has ???

Child with cystic fibrosis
Child has two abnormal genes for the trait

The mother's cells most likely contained

(1) a disease-causing virus
(2) one normal gene and one abnormal gene
(3) two normal genes
(4) an abnormal number of chromosomes

5. Bacteria in culture A produce slime capsules around their cell walls. A biologist removed the DNA from some of the bacteria in culture A. He then injected it into bacteria in culture B, which normally do not produce slime capsules. After the injection, bacteria with slime capsules began to appear in culture B. What conclusion could best be drawn from this investigation?

(1) The bacteria in culture A are mutations.
(2) Bacteria reproduce faster when they have slime capsules.
(3) The slime capsules of bacteria in culture B contain DNA.
(4) DNA is most likely involved in the production of slime capsules.

6. The letters in the diagram below represent genes on a particular chromosome.

Gene *B* contains the code for an enzyme that cannot be synthesized unless gene *A* is also active. Which statement best explains why this can occur?

(1) A hereditary trait can be determined by more than one gene.
(2) Genes are made up of double-stranded segments of DNA.
(3) All the genes on a chromosome act to produce a single trait.
(4) The first gene on each chromosome controls all the other genes on the chromosome.

7. Which cell structure includes all of the others?

(1) nucleus (3) DNA
(2) gene (4) chromosome

The Genetic Code

The inherited instructions (genes) that are passed from parent to offspring exist in the form of a chemical code. This genetic code, as the chemical code is called, is contained in the DNA molecules of all organisms. DNA molecules resemble a flexible, twisted ladder formed from many smaller repeating units, as shown in Figure 3-2.

DNA Structure

Like other large molecules of life, the DNA molecule is made of thousands of smaller sections called **subunits.** Each subunit has three chemical parts: a sugar, a phosphate, and a base. The subunits vary from one another according to the kind of bases they contain. The bases are represented by the letters A, G, C, and T. The four subunits of DNA molecules are

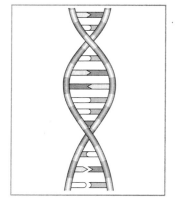

Figure 3-2. Model of a section of a DNA molecule

arranged in pairs, each subunit forming one side and half of one rung of the "twisted ladder." Base A of one subunit always pairs with the base T of another subunit. In a similar way, base G always pairs with base C. Figure 3-3 shows the details of the structure in an untwisted molecule.

Once the chemical and structural properties of DNA were discovered by scientists, it became clear how this molecule could contain a kind of message that functions as a code. Notice in Figure 3-3 that the sequence of bases on this molecule's left strand, reading from top to bottom, is ACAG. A different molecule might have a sequence in the same position reading GCAG or AACG. The specific sequence of bases in a DNA molecule forms a coded message. The message of a single gene is often a sequence of hundreds of bases. The code for an entire human is estimated to be around 3 billion base pairs!

DNA Replication

The ability to copy the coded instructions in the DNA molecule is critical to its function. Knowing the chemical makeup and structure of DNA molecules gave scientists an immediate clue to how the molecule could be copied, or **replicated.** When scientists realized that the bases used weak chemical bonds to pair with each other, they also realized that the DNA could separate at that weak **bond** to form two single strands. Each single strand became a **template**, or pattern, for a new molecule.

The new molecule was built by attaching new subunits to each template strand, always following the base pairing rules of linking A with T and C with G. The result is the formation of two new molecules whose base pair sequences are exactly alike. See Figure 3-4.

When the structure of DNA was determined, scientists finally understood how cells could copy and transfer information to new cells each time they divide and to new offspring during reproduction. Replication produces two identical copies of the cell's genetic information, each ready to be passed from the parent cell to two offspring cells during cell division. Offspring cells are commonly called daughter cells.

Proteins and Cell Functioning

The work of the cell is carried out by the many types of molecules the cell assembles (synthesizes). Many of these molecules are proteins. Protein molecules are long chains. They are formed from various combinations of 20 kinds of amino acids arranged in a specific sequence.

The sequence of amino acids in a particular protein influences the shape of the molecule. This is because some of the amino acid parts are attracted to (and may bond with) other amino-acid parts of the chain. The connections that form between different parts of the chain cause it to fold and bend in a specific way. The final folded shape

Figure 3-3. **Portion of a DNA molecule:** A single subunit is shown in black. The bases of the DNA molecule are arranged in pairs, represented here by letters. The base pairs form the rungs of the twisted DNA ladder. The sugar and phosphate of each subunit form the sides of the ladder and are connected by strong chemical bonds. The two sides are held together by weak chemical bonds between the paired bases. (Bonds are the links between atoms that hold molecules together.)

Figure 3-4. **The replication of a DNA molecule:** This is how cells copy their genetic information to be passed on to two offspring cells when cell division occurs. Both strands are replicated at the same time.

of the protein enables it to carry out its function in the cell. Many proteins made by a cell become enzymes that regulate chemical reactions. Remember that an enzyme can interact with a specific molecule because their shapes correspond.

Some of the proteins made in cells become parts of organelles, such as the cell membrane. Other proteins include the hormone insulin or the many antibodies that bind to antigen molecules on pathogens. The color of your eyes and skin are also the result of proteins synthesized by your body.

The DNA-Protein Connection

Cells store vast amounts of coded information in their genes. Much of this coded information is used to make the thousands of proteins that each cell requires for its functions and the structures it contains. The proteins for these structures and functions are made at the ribosomes according to the directions stored in the cell's DNA code.

Because offspring inherit genetic information from their parents, their cells make many of the same proteins. This is what causes the resemblance between some children and their parents. Making many of the same proteins causes both parent and offspring to form similar structures that give them similar features. One example of a protein-dependent trait includes hair texture (curly, straight, or kinky).

If a parent's DNA carries a code for a protein that does not function correctly, the children may also make that defective protein. For example, an albino does not produce the usual amount of eye, hair, or skin color pigment. The condition is caused by a defect in the gene that codes for the protein that produces color pigment. If albino parents pass this gene to their offspring, they, too, may not produce the normal color pigment.

Protein Synthesis The process of synthesizing a protein from DNA begins in the nucleus. There, the DNA code of a particular gene is "read" by a special enzyme and used to produce a "messenger" molecule. This messenger molecule then travels to the ribosomes in the cell's cytoplasm. With the aid of specialized transfer molecules, amino acids are moved to the ribosomes for assembly into protein. They are bonded in the order specified by the messenger molecule. In this way, the sequence of amino acids of any protein, and therefore its overall structure, is determined by the gene's DNA sequence in the nucleus. The process is shown in Figure 3-5.

Figure 3-5. Protein synthesis: Notice that the DNA in the nucleus supplies the instructions for how to assemble the protein to the messenger molecule. The transfer molecules help assemble amino acids. The assembly process occurs at a ribosome.

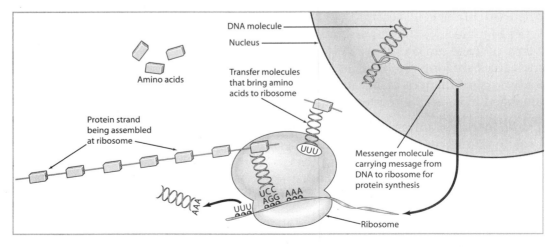

8. In a DNA molecule, the letters A, T, C, and G represent
   (1) bases
   (2) sugars
   (3) starches
   (4) proteins

9. The individuality of an organism is determined by the organism's
   (1) amino acids
   (2) nitrogen bases
   (3) DNA base sequence
   (4) order of ribosomes

10. What would most likely happen if the ribosomes in a cell were not functioning?
    (1) The cell would undergo uncontrolled mitotic cell division.
    (2) The synthesis of enzymes would stop.
    (3) The cell would produce antibodies.
    (4) The rate of glucose transport in the cytoplasm would increase.

11. The diagram below represents a portion of a DNA molecule.

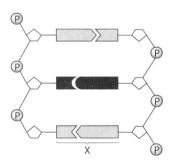

    The letter X represents two bases that are
    (1) identical and joined by weak bonds
    (2) identical and joined by strong bonds
    (3) a part of the genetic code of the organism
    (4) amino acids used to build folded protein molecules

12. The kinds of genes an organism possesses are dependent on the
    (1) type of proteins in the organism's nuclei
    (2) sequence of bases in the organism's DNA
    (3) number of ribosomes in the organism's cytoplasm
    (4) size of the mitochondria in the organism's cells

13. What is the role of DNA molecules in the synthesis of proteins?
    (1) They catalyze the formation of bonds between amino acids.
    (2) They determine the sequence of amino acids in a protein.
    (3) They transfer amino acids from the cytoplasm to the nucleus.
    (4) They supply energy for protein synthesis.

14. The diagram at the right represents a molecule of
    (1) ATP
    (2) protein
    (3) carbohydrate
    (4) DNA

15. During replication, the strands of a double-stranded DNA molecule separate when the bonds are broken between their paired bases.

    Explain why, in terms of the genetic code, it is important that the molecule separate between the bases and not at some other point. [1]

Base your answers to questions 16 and 17 on the diagram below and on your knowledge of biology.

16. Within which organelle does process A occur?
    (1) ribosome   (3) vacuole
    (2) nucleus   (4) cell membrane

17. Within a living cell, which organelles are directly necessary for process B to occur?
    (1) ribosomes   (3) vacuoles
    (2) mitochondria   (4) cell membranes

18. In all living cells, DNA controls cellular activities by
  (1) determining the order of amino acids in protein molecules
  (2) regulating the concentration of molecules on both sides of the cell membrane
  (3) varying the rates of starch synthesis
  (4) coordinating active and passive transport

19. Which cell organelle indicated in the diagram controls the synthesis of enzymes?
  (1) A
  (2) B
  (3) C
  (4) D

20. The sequence of amino acids that makes up a protein molecule is determined by the sequence of
  (1) bases in DNA
  (2) glucose in DNA
  (3) ribosomes in the cytoplasm
  (4) chloroplasts in the vacuoles

21. In DNA, the base represented by an A always pairs with the base represented by
  (1) A   (2) T   (3) C   (4) G

22. The presence of DNA is important for cellular metabolic activities because DNA
  (1) directs the production of enzymes
  (2) is a structural component of cell membranes
  (3) directly increases the solubility of nutrients
  (4) is a major component of the cytoplasm

Mutations

Genes are actually segments of DNA molecules. Any alteration of the DNA sequence is a **mutation**, which changes the normal message carried by the gene. Many mutations involve the substitution of one base for another. This often causes a different amino acid to be placed in a particular position in the growing protein chain. Some mutations involve the insertion of an additional base into an existing DNA sequence. This affects all of the code past the change, just as skipping a blank on the answer sheet for a test can cause all of the remaining answers to be shifted to the next blank, making almost all of them wrong. The deletion of a base from the normal gene sequence would also alter all the code past the change.

Some mutations occur when the bases within a gene are accidentally rearranged. This, too, alters the genetic code. Figure 3-6 shows several ways that DNA can mutate.

All of these alterations are totally random and can occur anywhere along the molecule, making the result of the change almost impossible to predict. However, when a DNA sequence is changed, it is quite likely that the protein it codes for may be assembled incorrectly. If some amino acids are replaced by others, or if their sequence is different, the folding of the protein may be different. Incorrect folding means that the protein's shape would not be normal. This could cause the protein to malfunction. One mutation caused by a substitution is sickle cell disease. (See Figure 3-7.)

Mutations can cause such serious changes that the cell may die. However, if a mutated cell does survive and can replicate its DNA, its changed instructions will be copied and passed on to every cell that develops from it. In sexually reproducing organisms, only mutations found in sex cells can be inherited by the offspring.

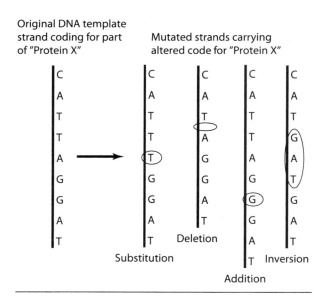

Original DNA template strand coding for part of "Protein X"

Mutated strands carrying altered code for "Protein X"

Substitution

Deletion

Addition

Inversion

Figure 3-6. Mutation of DNA: The DNA on the left is part of the original template strand that codes for protein X. The four strands on the right show the DNA that would result from several types of mutations.

DNA and Individuality Although an individual's body cells all originally come from a single cell, the body is made up of many types of cells. Each body cell's nucleus—whether it is a nerve cell, skin cell, or bone cell—has a complete set of identical genetic instructions for that individual.

For years, scientists wondered how cells with identical genetic instructions could be so different. The answer is that each kind of cell uses only some of the genetic information it contains. It uses only the instructions it needs to operate its own kind of cell. For instance, information for building all of a person's enzymes is coded in the chromosomes of each cell, but a muscle cell uses only the specific enzymes that are needed by a muscle cell.

Both the internal and external environment of the cell can influence which genes are activated in that cell. Some of this influence may occur during development, leading to the many different types of cells that an organism needs.

The selective activation of genes in a cell may continue as conditions change throughout life. For instance, chemical signals from within the cell or from other cells may activate a particular gene. Hormones are one kind of molecule that can activate parts of a cell's DNA code, leading to the production of a particular protein.

Although genes are inherited, an organism's environment can affect the way some genes are revealed, or **expressed,** in the organism. For example, in some animals, such as the Himalayan rabbit, the outside temperature can cause the activation or inactivation of the genes for fur color. When the rabbit's body area is cold, black fur grows. If the same body area becomes warm, white fur grows instead. (See Figure 3-8.) The environment can also influence human genes. Studies of identical twins (those with identical genetic information) who were raised in different environments show that they have differences that can only be explained by the influence of the environment on gene expression.

Normal cells   Sickled cells

Figure 3-7. Effects of a substitution mutation: Normal red blood cells are round. The abnormal cell shapes are due to a substitution mutation that forms a defective protein which changes the cell's shape.

Figure 3-8. Body temperature and fur color in the Himalayan rabbit: From what you know about the activation and inactivation of the genes for fur color in this animal, why do you think the ears, feet, nose, and tail are black?

Review Questions

Set 3.3

23. A dog breeder can determine that the sudden appearance of hairlessness in one of the puppies is a mutation if the dog

(1) is still hairless after 5 years
(2) shows no change in the hairless condition after its diet is changed
(3) develops other conspicuous differences from the parent
(4) is bred and the trait is capable of being inherited

24. Explain how a change in the sequence of nitrogen bases in a DNA molecule could result in a gene mutation. [1]

25. Which mutation could be passed on to future generations?

(1) a gene change in a liver cell
(2) cancer caused by excessive exposure to the sun
(3) a chromosomal alteration during gamete formation
(4) random breakage of a chromosome in a leaf cell of a maple tree

26. Mutations can be transmitted to the next generation if they are present in

(1) brain cells   (3) body cells
(2) sex cells   (4) muscle cells

27. Overexposure of animals to X-rays is dangerous because X-rays are known to damage DNA. A direct result of this damage is cells with

(1) unusually thick cell walls
(2) no organelles located in the cytoplasm
(3) abnormally large chloroplasts
(4) changes in chromosome structure

28. The diagram below shows a portion of a DNA molecule. The base sequence of the unlabeled strand shown in the diagram is *most* likely

(1) G-A-G-T
(2) C-U-C-A
(3) T-C-T-G
(4) G-A-G-U

29. The individuality of an organism is determined by the

(1) sequence of bases in DNA
(2) number of amino acids in a cell
(3) position of ribosomes in the cytoplasm
(4) number of bases in the mitochondria

30. In which situation could a mutation be passed on to the offspring of one of the organisms listed in the data table below?

Data Table	
Name of Organism	Number of Chromosomes in a Body Cell
Human	46
Fruit fly	8

(1) Ultraviolet radiation causes fruit-fly wing cells to undergo uncontrolled division, resulting in cells with 9 chromosomes.
(2) A cell in the wall of the human uterus undergoes a change, resulting in cells with 47 chromosomes.
(3) A primary sex cell in a human forms a sperm that contains 23 chromosomes.
(4) A cell in the ovary of the fruit fly undergoes a chromosomal change that results in 5 chromosomes per egg cell.

31. A change in the sequence of bases in a DNA molecule is most accurately referred to as

(1) an insertion, deletion, or substitution
(2) a chromosomal replication
(3) carbohydrate molecule synthesis
(4) selective breeding

Genetic Engineering

Genetic engineering is a new technology that humans use to alter the genetic instructions in organisms. The idea of altering organisms to have more desirable traits, however, is not new. In fact, **biotechnology**—the application of technology to biological science—has been producing useful products for thousands of years. Cheese and bread are just two examples of "biotech" products made with the use of microbes.

Throughout recorded history, humans have also used **selective breeding**—a process that produces domestic animals and new varieties of plants with traits that are particularly desirable. Many meat products, for example, come from animals that have been bred to contain less fat. In addition, many of the fruits and vegetables we consume have been selectively bred to be larger, sweeter, hardier, or even juicier.

To breed a better plant, farmers might select a bean plant that produces many pods and then crossbreed it with a bean plant that resists fungus infections. The farmers would expect to get seeds that would grow into bean plants with both features.

Gene Manipulation

In recent years, plants and animals have been genetically engineered by manipulating their DNA instructions. The result of this genetic manipulation is new characteristics and new varieties of organisms. Consequently, we have been able to produce plants with many beneficial traits. In one instance, plants can now contain genes with the instructions for making chemicals that kill the insects that feed on them. Scientists have also engineered bacteria that can be used to clean up oil spills or that produce human growth hormone.

The basic method that alters genes in organisms uses special enzymes. These enzymes cut DNA segments in a way that allows the segments to be spliced, or moved and attached, to the DNA of a new organism. Once in the new organism, the transferred genes direct the new organism's cells to make the same protein product as the original organism. For example, when we move a human insulin-producing gene into a bacterial cell, the bacterium—and all its offspring—will produce human insulin. This provides a way to produce large quantities of a hormone at low cost. Genes for other human proteins have also been inserted into bacterial cells, as illustrated in Figure 3-9.

Other enzymes have been found that can be used to make many copies of segments of DNA. These can be used to increase the amount of DNA available from a tiny sample. This procedure is helpful even when only a drop of blood or saliva is found at a crime scene. By copying and re-copying the DNA in the sample, criminal investigators can produce a sample that is large enough to test. The test results may identify or clear suspects.

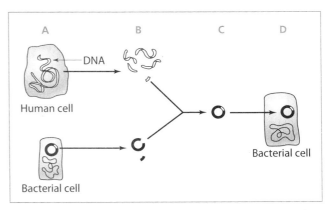

Figure 3-9. Genetic engineering using bacteria: On the left (area A), a special enzyme is used to cut a segment of DNA from a human cell and to also cut open a circular piece of DNA from a bacterial cell. When the piece of human DNA is mixed with the open loop of bacterial DNA (area B), they join to form a closed loop (area C). That loop is then taken up by another bacterial cell (area D). The transformed bacterial cell will produce the protein product of the human DNA segment and that DNA loop will be duplicated and passed to all future offspring.

Applications of Biotechnology

The health care field has much to gain through our increasing knowledge of genetics and biotechnology. New methods enable us to locate and decode genes that cause diseases. Once we have a better understanding of the gene's specific defect, we may be able to develop ways to treat the disease. In some cases, we may be able to alter the DNA in affected cells and cure the person.

Due to mutations in their genes, people with genetic diseases are sometimes unable to produce certain hormones, enzymes, or other body chemicals. At times, we can extract these chemicals from animals, such as sheep and cattle. These extractions, however, can be expensive, and the chemicals may contain contaminants that cause side effects. If scientists can produce the chemicals using genetically engineered organisms, we may be able to economically provide the missing chemicals in a pure enough form to avoid the side effects associated with chemicals obtained from animal sources.

32. Genetic engineering is used in the biotechnology industry to

(1) eliminate all infections in livestock
(2) synthesize hormones such as insulin and human growth hormone
(3) increase the frequency of fertilization
(4) eliminate asexual reproduction

33. Describe two examples of how an understanding of genetics is making new fields of health care (treatment or diagnosis) possible. [1]

34. The insertion of a human DNA fragment into a bacterial cell might make it possible

(1) for the bacterial cell to produce a human protein
(2) to clone the human that donated that DNA fragment
(3) for humans to become immune to an infection by this type of bacteria
(4) to clone this type of bacteria

35. In a DNA sample, 15% of the bases are thymine (T). What percentage of the bases in this sample are cytosine (C)?

(1) 15%   (3) 35%
(2) 30%   (4) 85%

Base your answers to questions 36 through 40 on the passage below and on your knowledge of biology.

Advances with Cells and Genes

Recent advances in cell technology and gene transplanting have allowed scientists to perform some interesting experiments, including splicing human DNA into the chromosomes of bacteria. The altered bacteria express the added genes.

Bacteria reproduce rapidly under certain conditions. This means that bacteria with the gene for human insulin could multiply rapidly, resulting in a huge bacterial population capable of producing large quantities of human insulin.

The traditional source of insulin has been the pancreases of slaughtered animals. Continued use of this insulin can trigger allergic reactions in some humans. The new bacteria-produced insulin is actually human insulin. As a result, it does not produce many side effects.

The bacteria used for these experiments are *E. coli*, which are found in the digestive system of humans and many other animals. Some scientists question these experiments and are concerned that the altered *E. coli* may accidentally get into water supplies.

For each of the statements below, write the number 1 if the statement is true according to the passage, the number 2 if the statement is false according to the passage, or the number 3 if not enough information is given in the passage.

36. Transplanting genetic material into bacteria is a simple task. [1]

37. Under certain conditions, bacteria reproduce at a rapid rate. [1]

38. The continued use of insulin from animals may cause harmful side effects in some people. [1]

39. The bacteria used in these experiments are normally found only in the nerve tissue of humans. [1]

40. Bacteria other than *E. coli* are unable to produce insulin. [1]

---

41. The headline "Improved Soybeans Produce Healthier Vegetable Oils" accompanies an article describing how a biotechnology company controls the types of lipids (fats) present in soybeans. The improved soybeans are most likely being developed by the process of

(1) natural selection
(2) asexual reproduction
(3) genetic engineering
(4) habitat modification

42. A product of genetic engineering technology is represented below.

Which substance was needed to join the insulin gene to the bacterial DNA as shown?

(1) a specific carbohydrate
(2) a specific enzyme
(3) hormones
(4) antibodies

43. In the past, diabetics used horse or cow insulin to control their glucose levels. Today, as a result of genetic engineering, human insulin can be synthesized by bacteria. State *one* advantage for a person with diabetes to receive genetically engineered insulin rather than insulin taken from a horse or cow. [1]

Directions

Review the Test-Taking Strategies section of this book. Then answer the following questions. Read each question carefully and answer with a correct choice or response.

Part A

1 Hereditary information for most traits is generally located in
(1) genes found on chromosomes
(2) chromosomes found on genes
(3) the ribosomes of sperm cells
(4) the mitochondria in the cytoplasm

2 An analysis of chromosomes in a culture containing mutated cells may show the loss of one or more bases making up the chromosome. This type of chromosomal change is known as
(1) an addition
(2) an insertion
(3) a deletion
(4) a substitution

3 What is the genetic engineering technique in which DNA is transferred from the cells of one organism to the cells of another organism?
(1) gene splicing   (3) electrophoresis
(2) chromatography   (4) selective deleting

4 A change that alters the base sequence in an organism's DNA is a
(1) mutation   (3) clone
(2) replication   (4) zygote

5 The technique illustrated in the diagram is known as

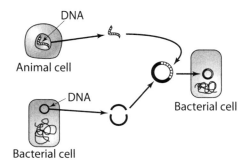

(1) genetic engineering
(2) protein synthesis
(3) internal fertilization
(4) external fertilization

6 The diagram represents a portion of DNA.

Which DNA strand could correctly pair with the one illustrated?

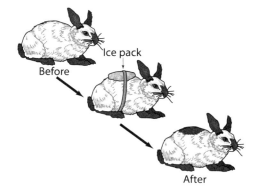

7 The diagram illustrates what happens to the fur color of a Himalayan rabbit after prolonged exposure to a low temperature.

The change in fur color is most likely due to
(1) the effect of heredity on gene expression
(2) the arrangement of genes on chromosomes
(3) environmental influences on gene action
(4) mutations resulting from a change in the environment

Part B

Base your answers to questions 8 and 9 on the diagram below and on your knowledge of biology. The diagram represents part of a double-stranded DNA molecule.

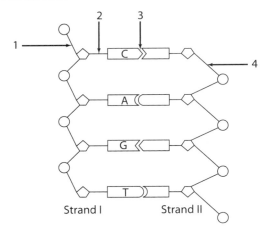

Strand I   Strand II

8 The base sequence of Strand II is most likely
   (1) C–G–G–A   (3) G–T–C–A
   (2) G–A–G–T   (4) T–G–A–C

9 Which event must occur if a nucleus containing this molecule is to undergo mitotic cell division?
   (1) The bonds at point 3 break, and the molecule replicates.
   (2) The molecule separates at point 2, and new bases attach.
   (3) The bonds at point 3 break, and the molecule deletes bases.
   (4) The bonds at points 1, 2, and 4 break, and new sequences of bases form.

---

10 Identify the process by which information in segments of human DNA can be expressed by a bacterial cell. [1]

Base your answers to questions 11 and 12 on the information below and on your knowledge of biology.

Some geneticists are suggesting the possibility of transferring some of the genes that influence photosynthesis from an efficient variety of crop plant to a less efficient crop plant. The goal is to produce a new variety with improved productivity.

11 To produce this new variety, the project would most likely involve
   (1) genetic engineering
   (2) a gene mutation
   (3) chromatography
   (4) vaccinations

12 Which technique would most likely be used to produce large numbers of genetically identical offspring from this new variety of plant?
   (1) cloning
   (2) sexual reproduction
   (3) electrophoresis
   (4) selective breeding

Base your answers to questions 13 through 17 on the information and data table below and on your knowledge of biology.

Certain chemicals cause mutations in cells by breaking chromosomes into pieces. Cells containing such broken chromosomes are known as mutated cells. Certain nutrients, such as beta carotene (a form of vitamin A), have the ability to prevent chromosome breakage by such mutagenic chemicals.

The results of an investigation of the effect of beta carotene in preventing chromosome damage are presented in the following data table. In the investigation, varying amounts of beta carotene per kilogram of body weight were added to the diets of hamsters. A mutagenic chemical at a constant dose rate was also added to the diets of the hamsters.

The Effect of Beta Carotene Added to Hamster Diet on Cell Mutation	
Amount of Beta Carotene per Kilogram of Hamster's Body Weight	Percentage of Mutated Cells
0 mg	11.5
20 mg	11.0
30 mg	8.0
40 mg	7.0
50 mg	4.5
75 mg	3.5
100 mg	2.0
150 mg	1.2

Using the information in the data table, construct a line graph on the grid provided. Follow the directions given.

13 Mark an appropriate scale, without any breaks, on each of the axes. [1]

14 Label the axes. [1]

15 Plot the data from the table. Surround each point with a small circle and connect the points. [1]

Example:

16 State an appropriate conclusion for the above experiment regarding the use of beta carotene for the prevention of chromosome damage. Use experimental data to support your conclusion. [1]

17 Vitamins A and E are essential vitamins that can dissolve in oil. A student, knowing this and seeing the above results with beta carotene, suggested that vitamin E will increase the percentage of mutations in the cells of hamsters. State whether or not this is a valid conclusion. Support your statement with an explanation. [1]

18 Animal cells utilize many different proteins. Discuss the synthesis of proteins in an animal cell. Your answer must include at least:
- the identity of the building blocks required to synthesize these proteins [1]
- the identity of the sites in the cell where the proteins are assembled [1]
- an explanation of the role of DNA in the process of making proteins in the cell [1]

Part C

Base your answers to questions 19 through 23 on the passage below and on your knowledge of biology.

Genetic Engineering

Genetic engineering is a technique used by scientists to combine or splice genetic material from different organisms. Gene splicing involves changing the normal base sequences of DNA by removing a section of DNA and introducing another gene. The technique may involve the use of the bacterium *E. coli*. The bacterium has one large chromosome and several small plasmids, which are ring-shaped pieces of DNA found in the cytoplasm.

Genetic engineers have been able to extract plasmids from *E. coli*. Restriction enzymes are used to cut the DNA of the plasmid at designated places in the base sequence. The same enzymes are used to cut a section of human DNA. This section of human DNA is then placed into the space in the cut DNA of the bacterial plasmid. The human DNA codes for the synthesis of a product such as human growth hormone.

The spliced bacterial DNA, which now contains a piece of human DNA, is referred to as a hybrid. This hybridized plasmid is then taken in by *E. coli* cells. When the bacterium reproduces, the hybrid DNA will replicate. The offspring will possess the ability to synthesize the human growth hormone.

19 Describe a bacterial plasmid. [1]

20 Describe a hybrid plasmid. [1]

21 Explain how genetic engineers remove sections from human DNA for splicing into bacterial DNA. [1]

22 State one benefit of gene splicing. [1]

23 Explain why it is not necessary to continue splicing the gene for human growth hormone into *E. coli* once cultures of the bacteria with the spliced gene are established. [1]

Base your answers to questions 24 through 26 on the statement below and on your knowledge of biology.

Selective breeding has been used to improve the racing ability of horses.

24 Define selective breeding.

25 State how selective breeding would be used to improve the racing ability of horses. [1]

26 State *one disadvantage* of selective breeding. [1]

27–28 Knowledge of human genes gained from research on the structure and function of human genetic material has led to improvements in medicine and health care for humans.
- state two ways this knowledge has improved medicine and health care for humans [1]
- identify one specific concern that could result from the application of this knowledge [1]

Base your answers to questions 29 and 30 on the information below and on your knowledge of biology.

A biologist at an agriculture laboratory is asked to develop a better quality blueberry plant. He is given plants that produce unusually large blueberries and plants that produce very sweet blueberries.

29 Describe one way the biologist could use these blueberry plants to develop a plant with blueberries that are both large and sweet. [1]

30 The biologist is successful in producing the new plant. State one method that can be used to produce many identical blueberry plants of this new type. [1]

Base your answer to question 31–34 on the information below and on your knowledge of biology.

Chickens as Drug Factories

Scientists in Scotland have successfully produced five generations of chickens that lay eggs containing certain protein-based drugs. The scientists changed the DNA of the chickens so that two drugs, one used to treat skin cancer and the other used to treat multiple sclerosis, were present in the egg whites. Cows, sheep, and goats have already been altered to produce protein-based drugs in their milk. Chickens are considered good "drug factories" because they are inexpensive to care for, they grow fast, and their chicks inherit the special drug-producing ability.

31–34 Discuss the process scientists used to alter the DNA of the chickens. In your answer, be sure to:
- state one reason why the scientists altered the DNA of the chickens instead of altering a protein already present in the chickens [1]
- identify the type of molecule used to cut the gene from the DNA of another organism and move it into the chicken's DNA [1]
- state one advantage of using chickens for this procedure [1]
- state one reason why some people might not support this method of drug production [1]

---

35 One variety of wheat is resistant to disease. Another variety contains more nutrients of benefit to humans. Explain how a new variety of wheat with disease resistance and high nutrient value could be developed. In your answer, be sure to:
- identify one technique that could be used to combine disease resistance and high nutrient value in a new variety of wheat [1]
- describe how this technique would be carried out to produce a wheat plant with the desired characteristics [1]
- describe one specific difficulty (other than stating that it does not always work) in developing a new variety using this technique [1]

Reproduction and Development

What do **YOU** Think?

Genes and Reproduction

One parent gives you the genes for some traits while the genes for your other traits come from the other parent.

Boys get most of their genes from their dad and girls get most of their genes from their mom.

Both parents contribute genes for each of the traits you have.

4 Reproduction and Development

Vocabulary

asexual reproduction	fetus	sex cell
cloning	gamete	sexual reproduction
development	gene expression	species
differentiation	meiosis	sperm
egg	mitosis	testes
embryo	ovaries	testosterone
estrogen	placenta	uterus
expressed	progesterone	zygote
fertilization	recombination	

Topic Overview

A **species** is a group of closely related organisms that share certain characteristics and can produce new individuals through reproduction. For any species to survive past a single generation, reproduction is essential. All individuals eventually die, but the species continues because individuals reproduce. When individuals reproduce, their offspring begin a period of **development** that ends in adulthood. Once an individual reaches adulthood, it is usually able to reproduce and continue the species for another generation.

Types of Reproduction

Two methods of reproduction are associated with living organisms: asexual and sexual. **Asexual reproduction** involves just one parent and results in one or more offspring that are genetically identical to that parent. **Sexual reproduction** involves two parents and results in offspring that have some genetic material (DNA) from each parent. The result is an organism that may be similar to one or both parents, but is not identical to either.

Asexual Reproduction Organisms that reproduce asexually produce their offspring in a variety of ways. In some cases they merely divide in two, producing two new individuals. (The parent in this case *becomes* the offspring!) Other organisms produce special cells that have a complete set of genetic information, and these individual cells can develop into new members of the species. Still others produce an outgrowth of the body that later detaches to become a separate individual. Many plants can develop from parts that are either broken off intentionally by humans or separated naturally from the parent plant. In every case, organisms produced by asexual reproduction have only one parent, and they have the same genetic information (in the form of DNA) as the parent. Figure 4-1 shows some examples of asexual reproduction.

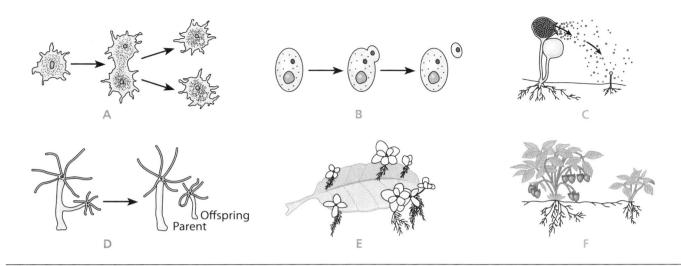

Figure 4-1. Examples of asexual reproduction: (A) An ameba divides to form two new amebas. (B) A yeast cell divides into two cells that are different sizes but genetically alike. (C) Mold spore cells reproduce the mold. (D, E, and F) Some offspring develop attached to the parent, but later separate to become independent individuals.

Sexual Reproduction In sexual reproduction, offspring receive half of their genes from one parent and half from the other. The genes are carried on chromosomes in **sex cells** (also known as **gametes** or egg or sperm cells), which join in **fertilization.** Each parent supplies half of the genetic information needed to form a complete individual. The **sperm,** which is the sex cell from the father, provides half of the information; the **egg,** which is the sex cell from the mother, provides the other half.

Offspring produced by sexual reproduction combine genes inherited from each parent's gametes. Since an offspring gets only half of its DNA from each parent, it will not be identical to either of its parents. Also, since each offspring gets a unique combination of genes from its parents, it will differ from its siblings (brothers and sisters).

Cloning **Cloning** is a technique that accomplishes the same end result as asexual reproduction. It is a way of making identical genetic copies. For example, if you cut a piece of stem from a plant and it grows roots and develops into a new plant, you have produced a genetically identical copy of the original plant. This could be called a clone of the plant.

Recently, however, it has also been possible to produce clones of animals that ordinarily only reproduce sexually. This is done by inserting a nucleus from a "parent" organism's cell (one that has a complete set of genetic information from that individual) into an egg cell from which the nucleus has been removed. The result is an egg that now contains not 50%, but 100% of the genetic information from a single parent. If this new egg cell with all of its genes can be made to develop normally, the resulting offspring is a clone of the individual that donated the original cell nucleus. (In mammals, the egg would be implanted and develop inside the body of the female.) Cloning has been accomplished with animals as complex as sheep and pigs.

1. Which statement best describes the process of asexual reproduction?

(1) It involves two parents.
(2) It requires the combination of sperm and egg.
(3) It results in variation in the offspring.
(4) It involves the production of genetic copies.

2. Which statement concerning an organism produced by cloning is correct?

(1) The clone is genetically identical to its parent.
(2) The clone has the combined genes of both of its parents.
(3) The genetic makeup of the clone will be somewhat different from each of its parents.
(4) The appearance of the clone will be entirely different from that of its parents.

3. A student using a compound light microscope to observe a cell saw a number of threadlike nuclear structures resembling those shown below.

These threadlike structures are composed primarily of

(1) fat
(2) glucose
(3) DNA
(4) ATP

4. Plants with desirable qualities can be rapidly produced from the cells of a single plant by

(1) cloning
(2) gamete fusion
(3) meiosis
(4) immune response

5. Asexual reproduction differs from sexual reproduction in that, in asexual reproduction

(1) new organisms are usually genetically identical to the parent
(2) the reproductive cycle involves the production of gametes
(3) nuclei of sex cells fuse to form a zygote
(4) offspring show much genetic variation

6. Orchid plants reproduce slowly and take many years to produce flowers when grown from seeds. One technique that can be used in genetic research to reproduce rare orchid plants more rapidly is

(1) sexual reproduction (3) selective breeding
(2) fertilization   (4) cloning

7. Some bacteria produce an enzyme known as penicillinase, which prevents their destruction by penicillin. Since these same organisms reproduce asexually, they normally produce offspring that

(1) can be killed by penicillin
(2) have an abnormally high rate of mutation
(3) have variable numbers of chromosomes
(4) are resistant to penicillin

8. In plants, one way sexual reproduction differs from asexual reproduction is that in sexual reproduction

(1) more offspring are produced
(2) more genetic variation is seen in the offspring
(3) the offspring and the parents are identical
(4) more offspring survive to maturity

9. A man cuts some stems from several plants that are growing in his garden. He places the stems in wet sand until they grow roots, and then he transplants them to new pots. This method of reproducing plants is most like

(1) sexual reproduction
(2) cloning
(3) natural selection
(4) fertilization

10. Compared to the offspring of sexual reproduction in animals, the offspring of asexual reproduction will

(1) show greater variety
(2) be more resistant to disease
(3) be genetically identical to the parent
(4) grow larger

Cell Division

Cell division is the orderly separation of one cell into two. Before a cell divides, the genetic information in the DNA of the cells is duplicated exactly.

The process, by which a cell's genetic material divides, creating two complete sets of the cell's genetic material, is known as **mitosis.** Mitosis produces two cells that each have a full set of identical genes and chromosomes (unless a mutation occurs somewhere along the way).

During mitosis, one copy of the genetic information is distributed to each new cell. As a result, each new cell has all the information it needs to function properly. One-celled organisms make use of mitosis for asexual reproduction. Multicellular organisms mainly use mitosis for growth and for cell replacement and repair.

A second type of cell division is **meiosis.** This process divides the genetic material in a way that results in the production of the sex cells required by organisms that reproduce sexually. Each sex cell has only half the genetic material needed for a cell to function properly.

Mitotic Division/Mitosis

During the process of mitotic cell division, the double-stranded chromosomes that are visible during mitosis split into two identical single strands and move apart to opposite ends of the cell. This process is shown in Figure 4-3.

The process concludes when the cytoplasm divides, resulting in two smaller, but genetically identical, cells. Mitotic cell division in plants is illustrated in Figure 4-4.

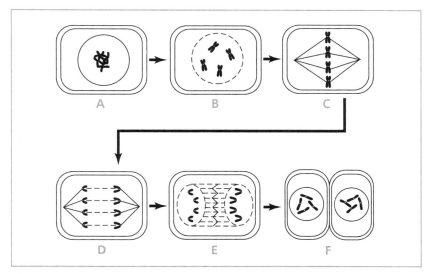

Figure 4-4. Mitotic cell division: The chromosomes in cell A have replicated, forming the double-stranded chromosomes that are finally visible in the cell at stage B. The four chromosomes line up single-file (C). Then the strands separate and move apart (D and E). The final result is two cells (F), each with four single-stranded chromosomes containing identical genetic information in their nuclei.

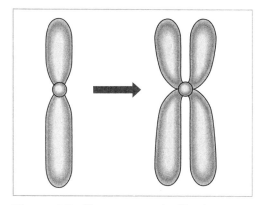

Figure 4-2. Chromosome duplication resulting from DNA replication: As a result of DNA replication, chromosomes become double-stranded.

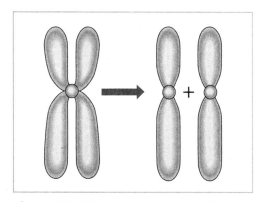

Figure 4-3. Chromosome during mitosis: When cells divide, each double-stranded chromosome separates into two identical single strands.

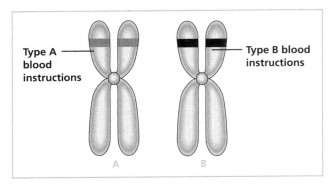

Figure 4-5. Two chromosomes with different information: The two chromosomes of each pair differ in the specific information they carry. For example, chromosome A may have coded gene instructions for type A blood, while the coded gene information on chromosome B may be for type B blood. Information for many other traits coded in the genes of these two chromosomes will be different, too, while some will be the same.

Meiotic Division/Meiosis

The gametes (sperm and eggs) formed during meiotic cell division each have only one half of the organism's genetic information—only one chromosome of each pair that is present in the body cells of that organism. However, a full set of genetic information is needed to produce a complete individual. When sperm and egg combine during **fertilization,** all of the newly paired chromosomes and all of the required genetic information are present in the fertilized egg.

Meiotic division begins with a body cell that has the full number of chromosomes typical of the species. Depending on the species, the cell contains one or more pairs of chromosomes that determine the traits of the organism. Figure 4-5 shows an example.

During the first phase of meiotic division, the double-stranded chromosomes line up in pairs in the center of the cell. The two chromosomes of each pair (still double-stranded) then separate, moving to opposite ends of the cell. Following this separation, the cell divides physically to form two cells.

The second phase involves the division of each of these two new cells. This time, however, the chromosomes line up in single file in the center of each cell. Each chromosome still consists of two strands. The strands separate and move to opposite ends of each of the dividing cells. When the process is complete, four cells have been formed, each having half the number of chromosomes of the organism's body cells. Each contains only one member of each original chromosome pair. Meiotic cell division is illustrated in Figures 4-6 and 4-7.

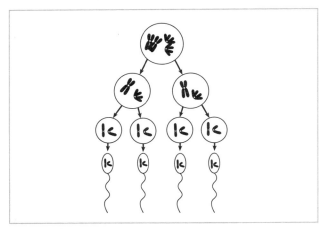

Figure 4-6. Meiotic cell division in the testes of males: Note the *four double-stranded chromosomes* (two pairs) present in the original cell. The pairs separate from each other during the first division—resulting in *two double-stranded chromosomes* in each of two cells. In the next division, the double-stranded chromosomes separate, leaving each final cell with *two single-stranded chromosomes*. These four cells can develop further into sperm cells in the testes of male individuals.

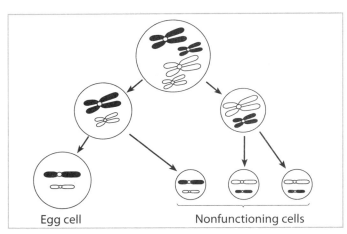

Figure 4-7. Meiotic cell division in the ovaries of females: This process is different from sperm cell formation because the cytoplasm divides unequally in each division, resulting in one large egg cell and three smaller cells that do not function. The egg cell is the one with the most cytoplasm.

Notice that the formation of cells during meiotic division, in which each cell has half the usual number of chromosomes, is very different from the duplication and distribution of a full set of chromosomes that occurs in mitotic division.

Meiotic division in females involves the same number of divisions and chromosome changes as in males. The division of the cytoplasm is where the two differ. The cytoplasm in a cell destined to become an egg cell divides unequally, resulting in one large egg cell and three small nonfunctioning cells. Meiotic division in females is shown in Figure 4-7.

Meiosis as a Source of Variation The events that occur during meiosis do more than simply divide chromosomes into smaller sets and form smaller cells. Meiosis is responsible for much of the genetic variation among the sex cells of each individual. For example, the two members of each pair of chromosomes carry different ways of expressing many of the organism's traits, so the way the different pairs randomly line up *in relation to other pairs* leads to many possible combinations in the sex cells that result. Two combinations are shown in Figure 4-8.

Another way variation can arise is by the exchange of parts of chromosomes, which occurs as they pair up during the first division. The process is sometimes called crossing-over. The result is shown in Figure 4-9. After separation, each set is unique. This means that there are no two sperm or egg cells, even from the same parent, that are alike. Each time a sperm and egg combine, a unique combination of genetic information results.

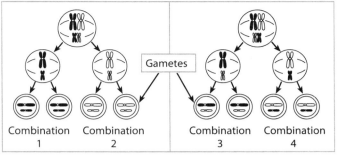

Figure 4-8. Two equally likely combinations of chromosomes lined up for meiotic division: A pair of chromosomes can be arranged in two ways when they pair up at the start of meiosis. This helps increase genetic variation. How many combinations do you see in the gametes? How would more pairs of chromosomes affect the number of possible arrangements?

Figure 4-9. Result of exchanging parts between chromosomes: When chromosomes line up in pairs during meiosis (Step 1), their strands may connect or cross over (Step 2) and then separate in a way that parts are exchanged. All four strands now carry different combinations of information (Step 3).

Table 4-1. Summary of Mitotic and Meiotic Cell Division		
Points of Comparison	**Mitotic Division**	**Meiotic Division**
Number of cell divisions	One	Two
Exchange of genetic material between chromosomes	No	Yes
Number of functioning cells produced from original	Two	Four sperm (in males) or one egg (in females)
Genetic makeup of final cells produced	Same as original	Highly variable gametes produced, each containing half of the genetic information of the original
Function of cells produced in multicellular organisms	Growth or replacement of body cells	Combine to form the zygote for reproduction

11. When complex plants are produced by cloning, which process is most directly involved?

(1) mitotic cell division
(2) meiotic cell division
(3) gamete production
(4) sperm cell fertilization

12. If a lobster loses a claw, it is capable of growing a new one. What process makes this possible?

(1) meiosis
(2) fertilization
(3) sexual reproduction
(4) mitosis

13. Organisms that reproduce asexually usually do so by a form of cell division called

(1) meiosis
(2) mitosis
(3) gamete formation
(4) sperm formation

14. A normal body cell of a fruit fly contains eight chromosomes. Each normal gamete of this organism contains

(1) four chromosomes as a result of meiosis
(2) four chromosomes as a result of mitosis
(3) eight chromosomes as a result of meiosis
(4) eight chromosomes as a result of mitosis

15. The process of mitotic cell division normally results in the production of

(1) four cells with half the number of chromosomes as the parent
(2) two cells with the same number of chromosomes as the parent
(3) two cells with only one chromosome from each parent
(4) one cell with a replicated set of matched chromosomes

16. Each of the two daughter (or offspring) cells that result from the normal mitotic division of the original parent cell contains

(1) the same number of chromosomes but different genes than the parent cell
(2) the same number of chromosomes and genes identical to those of the parent cell
(3) one half of the number of chromosomes but different genes than those of the parent cell
(4) one half of the number of chromosomes and genes identical to those of the parent cell

17. All types of asexual reproduction involve the process known as

(1) mitosis
(2) fertilization
(3) meiotic division
(4) aging

18. The diagrams below represent the sequence of events in a cell undergoing normal meiotic cell division.

- How many cells will finally be produced? [1]
- How many chromosomes will be in each cell? [1]
- Sketch one of the final cells, showing its chromosomes. [1]

19. The species chromosome number of orangutans is 48. Which diagram represents normal fertilization in orangutans?

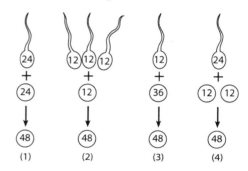

20. Which process is represented in the following photographs?

(1) mitotic cell division
(2) zygote formation
(3) fertilization
(4) recombination

21. If the sperm cells of a fish have 12 chromosomes, how many chromosomes would be found in the cells forming the scales of the fish?

(1) 6
(2) 12
(3) 24
(4) 48

Zygote Formation During fertilization, the gametes unite to form a **zygote**—a cell that contains all of the genetic information needed by the offspring. This process is known as **recombination,** since the genes from both parents recombine when fertilization occurs. Since a sex cell contains a unique combination of genetic material, the result of the random combination of any sperm and egg explains the variation found in offspring produced by sexual reproduction. This variation plays a key role in evolutionary change and species survival.

The zygote contains all the information necessary for growth, development, and eventual reproduction of the organism. The zygote divides by mitosis to form a multicellular organism. Fertilization, zygote formation, and some early mitotic divisions that occur in development are shown in Figure 4-10.

Early Development During the early stages of development, the cells that are formed by mitotic division begin to undergo **differentiation,** which simply means that they become different from one another. This leads to the formation of specialized cells, which form the tissues, and then the organs, of multicellular organisms.

In an **embryo,** an organism in an early stage of development, all the genetic information in each cell starts out the same. However, different genes are activated or deactivated in certain cells, causing them to make only some of the many proteins they are capable of synthesizing. As a result, these cells become different from others, and may develop into skin cells, muscle cells, or any of the other specialized cells of the organism. The activation or inactivation of genes can be due to environmental influences from within the cell, from surrounding cells, or from outside the organism.

When a gene is actively producing its protein, scientists say that the gene is **expressed.** There is much evidence that **gene expression,** which is the result of activated genes, can be modified through interaction with the environment. For example, fruit flies that have genes to develop curly wings will develop straight wings instead, if they are raised in a cooler than normal environment. Another example of an environmentally produced gene modification is a plant grown without light. Such a plant is white instead of green, because sunlight is needed to stimulate the gene that produces chlorophyll.

Figure 4-10. Fertilization, zygote formation, and early development: Note that all cell divisions here are by MITOTIC division.

Review Questions

Set 4.3

22. An exact duplication of the complete set of chromosomes of a cell, followed by the separation of these duplicate sets into two new cells, is known as

(1) mitotic cell division   (3) meiotic cell division
(2) zygote formation   (4) fertilization

23. New cells are produced within the uterus as a direct result of

(1) gamete formation
(2) meiotic cell division
(3) mitotic cell division
(4) ecological succession

24. The data table below summarizes the results of an experiment using primrose plants grown under different temperature conditions.

Data Table: Primrose Color Under Two Growing Conditions		
Flower Color	Temperature of 20°C	Temperature of 31°C
Color coded in DNA	Red White	Red White
Actual color expressed	Red White	White White

Which conclusion can be drawn from this data table?

(1) Color in primroses is determined only by gene action.
(2) Many traits are not inherited.
(3) Gene exchanges only occur when the plants are grown at lower temperatures.
(4) There is an interaction between environment and heredity.

---

25. When organisms reproduce sexually, the species number of chromosomes is maintained. This can be demonstrated with a diagram like the one below. Complete the diagram by filling in the blanks with the appropriate information.

Name of process A: _____

Number of chromosomes in gamete cell: _____

Name of process B: _____

Number of chromosomes in zygote: _____

Name of process C: _____

Number of chromosomes in new multicellular organism: _____

Base your answers to questions 26 through 29 on the diagrams below and on your knowledge of biology.

Diagram A represents the chromosomes in the nucleus of the body cell of a worm. Diagrams B through G represent chromosomal arrangements that may occur in other cells produced by this worm.

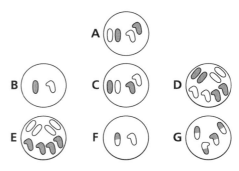

26. If meiosis failed to occur in both male and female worms, the zygote nucleus would resemble diagram

(1) E   (2) G   (3) C   (4) D

27. If genes were exchanged between a single pair of chromosomes during gamete formation, the gamete nucleus would most closely resemble diagram

(1) F   (2) B   (3) C   (4) G

28. The nucleus of a normal zygote formed when fertilization occurs in this species would most likely resemble diagram

(1) E   (2) F   (3) C   (4) D

29. The nucleus of a mature gamete from a female worm would most likely resemble diagram

(1) E   (2) B   (3) C   (4) D

---

30. In human females, gametes are produced in the

(1) uterus   (3) ovaries
(2) testes   (4) estrogen

31. Complex organisms produce sex cells that unite during fertilization forming a single cell known as

(1) an embryo   (3) a clone
(2) a gamete   (4) a zygote

Human Reproduction and Development

Human reproduction and development are carried out by specialized organs. The function of these organs is regulated by hormones from the endocrine system. In humans, as in nearly all mammals, fertilization and development occur internally—within the mother's body. Reproductive organs in other mammals are similar in appearance and function.

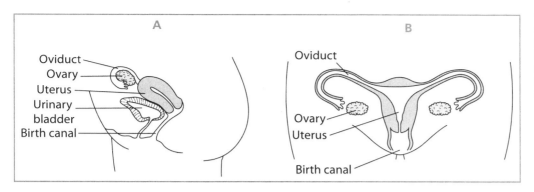

Figure 4-11. Two views of essential parts of the human female reproductive system and other structures: View A is from the side; View B is from the front.

Female Reproductive System The human female reproductive system is organized to produce gametes, to support internal fertilization and development, to exchange materials through the placenta, and to provide milk to the offspring.

In human females, the **ovaries** produce egg cells (female gametes) and the hormones **estrogen** and **progesterone.** These hormones are associated with sexual development and the reproductive process. The ovaries are located near the open ends of tubes called oviducts (egg ducts). The egg cell can be fertilized in the oviduct if sperm are present. The oviducts lead to the **uterus,** where the embryo develops into a fetus. The main parts of the female reproductive system are illustrated in Figure 4-11.

After the fertilized egg sinks into the thickened wall of the uterus, a placenta begins to form. The **placenta** is the organ responsible for the passage (by diffusion) of nutrients and oxygen from the mother's blood to the fetus. Wastes from the fetus also diffuse to the mother's blood through the placenta. During birth, the muscular uterus undergoes a series of contractions that eventually push the baby out of the mother's body. The early events of pregnancy are shown in Figure 4-12.

Male Reproductive System The **testes** of the male reproductive system are the organs that produce sperm cells. The testes also produce the hormone **testosterone,** which is associated with male sexual development and reproduction. Other structures associated with the male reproductive system produce the fluids and nutrients that are needed for the proper function and delivery of the male gametes to the female reproductive system. The essential parts of the human male reproductive system are shown in Figure 4-13.

Figure 4-12. Early events of pregnancy: The egg released by the ovary travels down the oviduct where fertilization occurs. Mitotic divisions of the zygote begin as it continues to the uterus, where the developing embryo sinks into the uterine wall, and the placenta forms. The placenta will supply essential materials and remove wastes throughout the rest of the pregnancy.

Table 4-2. The Functions of the Parts of the Human Female Reproductive System

Structure	Function
Ovary	Produces egg cells; releases the hormones estrogen and progesterone
Oviduct	Site of fertilization; carries egg to uterus
Uterus	Site where embryo and fetus develop in association with placenta
Birth canal (vagina)	Site where sperm enter and swim to egg in oviduct; passageway for the birth of baby

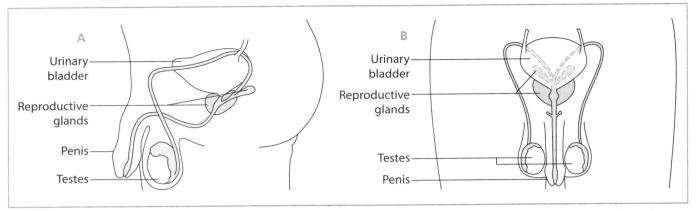

Figure 4-13. **Two views of the essential parts of the human male reproductive system and other structures:** View A is from the side; View B is from the front.

Hormonal Regulation The male reproductive system and other male characteristics, such as facial hair and a deep voice, that develop as sexual maturity is reached are influenced by several hormones, including testosterone from the testes. The development of the female reproductive system and female features, such as breast development and widening of the hips, also involves several important hormones, such as estrogen and progesterone.

Once sexual maturity is reached, females begin a regular cycle of about 28 days, during which an egg is released on about day 14. The timing of the events of this cycle is regulated by two hormones from the ovaries, along with several others from an endocrine gland in the brain. Figure 4-14 illustrates the changes in the level of several hormones associated with regulating this monthly cycle. The cycle varies slightly from individual to individual.

Although the interactions of the hormones are quite complex, estrogen and progesterone play important roles in the female reproductive cycle. Estrogen from the ovaries influences the sexual development of females. Together, estrogen and progesterone influence the preparation of the lining of the uterus so that a fertilized egg that embeds itself there can develop normally. Progesterone also maintains the uterine lining throughout pregnancy. For this reason, progesterone is often called the hormone of pregnancy. At the end of the cycle, if an egg is not fertilized, the levels of estrogen and progesterone decrease, and the lining of the uterus breaks down. Then the cycle begins again.

Figure 4-14. **Hormones and events associated with the monthly reproductive cycle in human females:** Notice the rise and fall in hormone levels at various times. These changes influence such events as the release of the egg from the ovary, the preparation of the uterus for a possible pregnancy, and the breakdown of the uterine lining if no pregnancy occurs. Remember that the timing of this cycle is NOT the same for everyone.

Human Development As with most other mammals, embryonic development continues in the uterus. Figure 4-15 shows some of the features of the uterus during pregnancy.

During the first part of pregnancy, cells continue to divide by mitotic division and begin to differentiate, forming tissues and organs. The placenta and a fluid-filled sac that cushions and protects the developing embryo both form at this time, too. After about two months, when all the major organs have begun to form, the embryo is called a **fetus.**

During the first few months, when essential organs are forming in the embryo, things can go wrong. Problems associated with either the embryo's inherited genes or the mother's exposure to various harmful environmental factors can affect the embryo. Harmful environmental factors that a woman should avoid at any time during pregnancy include alcohol, drugs, and tobacco. Use of these can lead to the birth of a baby with brain damage, drug addiction, and/or low birth weight and the problems associated with it. An embryo or fetus may also be harmed if the mother has a poor diet, is exposed to certain toxic substances, or gets certain infections, such as German measles or AIDS.

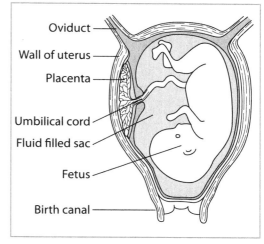

Figure 4-15. **The uterus during pregnancy**

After birth, cell differentiation and body growth continue until adulthood. During adulthood, the structures of the body slowly begin to age. Eventually, the organism weakens and dies. This process of birth, growth, development, aging, and death is a predictable pattern that applies not just to humans, but to all organisms.

Applications of Reproductive Technology

Recent discoveries by scientists have greatly changed the way we can deal with many problems involving the reproduction of humans as well as plants and other organisms. The knowledge we have gained has a variety of agricultural, ecological, and medical applications.

In the field of agriculture, scientists have produced plants that are resistant to insects, weed killers, and even frost. Such altered plants can then be cloned to produce thousands of genetically identical offspring. Using artificial insemination, scientists can generate hundreds of offspring from one farm animal. They can also freeze the sperm or fertilized eggs of an animal and transport them to animals thousands of miles away, at far less cost than transporting the animals themselves.

In the field of ecology, reproductive technology is being used to help build up populations of endangered species. Embryos from the endangered species have been transplanted into related species, who later give birth to offspring that are no different than they would be if they developed in the bodies of the endangered animals themselves. Also, hormones of insects that regulate their reproduction and development have been studied in an attempt to find ways to control insects without using poisonous chemicals.

In the field of medicine, recent scientific discoveries have led to new ways of dealing with reproductive problems in humans, other animals, and plants. Some women cannot become pregnant because of problems with their hormones, ovaries, or other parts of their reproductive systems. Reproductive technologies have enabled doctors to help infertile women become pregnant by using hormone therapy to adjust their hormones to normal levels. Sometimes doctors can extract several eggs from a woman's ovaries and fertilize them with sperm in a laboratory dish. When these

Figure 4-16. **Obtaining fetal cells and fluids during pregnancy:** Biochemical studies and chromosome analysis of the fetus can be done with cells and fluids removed during pregnancy.

fertilized eggs are implanted in the woman's uterus, a successful pregnancy may result.

Ultrasound and miniature video cameras allow doctors to view ovaries, oviducts, and other reproductive structures, or even a developing fetus, to determine if or where problems exist. Methods have also been developed to retrieve fetal cells that are present in the fluids around the developing fetus. (See Figure 4-16.) Doctors can then analyze the cells for chromosome abnormalities and the fluids for biochemical deficiencies that may threaten the health or development of the fetus.

Review Questions

32. What substances are involved in controlling the production of sperm and eggs in humans?

  (1) vitamins   (3) starches
  (2) hormones   (4) minerals

33. Which practice is essential to good prenatal care?

  (1) increased egg production
  (2) frequent dieting
  (3) avoidance of drugs
  (4) intake of antibiotics

34. Which part of the human male reproductive system produces hormones that influence the development of male sex characteristics?

  (1) penis   (3) gametes
  (2) testes   (4) ovaries

35. The diagram below represents a sequence of events in a human ovary.

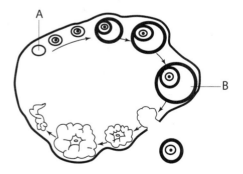

The process that occurs between stage A and stage B is known as

  (1) egg formation   (3) mitotic cell division
  (2) sperm formation   (4) cell recombination

36. The diagram below represents a series of events that takes place in the life cycle of humans.

Which term best describes the event taking place in the box labeled X?

  (1) fertilization   (3) meiosis
  (2) immune response   (4) protein synthesis

Base your answers to questions 37 through 41 on the diagram below and on your knowledge of biology. The diagram represents the human female reproductive system.

37. Fertilization usually occurs within structure

  (1) A   (2) B   (3) C   (4) D

38. A placenta normally develops in structure

  (1) A   (2) B   (3) C   (4) D

39. The structure that produces estrogen and progesterone is

  (1) A   (2) B   (3) C   (4) D

Base your answers to questions 40 through 42 on the diagram below and on your knowledge of biology. The diagram represents the human male and female reproductive systems.

40. Gametes are produced in
    (1) A, only   (3) both A and B
    (2) B, only   (4) neither A nor B

41. Estrogen and progesterone are produced in
    (1) A, only   (3) both A and B
    (2) B, only   (4) neither A nor B

42. A substance is produced that influences both the reproductive cycle and the development of sex characteristics in
    (1) A, only   (3) both A and B
    (2) B, only   (4) neither A nor B

---

43. In humans and other mammals, nutrients are transferred from the mother's bloodstream to the embryo's bloodstream across the
    (1) placenta   (3) ovary
    (2) uterus   (4) intestine

44. Which substance is a waste that would normally diffuse across the placenta from the embryo to the mother?
    (1) glucose   (3) amino acid
    (2) oxygen   (4) carbon dioxide

45. The egg of a mammal is smaller than that of a bird because the embryo of the mammal obtains its nutrients from the
    (1) placenta through the process of diffusion
    (2) mammary glands of the mother
    (3) blood of the mother when it mixes with the blood of the embryo
    (4) yolk stored in the uterus of the mother

Base your answers to questions 46 and 47 on the diagram below, which represents an experiment, and on your knowledge of biology.

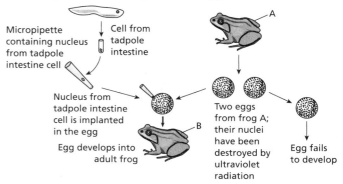

Micropipette containing nucleus from tadpole intestine cell

Cell from tadpole intestine

Nucleus from tadpole intestine cell is implanted in the egg

Egg develops into adult frog

Two eggs from frog A; their nuclei have been destroyed by ultraviolet radiation

Egg fails to develop

46. An inference that can be made from this experiment is that
    (1) adult frog B will have the same genetic traits as the tadpole
    (2) adult frog A can develop only from an egg and a sperm
    (3) fertilization must occur in order for frog eggs to develop into adult frogs
    (4) the nucleus of a body cell fails to function when transferred to other cell types

47. Other scientists substituted a nucleus from a frog sperm cell and no adult frog developed. Explain why a sperm cell nucleus would not work in this procedure. [1]

Base your answers to questions 48 through 51 on the diagram below and on your knowledge of biology. The diagram represents the human female reproductive system.

Fill in the boxes numbered 48 through 51 in the chart below using the information from the diagram.

Name of Structure	Letter on Diagram	Function of Structure
48. _____ [1]	49. _____ [1]	produces gametes
uterus	D	50. _____ [1]
51. _____ [1]	B	transports oxygen directly to the embryo

Practice Questions
for the New York Regents Exam

Directions
Review the Test-Taking Strategies section of this book. Then answer the following questions. Read each question carefully and answer with a correct choice or response.

Part A

1 Compared to the number of chromosomes in a normal human body cell, the number of chromosomes in a normal sperm cell is
   (1) the same
   (2) twice as great
   (3) half as great
   (4) four times as great

2 Children born to the same parents are usually very different from each other. These differences result primarily from the process of
   (1) mitotic division
   (2) meiosis
   (3) asexual reproduction
   (4) cloning

3 Human growth and sexual development are controlled by
   (1) nerves
   (2) hormones
   (3) the digestive system
   (4) the excretory system

4 The diagram below represents the human male reproductive system.

If structure X were cut and tied off at the line, which change would occur immediately?
   (1) Hormones would no longer be produced.
   (2) Sperm would no longer be produced.
   (3) Sperm would be produced but no longer released from the body.
   (4) Urine would be produced but no longer released from the bladder

Base your answers to question 5 through 7 on the diagram below, which represents a stage in human development.

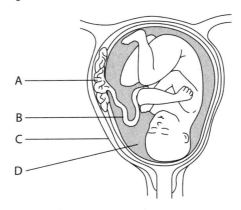

5 The exchange of oxygen, food, and wastes between mother and fetus occurs at
   (1) A
   (2) B
   (3) C
   (4) D

6 What is the function of the fluid labeled D?
   (1) nourishment
   (2) protection
   (3) excretion
   (4) respiration

7 The structure labeled C, within which development occurs, is known as the
   (1) birth canal
   (2) uterus
   (3) ovary
   (4) placenta

8 Which is arranged in the correct sequence?
   (1) fertilization → embryo development → meiosis → birth
   (2) embryo development → meiosis → fertilization → birth
   (3) meiosis → fertilization → embryo development → birth
   (4) fertilization → meiosis → embryo development → birth

9 The diagram at the right represents a cell that will undergo mitosis.

Which of the diagrams best illustrates the daughter cells that result from a normal mitotic cell division of the parent cell shown?

(1)   (3)

(2)   (4)

Part B

Base your answers to questions 10 through 14 on the diagram below, which shows some events in the human female reproductive cycle, and on your knowledge of biology.

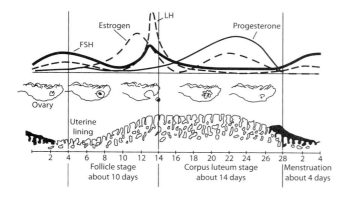

10 During which part of this cycle does the breakdown of the thickened uterine lining occur?
(1) ovulation
(2) corpus luteum stage
(3) menstruation
(4) follicle stage

11 On or about which day is the egg released from the ovary?
(1) day 8
(2) day 14
(3) day 20
(4) day 28

12 What is the average length of this reproductive cycle?
(1) 32 days   (3) 14 days
(2) 28 days   (4) 4 days

13 The hormone FSH stimulates the development of a follicle in the ovary of a human female. As the follicle develops, it secretes estrogen. A high level of estrogen decreases the secretion of FSH. This mechanism is an example of
(1) gamete development
(2) cell differentiation
(3) positive feedback
(4) negative feedback

14 Identify another human reproductive hormone that is *not* shown on this diagram. [1]

---

15 Compare the number of chromosomes present in the offspring with the number of chromosomes present in the parent organism in the process of cloning. [1]

Base your answers to questions 16 through 19 on the diagram below and on your knowledge of biology. The diagram represents a single-celled organism, such as an ameba, undergoing the changes shown.

16 As a result of these processes, the single-celled organism accomplishes
(1) gamete production   (3) sexual reproduction
(2) energy production   (4) asexual reproduction

17 Process 1 is known as
(1) replication   (3) differentiation
(2) meiosis   (4) digestion

18 Process 1 and process 2 are directly involved in
(1) meiotic cell division (3) fertilization
(2) mitotic cell division (4) recombination

19 The genetic content of *C* is usually identical to the genetic content of
(1) *B* but not *D*   (3) *D* but not *A*
(2) both *B* and *D*   (4) both *A* and *D*

Base your answers to questions 20 and 21 on the information below and on your knowledge of biology.

The reproductive cycle in a human female is not functioning properly. An imbalance of hormones is diagnosed as the cause.

20 Identify one hormone directly involved in the human female reproductive system that could cause this problem. [1]

21 Explain why some cells in a female's body respond to reproductive hormones while other cells do not. [1]

22 The data in the table below indicate the presence of specific reproductive hormones in blood samples taken from three individuals. An X in the hormone column indicates a positive lab test for the appropriate levels necessary for normal reproductive functioning in that individual.

Data Table			
Individuals	Hormones Present		
	Testosterone	Progesterone	Estrogen
1		X	X
2			X
3	X		

Which processes could occur in individual 3?

(1) production of sperm, only
(2) production of sperm and production of eggs
(3) production of eggs and embryonic development
(4) production of eggs, only

Base your answers to questions 23 through 25 on the diagram below, which represents some stages in the development of an embryo, and on your knowledge of biology.

23 This entire sequence (A through embryo) started directly after

A B C D E F G

(1) the periodic shedding of a thickened uterine lining
(2) mitotic cell division in a testis
(3) meiotic cell division in the placenta
(4) the process of fertilization

24 If cell A has 46 chromosomes, how many chromosomes will most likely be found in each cell of stage G?
(1) 23   (3) 69
(2) 46   (4) 92

25 The arrow labeled X represents the process of
(1) meiosis   (3) differentiation
(2) recombination   (4) cloning

26 An incomplete diagram of meiosis in the ovary of an animal is shown below.

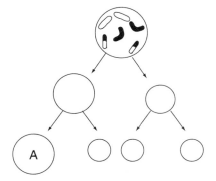

On the diagram below, draw in the chromosomes of cell A. Your drawing should show the usual result of the process of meiosis. [1]

Base your answers to questions 27 and 28 on the diagram below and on your knowledge of biology.

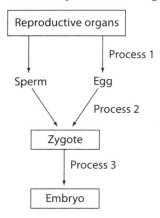

27 State why Process 2 is necessary in sexual reproduction. [1]

28 State one difference between the cells produced by Process 1 and the cells produced by Process 3. [1]

Directions (29–31): The diagrams below represent organs of two individuals. The diagrams are followed by a list of sentences. For each phrase in questions 29 through 31, select the sentence from the list below that best applies to that phrase and record its number.

Individual A   **Individual B**

Sentences

1. The phrase is correct for both Individual *A* and Individual *B*.
2. The phrase is not correct for either Individual *A* or Individual *B*.
3. The phrase is correct for Individual *A*, only.
4. The phrase is correct for Individual *B*, only.

29 Contains organs that produce gametes [1]

30 Contains organs involved in internal fertilization [1]

31 Contains a structure in which a zygote divides by mitosis [1]

32 Which activity most directly involves the process represented in the diagram below?

(1) a gamete reproducing sexually
(2) a white blood cell engulfing bacteria
(3) a zygote being produced in an ovary
(4) an animal repairing damaged tissue

Part C

Base your answer to question 33–35 on the information below and on your knowledge of biology.

The Critical Role of the Placenta

The proper functioning of the placenta is critical to the growth and development of a healthy fetus. For example, the placenta appears to act as a nutrient sensor. It regulates the amounts and types of nutrients that are transported from the mother to the fetus.

Improper functioning of the placenta can alter the structure and function of specific cells and organ systems in the developing fetus, putting it at risk for health problems as an adult. For example, in some pregnancies, the placenta develops a resistance to blood flow.

This resistance appears to force the heart of the fetus to work harder. This could result in an increased chance of the individual developing heart disease as an adult. A group of hormones known as glucocorticoids affects the development of all the tissues and organ systems. One of the things this group of hormones does is to alter cell function by changing the structure of cell membrane receptors.

33–35 Discuss the importance of the placenta in the development of a healthy fetus. In your answer, be sure to:
- identify two factors that could influence the nutrients that can pass from the mother to the fetus [1]
- identify the group of hormones that alter cell membrane receptors and explain how this alteration can affect cell function [1]
- state the role of the uterus in the development of the fetus and the placenta [1]

---

36 The production of a normal baby involves protecting the developing embryo from harmful environmental factors. State three ways in which the pregnant woman could avoid exposing the developing embryo to environmental risks. [1]

37 The diagram below shows some steps involved in preparing tissue cultures in plants.

Remove leaves, roots, and top third of plant

Wash, break, and sterilize stem pieces

Insert cork borer to remove pith

Cut pith transversely in sterile petri dish

Place pith disks on growth medium

Transfer to root initiation media

Transfer to soil

Compare the genetic makeup of the offspring plants that are transferred to the soil to that of the parent plant that provided the stem pieces. [1]

38 The process of meiosis followed by fertilization is necessary to maintain the species chromosome number of a sexually reproducing species. For instance, a species with 24 chromosomes in each body cell normally has offspring that also have 24 chromosomes in their body cells.

Explain the specific way that meiotic cell division and fertilization interact to help maintain the species chromosome number. [1]

Base your answers to questions 39 through 41 on the information below and on your knowledge of biology.

Egg Laying vs. Bearing Live Young

Three groups of animals in which most species lay eggs for reproduction are amphibians, reptiles, and birds.

Most female amphibians lay hundreds of eggs in water, which are then fertilized by sperm from the male. Many reptiles lay between 1 and 200 eggs at a time, often in nests on land. The eggs have a leathery shell.

Birds usually lay between one and four eggs at a time in nests on land. Wild bird eggs usually have shells similar to those of the domestic chicken.

Most mammals bear live young. Some of these mammals, humans, for example, usually give birth to one live offspring at a time.

39 State one reason that individuals of some species must lay hundreds of eggs in order for the species to survive. [1]

40 Explain why fertilization in reptiles and birds must be internal. [1]

41 State two reasons that the human species has been able to survive, even though usually only one offspring is born at a time. [1]

Base your answers to question 42–46 on the information below and on your knowledge of biology.

Scientists have successfully cloned sheep and cattle for several years. A farmer is considering having a flock of sheep cloned from a single individual.

42–46 Discuss the process of cloning a flock of sheep. In your answer be sure to:
- state how a cloned flock would differ from an flock of sheep that was not cloned [1]
- state one advantage of having a cloned flock [1]
- state one disadvantage of having a cloned flock [1]
- state one reason the farmer would be able to mate the sheep in his flock with others in the flock [1]
- explain why breeding a sheep from his flock with sheep not in his flock would produce offspring that are not all identical clones [1]

Base your answers to question 47–48 on the information below and on your knowledge of biology.

47–48 Sexual and asexual reproduction are similar in some ways and different in others. Compare the two types. In your answer be sure to:
- Identify which type of reproduction results in genetically identical offspring. Explain why this occurs [1]
- describe one other way the two methods differ from each other [1]

49–53 Base your answers to question 49-53 on the information below and on your knowledge of biology.

A human is a complex organism that develops from a zygote. Briefly explain some of the steps in this process. In your answer be sure to:
- explain how a zygote is formed [1]
- compare the genetic content of the zygote to that of a body cell of the parents [1]
- identify one developmental process involved in the change from a zygote into an embryo [1]
- identify the structure in which fetal development usually occurs [1]
- identify one factor that can affect fetal development and explain how that factor affects fetal development [1]

Base your answers to questions 54 and 55 on the information below and on your knowledge of biology. The reproductive cycle in a human female is not functioning properly. An imbalance of hormones is diagnosed as the cause.

54 Identify one hormone directly involved in the human female reproductive system that could cause this problem. [1]

55 Explain why some cells in a female's body respond to reproductive hormones while other cells do not. [1]

Evolution

What do **You** Think?

Evolution

Natural selection is a process that allows the best adapted of the species to survive and reproduce.

Evolution is based on natural selection, which is very, very slow.

Evolution explains how life originated on Earth millions of years ago.

Natural selection is a process that gives organisms what they need when they need it to survive and reproduce.

Vocabulary

adaptive value

evolution

extinction

fossil record

genetic variation

geologic time

mutation

natural selection

overproduction

theory

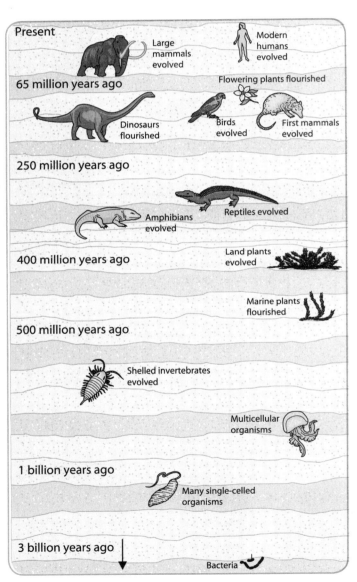

Present

Large mammals evolved

Modern humans evolved

65 million years ago

Flowering plants flourished

Dinosaurs flourished

Birds evolved

First mammals evolved

250 million years ago

Reptiles evolved

Amphibians evolved

400 million years ago

Land plants evolved

Marine plants flourished

500 million years ago

Shelled invertebrates evolved

Multicellular organisms

1 billion years ago

Many single-celled organisms

3 billion years ago

Bacteria

Figure 5-1. Examples from the fossil record

Topic Overview

Extensive evidence indicates that life on Earth began more than three billion years ago. Fossils found in ancient rocks have given us many clues to the kinds of life that existed long ago. The first living organisms were simple, single-celled organisms. Over time, more complex single-celled creatures developed. Then, about a billion years ago, increasingly complex, multicellular organisms began to appear. The idea that explains how this change in species has occurred over time is known as **evolution.**

The Theory of Evolution

The theory of evolution is accepted as the central theme of modern biology. It helps biologists understand how the variations among individuals can lead to changes in an entire species of organism. Since it was first suggested by Charles Darwin, the concept of evolution has been refined by massive amounts of evidence offered by thousands of scientists. So much evidence has been collected that evolution now has the stature of a **theory,** which is a concept that has been tested and confirmed in many different ways and can be used by scientists to make predictions about the natural world.

The theory of evolution helps biologists understand the similarities (such as bone structure and biochemistry) among different organisms. It also helps to explain the history of life that is revealed by the **fossil record,** which is a collection of fossils that provides clues to the history of Earth's organisms.

The fossil record spans much of **geologic time**—the billions of years of Earth's history—revealing many changes in environments as well as species. Figure 5-1 shows examples from the fossil record through geologic time.

Evolution does NOT necessarily produce long-term progress in any set direction. Instead, evolutionary change appears to be more like the growth of a bush. Notice in Figure 5-2 that some branches survive from the beginning with little or no change. Some die out altogether. Others branch repeatedly, with each new branch representing a new species.

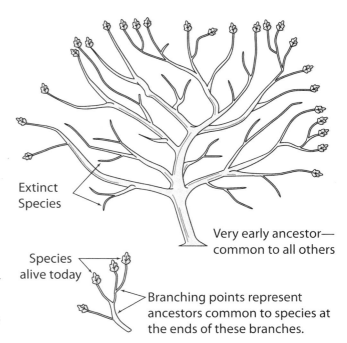

Figure 5-2. Evolution modeled as the growth of a bush: Evolutionary changes in species are like the growth of a bush in which some twigs grow and branch, while others die. The tips of the living twigs represent species that are alive now.

Review Questions

Set 5.1

1. Evolution is the process of
   (1) development of one-celled organisms from mammals
   (2) change in species over long periods of time
   (3) embryonic development of modern humans
   (4) changing energy flow in food webs

2. Which phrase best defines evolution?
   (1) an adaptation of an organism to its environment
   (2) a sudden replacement of one community by another
   (3) the isolation of organisms from each other for many years
   (4) a process of change in species over a period of time

3. The study of fossils has allowed scientists to
   (1) describe past environments and the history of life
   (2) study present ocean temperatures at different depths
   (3) analyze the chemical composition of sedimentary rocks and minerals
   (4) describe the details of the process by which life first began on Earth

4. The evolution of species is often represented as a branching tree similar to the one shown in the diagram below. The names shown represent different groups of organisms alive today; the lines represent their evolutionary histories.

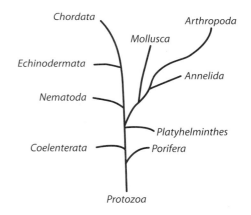

The statement that is best supported by the diagram is that
(1) *Annelida* and *Arthropoda* have an ancestor in common
(2) *Echinodermata* are more closely related to *Mollusca* than they are to *Chordata*
(3) *Mollusca* and *Arthropoda* evolved before *Porifera*
(4) *Annelida* and *Arthropoda* evolved from *Echinodermata*

5. The diagram below represents possible lines of the evolution of primates.

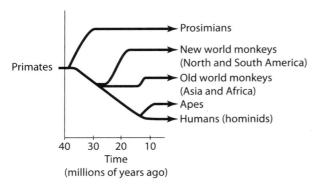

Which inference can best be made based on the diagram?

(1) Adaptations for living in trees are inherited by all primates.
(2) Humans and apes have a common ancestor.
(3) The embryos of monkeys and apes are identical.
(4) The period of development is similar in most primates.

The Mechanics of Evolution

Darwin did not only suggest that species evolved. He also suggested how that evolution might have occurred. Darwin thought that the mechanism of evolution was like the process of artificial selection practiced by breeders of plants and animals. (See Figure 5-3.) He used the term **natural selection** to indicate that the process of evolution was controlled by "nature" rather than by people. In the process of natural selection, individuals that survive are able to breed and pass their genetic information to the next generation. Those that are not as successful in the environment often die without leaving any offspring.

Figure 5-3. Racehorses are bred for speed and stamina: When humans breed plants or animals, they select specific traits, such as speed, flower color, or resistance to insects. In a similar way, "nature" selects any trait that increases an organism's ability to survive and reproduce.

Overview of Evolution

Darwin's ideas are easy to understand: In any environment, an individual may be born with a characteristic that makes it stronger, faster—any sort of advantage that will help it survive and reproduce. The individuals that prove to be the best adapted to their environment will be more likely to survive. If they do survive, their favorable characteristics will be passed on to many of their offspring. As a result, these useful adaptations, which first appeared randomly, are likely to become more and more common with each generation. Similarly, characteristics that reduce an individual's chance of surviving and reproducing will tend to decrease over time.

The long-term result of natural selection is a change in the frequency of certain traits in a population. Beneficial traits tend to become more common; harmful traits tend to become less common. As the frequency of a trait in a population increases or decreases over time, it can be said that the species is evolving. Note that the population—not the individual—changes as a result of evolution. An individual does not evolve; each is born with genetic information that may or may not help it survive and reproduce. As natural selection leads to changes in the composition of a population, that population may have more individuals with a certain favorable characteristic than it did earlier.

Interactions and Evolution

The driving force behind evolution is the interaction between individual organisms and their environment. Conditions that are vital to the process of evolution include

- the potential for a species to increase its numbers, known as **overproduction**
- the <u>finite</u> (limited) supply of resources needed for life
- the genetic variation of offspring due to mutation and genetic "shuffling"
- the selection by the environment of those offspring better able to survive and reproduce

All of these conditions, which are explained below, are involved in the process of evolutionary change.

Overproduction In each generation, a species has the potential to produce more offspring than can possibly survive. Species with high reproductive potential include bacteria, insects, dandelions, and rabbits. (See Figure 5-4.) If all the offspring of these organisms survived, they would overrun Earth. However, that does not happen.

Scientists have learned that, in stable environments, the population of a species remains about the same from one year to the next. For example, no matter how many deer are born in one year, at the same time the next year, there will be about the same number of deer as there was the year before. Similarly, some fish species lay millions of eggs, but by the next year, the population of that species is the same as it was the previous year. This happens because not all of the new individuals that are born or hatched will survive to adulthood.

The Struggle for Survival Overproduction leads to competition among the members of a species. Not all offspring survive long enough to reproduce. In many cases, chance determines which offspring survive. For example, wind may blow a dandelion seed to a patch of fertile soil or into a lake. A deer may be born in a wildlife preserve or in the path of a forest fire.

But chance is not the only factor that determines which offspring will survive and which will die. The offspring all have to cope with environmental conditions, such as temperature, disease, parasites, and predators. They also need resources, such as oxygen, water, food, and shelter. However, the supply of these resources is finite. If they are to survive, organisms of the same species must compete for limited resources. Depending on their success as competitors, individuals will get the resources they need to survive, or they will not. Those that are the best suited to their environment are more likely to survive. Many of the losers in this struggle for resources will die before they have a chance to reproduce.

Variation The new traits that can lead to evolution come from normal variation within species. As shown in Figure 5-5, organisms within a species are never exactly alike. For example, some adult grasshoppers have longer legs than others; some have a lighter body color. In any group of gray squirrels, some have sharper or longer claws,

Rabbit Population Group	
Number of Generations	Number of Rabbits
1	100
72	3,354
100	13,150

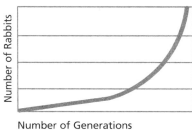

Figure 5-4. Overproduction: Rabbits are known for their high reproductive potential.

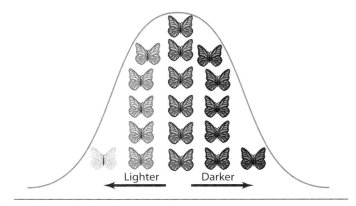

Figure 5-5. Genetic variation: In this example, a species of green butterflies might have individuals that vary in color from very dark green to very light green.

lighter or darker fur, bigger or smaller ears, and so on. The differences among offspring are due to **genetic variation**—the unique combination of traits each organism inherits from its parents.

Some variations give individuals an advantage over others in their struggle for resources. Any trait that helps an organism survive and reproduce under a given set of environmental conditions is said to have **adaptive value.** For example, a rabbit's ability to blend in with its surroundings may allow it to escape capture by a fox. The coloration it inherited has adaptive value for the rabbit, allowing it to escape predators and survive. When the fox population is high, this adaptation may be especially valuable to rabbits that inherited it.

Selection by the Environment As Darwin proposed with his idea of natural selection, traits with an adaptive value in a specific environment give individuals in that environment a competitive advantage. If the beneficial trait is passed to the offspring, they, too, are more likely to survive and reproduce. The proportion of individuals with these advantageous characteristics will increase because they are better able to compete than individuals without the beneficial trait. Eventually, nearly all the individuals in the population will have the beneficial trait. This change in the characteristics present in population over time is evolution.

Although some evolution may occur without much change in the environment, it is usually the adaptation of a species to changes in its environment that brings about evolution. Therefore, a changing environment is often the driving force for evolutionary change.

Review Questions
Set 5.2

6. The process of natural selection is based on the assumption that
   (1) environmental changes will cause changes in body structure in individuals
   (2) most changes from generation to generation are the result of mutations
   (3) part of the population of organisms always remains stable
   (4) different traits inherited by offspring have different survival value.

Base your answers to questions 7 and 8 on the information below and on your knowledge of biology.

A study of beetles on an isolated oceanic island formed by volcanic action and far from any other land shows that all of the beetles that are presently on the island are incapable of flying. A study of fossils from different rock layers of the island shows that the island was once populated with flying beetles. The graph shows the probable change over the last 5,000 years.

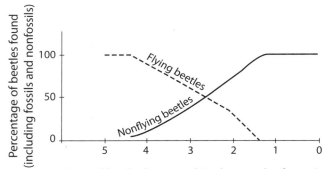

Ages of fossils discovered (in thousands of years)

7. The loss of flying ability by the beetle is most probably the result of
   (1) predators eating the beetles' wings
   (2) beetles not using their wings
   (3) genetic changes in the beetles
   (4) lack of vegetation for the beetle to feed on

8. The graph indicates that the non-flying beetles probably

(1) were better adapted to the environment
(2) arrived from other islands 5000 years ago
(3) mutated and produced flying beetles
(4) became extinct about 1.5 thousand years ago

9. When lions prey on a herd of antelope, some of the antelope are eliminated. Which part of the theory of evolution can be used to describe this situation?

(1) asexual reproduction of the fittest
(2) isolation of the species
(3) survival of the best adapted
(4) new species development due to mutation

10. Every spring, each mature female fish of a particular species produces several million eggs. However, the total population of this species remains at around 10,000 from one year to the next.

State two reasons why the fish population remains approximately the same from one generation to the next. [1]

Base your answers to questions 11 and 12 on the diagram below and on your knowledge of biology.

The diagram represents a small island divided by a mountain range. The mountain range prevents populations A and B from making contact with each other. At one time in the past, however, lowlands existed in the area indicated, and the ancestors of population A and population B were members of the same population.

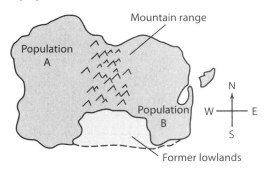

11. Over many years, the climate on the west side of the island has undergone drastic changes while the climate on the east side has remained the same. It is most likely that population B will

(1) migrate and intermix with population A
(2) become extinct
(3) have evolved more than population A
(4) have evolved less than population A

12. The organisms of population A and population B are now incapable of interbreeding and producing offspring. Which biological process most likely caused this situation to occur?

(1) artificial selection   (3) natural selection
(2) cloning   (4) asexual reproduction

Base your answers to questions 13 and 14 on the information and graph below and on your knowledge of biology.

Scientists studying a moth population in a wooded area of New York State recorded the distribution of moth wing color as shown in the following graph. While observing the moths, scientists noted that the moths spent most of the day resting on trees and looking for food during the night. The woods contained trees with a bark color that was predominantly brown.

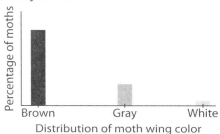

Distribution of moth wing color

13. A fungus infection affected nearly all trees in the woods so that the color of the tree bark was changed to a gray-white color. Which graph shows the most probable results that would occur in the distribution of wing color in this moth population after a long period of time?

14. As a result of the fungus infection, the change in moth wing color distribution would most probably occur by the

(1) production of sex cells by mitosis
(2) natural selection of favorable variations
(3) eating of pigments in fungus spores
(4) production of mutations as a result of eating the fungus

Sources of Variation

As you may recall, the arrangement of an individual's DNA bases determines all the inherited characteristics of that individual. Any change in bases or their sequence may bring about a change in the individual. But not all of those changes can be passed on to the individual's offspring. In sexually reproducing organisms, only changes in the genes of sex cells can be passed on to the next generation and become the basis for evolutionary change. Other types of variation (such as changes to body cells) die with the individual. For example, a father who has built huge muscles due to exercise does NOT pass those large muscles to his offspring.

There are two major ways an organism can wind up with genes that differ from those of its parents. Some genetic variations arise because of mutations in the genes of an organism. Others are due to "genetic shuffling," the routine sorting and recombination of genes that occurs during sexual reproduction.

Mutation A **mutation** is a change in the base sequence of a DNA molecule. Mutations occur as random, chance events that cannot be predicted. Some mutations occur as errors in DNA as cells function. Radiation and some chemicals can also cause them. Mutations are an important source of totally new forms of genes.

When mutations occur in body cells, they affect only that individual. However, a mutation in a single-celled organism or in the sex cells of a multicellular organism can be passed on to the offspring. In organisms that reproduce sexually, only mutations in the genes of sex cells can become the basis for evolutionary change.

Nearly all mutations are harmful and may affect the offspring so severely that it cannot survive. A few mutations benefit the individual, however, and can increase its chance of surviving, reproducing, and passing the mutation to the next generation. A beneficial mutation may lead to the evolution of a new species. For example, the ancestors of polar bears probably had dark fur. If a mutation resulted in a bear with white fur, that bear probably would have died young. However, if the mutation occurred in a snowy environment, the white fur would be a useful mutation, allowing the bear to stalk its prey more effectively.

Genetic Shuffling The sorting and random recombining of genes during meiosis and fertilization results in new and different combinations of genes. These genes can be passed on to individual offspring. The process is similar to shuffling and dealing cards. The deck stays the same, but nearly every hand will be slightly different because of mixing and rearranging during shuffling. At fertilization, even more variety is introduced because now cards from "two decks" are combined. Although mutations provide new genetic instructions, genetic shuffling is the main source of the variation that exists among the members of any sexually reproducing species.

15. Which statement is basic to the theory of evolution by natural selection?

   (1) In general, living organisms maintain a constant population from generation to generation.
   (2) Changes in living organisms are almost completely the result of mutations.
   (3) Natural variations are inherited.
   (4) There is little competition between species.

16. Which statement is *not* included as part of our modern understanding of evolution?

   (1) Sexual reproduction and mutations provide variation among offspring.
   (2) Traits are transmitted by genes and chromosomes.
   (3) More offspring are produced than can possibly survive.
   (4) New organs are formed when organisms need them.

17. The modern theory of evolution states that a basis for variation within a species is provided by

   (1) mutations
   (2) asexual reproduction
   (3) cloning
   (4) overproduction

18. Sexual reproduction is related to evolution because sexual reproduction

   (1) occurs only in more recently evolved forms of animal life
   (2) increases the chances of extinction of different species
   (3) increases the chances for variations to occur
   (4) is the more usual kind of reproduction

19. Mutations can be transmitted to the next generation if they are present in

   (1) hormones   (3) body cells
   (2) gametes   (4) muscle cells

20. A new chemical was discovered and introduced into a culture containing one species of bacteria. Within a day, most of the bacteria were dead, but a few remained alive. Which statement best explains why some of the bacteria survived?

   (1) They had a genetic variation that gave them resistance to the chemical.
   (2) They were exposed to the chemical long enough to develop a resistance to it.
   (3) They mutated and became a different species after exposure to the chemical.
   (4) They absorbed the chemical and broke it down in their digestive systems.

21. Which characteristics of a population would most likely indicate the lowest potential for evolutionary change in that population?

   (1) sexual reproduction and few mutations
   (2) sexual reproduction and many mutations
   (3) asexual reproduction and few mutations
   (4) asexual reproduction and many mutations

22. Which two factors provide the genetic basis for variation within many species?

   (1) asexual reproduction and meiosis
   (2) mutations and sexual reproduction
   (3) competition and the synthesis of proteins
   (4) ecological succession and mitosis

23. Which statement best describes a current understanding of natural selection?

   (1) Natural selection influences the frequency of an adaptation in a population.
   (2) Natural selection has been discarded as an important concept in evolution.
   (3) Changes in gene frequencies due to natural selection have little effect on the evolution of species.
   (4) New mutations of genetic material are due to natural selection.

The Results of Genetic Variation

The changes that result from mutation or genetic shuffling in the sex cells may affect the offspring in several ways. Most of the changes can be categorized as structural, functional, or behavioral.

Structural Change The structure of any organism is the result of its species' entire evolutionary history. There are millions of examples of variations that have resulted in structural changes. For example, the polar bear (like other bears) has thick fur that keeps it warm in its cold environment.

Bird wing

Human arm

Whale flipper

Bat wing

Figure 5-6. Similar bone structure of different species: The limbs shown above are from different species and have different functions, but they share many structural similarities. They are all made of the same type of bones and are attached in a similar way. The whale flipper is actually much larger than the other limbs. Notice that the ulna and radius of the bat wing are almost fused.

Polar bears, however, have evolved an extra protection from the cold. The soles of their feet are also mostly covered with thick fur. This extra fur not only keeps their skin off the ice but also improves traction.

The theory of evolution has helped scientists explain many of the structural variations and similarities found in organisms. For example, in Figure 5-6, notice that each limb has one thick "long" bone, two thinner "long" bones, and a "hand" with five digits. The ancestor of these animals most likely had a similar limb structure. At one point, however, limbs began to vary, evolving into arms, legs, wings, or flippers.

Structures that are no longer used by modern organisms give scientists clues to the evolutionary history of a species. Some snakes, for example, have tiny, nonfunctional leg bones—an indication that they probably evolved from four-legged, lizard-like ancestors.

Functional Change Molecular or biochemical changes affect how an organism works. These are functional changes. For example, all working muscles emit an extremely tiny electrical output. In some eels, however, that electrical output has evolved into an adaptation that helps it find and capture food. The muscles of these eels can produce a massive shock that stuns or kills its prey.

Changes in DNA often lead to functional changes. One example is a mutation in the DNA of certain one-celled organisms that led to their ability to make enzymes that digest wood. Another is the evolution of the ability of some snakes to make a poisonous venom.

Behavioral Change Behaviors have also evolved through natural selection. Many of the specific behaviors we find in species today have become common because they resulted in greater reproductive success.

- Fighting among the males of a walrus population for a harem of females is one evolved behavior. Because of the fighting, the stronger, healthier male mates with the most females.
- The correct rate of "blinking" allows males and females of firefly species to find each other. A different pattern or rate of blinking would isolate the individual from potential mates.

The Importance of Variation

If environmental conditions change, organisms that have adapted to those conditions may die. If all the members of the species had exactly the same combination of characteristics, an environmental change could be disastrous, wiping out the entire species. The variation of organisms within a species increases the likelihood that at least some members of the species will survive in a changed environment. Once the diversity present in a species is lost, it is next to impossible to get it back. Today's endangered species have such small populations that biologists worry that they may not have the genetic diversity to adapt to even slight changes in their environment.

24. The changes in the foot structure in a bird population over many generations are shown in the diagram below.

Present day

These changes can best be explained by the concept of

(1) natural selection
(2) extinction
(3) stable gene frequencies
(4) cloning

25. Explain how the lack of genetic diversity found in populations of endangered species might hinder their recovery. [1]

26. The Florida panther, a member of the cat family, has a population of fewer than 100 individuals and has limited genetic variation. Which inference based on this information is valid?

(1) These animals will begin to evolve rapidly.
(2) Over time, these animals will become less likely to survive in a changing environment.
(3) These animals are easily able to adapt to the environment.
(4) Over time, these animals will become more likely to be resistant to disease.

27. Which statement could be used as evidence to show that two different species of organisms most likely developed from a single, common ancestor?

(1) They eat the same types of food.
(2) They have different digestive enzymes.
(3) They lived during the same time period.
(4) They contain similar amino acid sequences.

28. The diagrams below show the bones in the forelimbs of three different organisms.

Human   Whale   Bat

Differences in the bone arrangements support the hypothesis that these organisms

(1) are members of the same species
(2) may have descended from the same ancestor
(3) have adaptations to survive in different environments
(4) all contain the same genetic information

29. In most populations, the individuals that produce the greatest number of offspring are

(1) always the strongest
(2) usually the best adapted
(3) those that have only inheritable traits
(4) those that are the most intelligent

30. The best scientific explanation for differences in structure, function, and behavior found in different species of organisms is provided by

(1) carbohydrate electrophoresis
(2) population chromatography
(3) the theory of carrying capacity
(4) the theory of evolution

Patterns of Change

Evolution appears to follow certain patterns that appear repeatedly in the fossil record. For example:

- Changes in species are often related to environmental change.
- Species with short reproductive cycles that produce many offspring tend to evolve more quickly than species with long lifespans and few offspring.
- The failure to adapt to a changing environment may result in the death of the species.

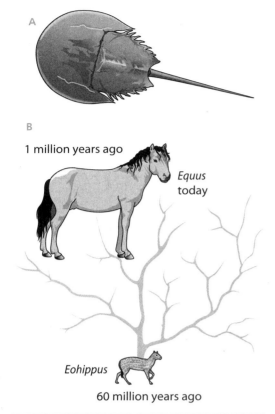

A

B

1 million years ago

Equus today

Eohippus

60 million years ago

Figure 5-7. **The rate of evolution:** For some species, the rate of evolutionary change has been very slow. For example, the horseshoe crab (A) has shown little change from fossils of its ancestors that lived 300 million years ago. However, the horse (B) has evolved tremendously over the past 60 million years.

The Rate of Evolution

Most of the diversity of life on Earth today is believed to be the result of natural selection occurring over a vast period of geologic time. The amount of change seems to be linked to changes in the environment. Minimal environmental change often results in stable populations. Rapid environmental change often leads to rapid changes in species. However, for any species, it may take millions of years to accumulate enough differences from its ancestors to be classified as a new or different species. As shown in Figure 5-7, some species have hardly changed in many millions of years. Others have changed so much that the relationships may not be obvious.

The rate of evolutionary change may also be influenced by the number of offspring produced by a species. Those that have few offspring and live a long time generally evolve quite slowly. Those that have brief lifespans and numerous offspring can change so quickly that evolution may occur in just a few years.

One example of rapid change involves the evolution of antibiotic resistance by pathogenic bacteria. When a population of millions of bacteria is exposed to an antibiotic, there is a chance that a few might have a gene that makes them resistant to the antibiotic. (This gene probably occurred as a chance mutation at some earlier time. It was most likely present in some of the bacteria before the antibiotic was used, and its appearance was totally unrelated to the presence of the antibiotic.) The antibiotic could kill almost all of the bacteria except for a few that escape exposure to the antibiotic. The ones with the resistance gene would also survive.

Because the antibiotic eliminated most of the competition, the few survivors, including the resistant ones, reproduce quickly, giving rise to a new population of the bacteria. In this new population, a higher proportion of individuals is now resistant to the drug. When the same antibiotic is used on the descendants of this new population, even more resistant bacteria will survive. Now the proportion of resistant bacteria is even higher. In this case, the antibiotic has become an agent of selection. The antibiotic did not cause the original mutation that made the bacteria resistant to the antibiotic. It merely determined which bacteria would live to reproduce. Figure 5-8 shows the process.

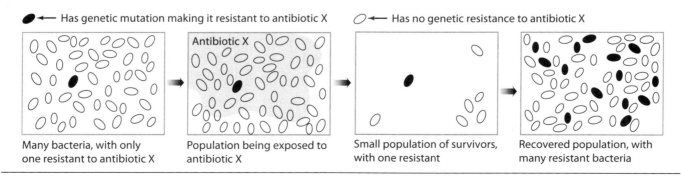

← Has genetic mutation making it resistant to antibiotic X   ← Has no genetic resistance to antibiotic X

Antibiotic X

Many bacteria, with only one resistant to antibiotic X

Population being exposed to antibiotic X

Small population of survivors, with one resistant

Recovered population, with many resistant bacteria

Figure 5-8. **How resistance to antibiotics can develop**

Insects also have short reproductive cycles and produce many offspring. Many insect species have changed significantly in response to pesticide use. For example, the widespread use of the pesticide DDT led to insect species becoming resistant in just a few years. As was the case with bacteria and antibiotics, there may have been a few DDT-resistant insects in the population before the chemical was ever used. They probably had a random mutation that had no adaptive value before the use of DDT. Once the DDT was sprayed, nearly all of the nonresistant insects were killed, leaving a high proportion of resistant insects to repopulate the area. Later, if DDT was sprayed again, it was less effective against the resistant offspring of the survivors of the earlier spraying.

As a result of these kinds of rapid evolutionary events, we are finding more and more bacteria that are resistant to antibiotics and more and more insect species that are resistant to our pesticides. This has created many problems in the fields of medicine and agriculture and will continue to be a problem in the future.

Extinction

Extinction is the disappearance of an entire species. Any time the death rate of individuals within a species is greater than the birth rate, extinction is a possibility. Generally, extinction occurs when the environment changes. Temperatures change; sea levels rise and fall. Grasslands become deserts; clear lakes become polluted. The variation of organisms within a species increases the likelihood that at least some members of the species will survive the changing environmental conditions. However, when the adaptive characteristics of a species are insufficient to allow its survival in a new environment, the species will become extinct.

The fossil record shows that throughout geologic time, millions of species have evolved, survived for a while, then failed to adapt successfully, and finally became extinct. It is a surprisingly common process. In fact, from the number of fossils of extinct organisms found, it is apparent that a majority of the species that ever lived on Earth is now extinct. Figure 5-9 shows a fossil of the extinct *Archaeopteryx*, an ancestor of modern birds.

Figure 5-9. An artist's conception of how the extinct *Archaeopteryx* might have looked, and the fossilized skeleton of this animal.

Review Questions

Set 5.5

31. The shark has changed very little in the last 50 million years. Which statement best explains why this is the case?

(1) The shark is well adapted to its relatively unchanged environment.

(2) Sharks have a high reproductive rate and show little change in their genetic makeup from one generation to the next.

(3) Sharks need to change only if humans are present in their environment.

(4) Sharks have a high mutation and genetic recombination rate.

32. Fossil evidence indicates that many species have existed for relatively brief periods of time and have then become extinct. Which statement best explains the reason for their short existence?

(1) These organisms lacked the energy to produce mutations.

(2) Humans modify plant and animal species through the knowledge of genetics.

(3) These organisms lacked variations having adaptive value.

(4) Within these species, increasing complexity reduced their chances of survival.

Base your answers to questions 33 through 35 on the diagram below and on your knowledge of biology. The diagram shows an interpretation of relationships based on evolutionary theory. The letters represent different species.

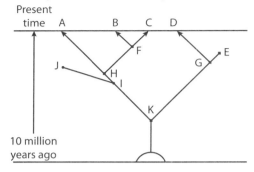

33. Explain why species B and C are more closely related than species A and C are.

34. The diagram indicates that a common ancestor for species C and E is species

(1) F   (2) G   (3) H   (4) K

35. Which species are least likely to be vital parts of a present-day ecosystem?

(1) A and E   (3) E and J
(2) C and D   (4) B and F

Base your answers to questions 36 and 37 on the information below and on your knowledge of biology.

Joshua Lederberg discovered that, in a large population of *Escherichia coli (E. coli)* about 1 in 10 million of the offspring was naturally resistant to the antibiotic streptomycin. When these naturally resistant bacteria were isolated and grown separately, they soon formed a larger population. The entire population so formed was also naturally resistant to streptomycin.

36. The formation of the large streptomycin-resistant population is based on

(1) variations and survival of the fittest
(2) mutations and asexual reproduction
(3) sexual reproduction and no mutations
(4) survival of the fittest and cloning

37. According to modern evolutionary theory, the resistance to streptomycin probably resulted directly from

(1) culturing the *E. coli*
(2) changes in temperature under which *E. coli* are grown
(3) a change in the DNA of *E. coli*
(4) the presence of streptomycin in the environment of *E. coli*

38. A large population of cockroaches was sprayed with a newly developed, fast-acting insecticide. The appearance of some cockroaches that are resistant to this insecticide supports the concept that

(1) species traits tend to remain constant
(2) variation exists within a species
(3) insecticides cause mutations
(4) the environment does not change

39. Compounds like the pesticide DDT may bring about the evolution of new strains of organisms by

(1) destroying food producers
(2) acting as a natural selecting agent
(3) mixing two different sets of genes
(4) creating new ecological niches

40. Some evolutionary pathways are represented in the diagram below.

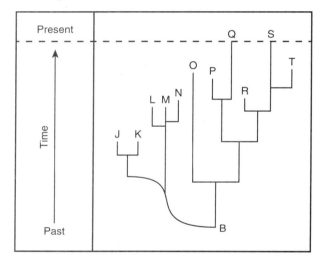

An inference that can be made from information in the diagram is that

(1) many of the descendants of organism B became extinct
(2) organism B was probably much larger than any of the other organisms represented
(3) most of the descendants of organism B successfully adapted to their environment and have survived to the present time
(4) the letters above organism B represent members of a single large population with much biodiversity

41. Explain why changes in climate can result in the extinction of a species. [1]

Directions

Review the Test-Taking Strategies section of this book. Then answer the following questions. Read each question carefully and answer with a correct choice or response.

Part A

1 How does natural selection operate to cause change in a population?
   (1) The members of the population are equally able to survive environmental change.
   (2) The members of the population differ so that only some survive when the environment changes.
   (3) The members of the population cause environmental changes and adapt to them.
   (4) All the members of the population adapt to environmental changes.

2 Which mutation could be passed on to future generations?
   (1) a gene change in a liver cell
   (2) cancer caused by excessive exposure to the sun
   (3) a chromosomal alteration during gamete formation
   (4) random breakage of a chromosome in a leaf cell of a maple tree

3 A trait with low survival value to the members of a population will most likely
   (1) undergo a series of mutations in succeeding generations
   (2) cause the reproductive rate of the individual to increase
   (3) decrease in frequency from one generation to the next
   (4) remain unchanged in frequency through many generations

4 A change in the genetic material that produces variation in a species may be the result of
   (1) the struggle for survival
   (2) the overproduction of a species
   (3) a mutation
   (4) competition

5 The DNA sequences found in two different species are 95% the same. This suggests that these species
   (1) are evolving into the same species
   (2) contain identical proteins
   (3) may have similar evolutionary histories
   (4) have the same number of mutations

6 The process by which a species passes out of existence is known as
   (1) endangerment
   (2) deforestation
   (3) extinction
   (4) adaptation

7 The diagram below illustrates the change that occurred in the frequency of body pattern traits shown by an insect population over ten generations.

First generation   Tenth generation
10 years later

A probable explanation for this change would be that over time there was
   (1) a decrease in the adaptive value of the spotted trait
   (2) an increase in the adaptive value of the spotted trait
   (3) an increase in the population of the insect
   (4) a decrease in the mutation rate of the gene for body pattern

8 The fact that a healthy deer can outrun a timber wolf is an example of
   (1) mutation
   (2) isolation
   (3) non-random mating
   (4) natural selection

9 A maple tree releases hundreds of seeds in a single season. This is an example of
   (1) a mutation
   (2) isolation
   (3) overproduction
   (4) non-random mating

Part B

Base your answers to questions 10 through 15 on the information below and on your knowledge of biology.

The bark of trees around Manchester, England, was mostly light in color before the Industrial Revolution. Light-colored peppered moths that rested on the trees were camouflaged from bird predators, while dark-colored peppered moths were easily preyed upon. After a few years of industrialization, the tree bark became darkened from pollution. The table below represents a change in the number of light- and dark-colored moths within the peppered moth population over a period of six years from the beginning of industrialization.

End of Year	Number of Light Moths	Number of Dark Moths
1	556	64
2	237	112
3	484	198
4	392	210
5	246	281
6	225	357

Using the information in the data table, construct a line graph on the grid provided. Follow the instructions below.

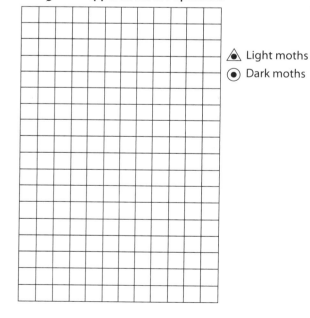

Changes in Peppered Moth Population

▲ Light moths
◉ Dark moths

Number of moths

End of year

10 Mark an appropriate scale, without any breaks, on each axis. [1]

11 Plot the data for the number of dark moths on the grid. Surround each point with a small circle and connect the points. [1]

Example: ◉——◉——◉

12 Plot the data for the number of light moths on the grid. Surround each point with a small triangle and connect the points. [1]

Example: △——△——△

13 At the end of which year of study was the number of dark-colored moths closest to the number of light-colored moths?
(1) 1 (2) 2 (3) 5 (4) 6

14 Which aspect of the evolutionary process is suggested by the information provided?
(1) The light-colored moths will eventually increase in number.
(2) The darker moths appeared when the tree trunks became lighter.
(3) The changing environment caused a darkening of the pigments of the moths.
(4) The darker moths increased in number when the environment became more favorable for their traits.

15 The biological concept that is most closely associated with the changes in the peppered moth population in England is known as
(1) natural selection (3) asexual reproduction
(2) positive feedback (4) homeostatic control

Base your answers to questions 16 through 19 on the paragraph below and on your knowledge of biology.

Two different species of crickets inhabited a meadow. One species of cricket had a straw-colored body and made up 90% of the total cricket population. The other species of cricket had a dark red body and made up 10% of the population. This proportion between the species had been constant for many years.

A new variety of grass with purple blades appeared in the meadow. The purple grass was better adapted to the meadow environment than the native green grass and replaced the green grass within a period of 50 years.

16 The appearance of the purple grass was most likely the result of

(1) asexual reproduction (3) cloning
(2) genetic engineering (4) mutation

17 Which graph most likely indicates the percentages of the straw-colored crickets (%S) over the 50-year period after the appearance of purple grass?

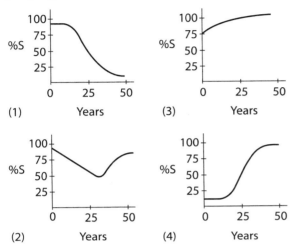

18 The evolutionary concept that would explain the changes taking place during the 50-year period in both the crickets and grasses is called

(1) common ancestry
(2) natural selection
(3) homeostatic balance
(4) selective breeding

19 What is the most likely reason for the large proportion of straw-colored crickets in the original population?

(1) The straw-colored crickets were larger and killed off most of the red crickets.
(2) Few natural enemies of the straw-colored crickets lived in the meadow.
(3) More straw-colored crickets than red were able to survive in the green grass.
(4) Red-colored crickets were not a part of the fossil record for the meadow.

20 State what could happen to a species in a changing environment if the members of that species do not express any genetic variations. [1]

Part C

21 Genetic variation is the raw material of evolution. Identify two different sources of genetic variation in a plant or animal population. [1]

Base your answers to questions 22 through 25 on the information below and on your knowledge of biology.

A hawk has a genetic trait that gives it much better eyesight than other hawks of the same species in the same area. Explain how this could lead to evolutionary change within this species of hawk over a long period of time. In your answer, be sure to include an explanation of:

- competition within the hawk population [1]
- survival of various individuals in the population [1]
- how the frequency of the better-eyesight trait would be expected to change over time within the population [1]
- what would most likely happen to the hawks having the better-eyesight trait if they also had unusually weak wing muscles [1]

Base your answers to questions 26 and 27 on the information below and on your knowledge of biology.

Scientists have observed thousands of female leatherback turtles during egg laying. Every female leatherback exhibits the same remarkable behavior. When she first comes up on the beach to lay her eggs, she digs a deep hole, lays her eggs in the hole, and then covers the eggs with sand. She then travels about 100 meters away from the first hole and digs another. She doesn't lay any eggs in this hole, but goes through the same process of covering the hole just as if there had been eggs present.

26 Write a hypothesis to explain why the female leatherback digs two holes. [1]

27 In the past, some leatherbacks may have only dug one hole and laid their eggs in it. In terms of evolution, how can this modern behavior of digging two holes be explained? [1]

Base your answers to questions 28 and 29 on the information below and on your knowledge of biology.

Two adaptations of the monarch butterfly that aid in its survival are the production of a certain chemical and a distinctive coloration that other animals can easily recognize. When a monarch butterfly is eaten, the presence of the chemical results in a bad taste to the predator. Although the viceroy butterfly does not contain the chemical that tastes bad to a predator, it does resemble the monarch in size, shape, and coloration.

28 Explain how the combination of this chemical and the distinctive coloration aid in the survival of the monarch butterfly. [1]

29 Explain how the characteristics of the viceroy butterfly aid in its survival. [1]

Base your answers to question 30–33 on the information below and on your knowledge of biology.

In the past, a specific antibiotic was effective in killing a certain species of bacteria. Now, most members of this bacterial species are resistant to this antibiotic.

Explain how this species of bacteria has become resistant. In your answer be sure to include the concepts of:

- overproduction [1]
- variation [1]
- natural selection [1]
- adaptation to the environment [1]

Base your answers to questions 34 through 37 on the passage below and on your knowledge of biology.

Dandelions are weeds that are very common in many grassy areas of New York State. Dandelion flowers first open up in a bright-yellow stage, and later turn a fluffy white when they are ready to release their seeds. The seeds are carried by the wind, and can sometimes travel great distances before landing and growing into new plants.

The stems of dandelions are usually very long, typically about 20–30 centimeters (cm), and stand high above the surrounding grass.

A science teacher in Niagara County discovered an area in her lawn where nearly every dandelion had a stem less than 1 cm long. These short dandelions were replacing large amounts of grass in the lawn surrounding her house. They were growing much more thickly than the taller dandelions in other nearby areas. The short dandelions appeared to be growing very successfully in one area of her lawn, but did not appear to have spread to other areas of her lawn.

The teacher noticed that every time she mowed her lawn, the short dandelions were left untouched by the mower blades, and that their numbers were steadily increasing.

34 State *one* possible cause of the genetic variation in dandelion height. [1]

35 State *one* possible explanation for the fact that the short dandelions had not yet spread to other areas of her lawn. [1]

36 State *one* possible reason why the amount of grass was decreasing, while the number of short dandelions was increasing in the lawn of the science teacher. [1]

37 State *one* possible advantage the short dandelions may have over the tall dandelions in this yard. [1]

Base your answers to question 38 through 40 on the information below and on your knowledge of biology.

Growers of fruit trees have always had problems with insects. Insects can cause visible damage to fruits, making them less appealing to consumers. As a result of this damage, much of the fruit cannot be sold. Insecticides have been useful for controlling these insects, but, in recent years, some insecticides have been much less effective. In some cases, insecticides do nothing to stop the insect attacks.

38 Identify the original event that resulted in the evolution of insecticide resistance in some insects [1]

39 Explain why the percentage of resistant insects in the population has increased [1]

40 Describe one alternative form of insect control, other than using a different insecticide, that fruit growers could use to protect their crops from insect attack [1]

Ecology

What do You Think?

Succession

Succession is the changes that occur in a species as it evolves into a series of new species.

Succession is the series of changes that take place in plant and animal communities as the habitat changes.

Succession is the series of changes a species makes as it adapts to new conditions.

Ecology

Vocabulary

abiotic

autotroph

biodiversity

biosphere

biotic

carnivore

carrying capacity

community

competition

consumer

decomposer

ecological niche

ecological succession

ecology

ecosystem

energy pyramid

environment

finite

food chain

food web

habitat

herbivore

heterotroph

host

limiting factors

parasite

population

predator

prey

producer

scavenger

Topic Overview

Our Earth is home to trillions of different organisms. None of these organisms can survive alone. All organisms—including humans—must interact with both the living and nonliving things around them. **Ecology** is the study of how organisms interact with the living and nonliving things that surround them.

Organisms and Their Environment

As you read this book, you are surrounded by your environment, which includes this book and perhaps your chair, light streaming through the window, a dog barking outside, and a pretzel on the table. If you're in class, your environment may include other students reading nearby, your teacher pacing the aisles, the drone of an airplane, the smell of the lunchroom, sunlight coming in the window, and the unseen mite picking skin flakes off your arm. In short, the **environment** is every living and nonliving thing that surrounds an organism.

Parts of an Ecosystem

Ecosystem is a short way of saying "ecological system." Scientists use the term to describe any portion of the environment. An ecosystem is made up of all the living things, such as bacteria, plants, and animals, that interact with one another. These interacting living things are termed **biotic** factors. When scientists study ecosystems, they also study the nonliving things, such as soil, water, physical space, and energy, that influence the organisms. Nonliving influences are termed **abiotic** factors.

A decaying log, a pond, a field of corn, and even a fish tank are ecosystems. In each of these ecosystems, organisms interact with both the biotic and abiotic parts of their environment. For example, frogs in a pond ecosystem may interact with insects, fish, hawks, and children chasing them with nets. They are also affected by abiotic factors, such as rainfall, the acidity of their pond, temperature, and the amount of light. Some biotic and abiotic parts of an ecosystem are shown in Figure 6-1.

Because the world contains a wide variety of physical conditions, many different kinds of environments are available to organisms. Some are shown in Figure 6-2. Most species, however, have a specific environment that is their "home." That specific environment is known as the species' **habitat.** Familiar habitats include fields, forests, oceans, streams, and deserts.

All the organisms of a species that live in the same area make up a **population.** Ants in a single anthill would be one population. All the different populations are combined to form a <u>community.</u>

Collectively, all of Earth's ecosystems make up the **biosphere**—the biologically inhabited portions of the planet. Earth's biosphere extends from the deepest ocean troughs to high above the surface of the planet. It includes all the water, land, and air in which organisms live. Throughout the biosphere, organisms interact and compete for vital resources, such as food, space, and shelter.

The fundamental concept of ecology is that all living organisms are interdependent, and they interact with one another and with the physical environment. These interactions result in a flow of energy and a cycling of materials essential for life.

Environmental Limits on Population Size

In any ecosystem, the growth and survival of organisms depends on the physical conditions and on the resources available to the organism. If they had unlimited resources, living things could produce populations of <u>infinite</u> (unlimited) size. Within any ecosystem, however, resources, such as oxygen and carbon dioxide, water, nutrients, space, and sunlight, are

Abiotic Factors

Biotic Factors

Figure 6-1. Parts of an ecosystem: The biotic part of the ecosystem includes all the living things that make up the community.

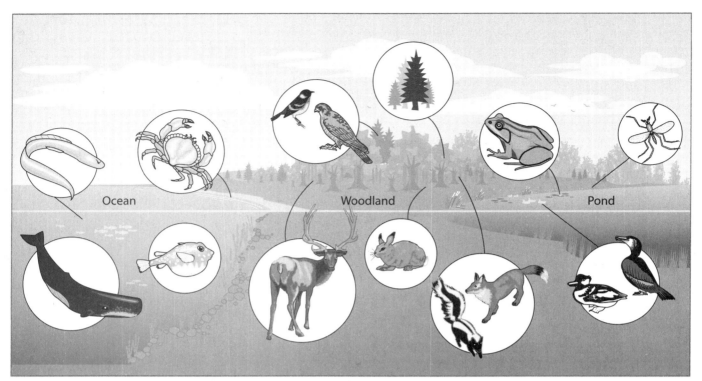

Figure 6-2. Some ecosystems in Earth's biosphere: In each ecosystem, the organisms interact with one another and with their environment. The degree to which each abiotic factor is present determines the types of organisms that can live there.

finite (limited). This has a profound effect on the interactions among organisms: Because the resources are finite, organisms must compete with one another to survive.

Competition is the struggle for resources among organisms. Within any one species, competition keeps the size of that species' population in check. In established ecosystems, populations tend to increase or decrease depending on the resources that are available at the time. This variation in population size tends to follow a predictable cycle. Many populations, for example, vary with the seasons. Over time, however, the size of the population remains stable.

Factors in the environment that limit the size of populations are known as **limiting factors.** Some limiting factors are abiotic; others are biotic. For example, abiotic factors, such as the amount of dissolved oxygen in a pond, may limit the kinds and numbers of fish that can live there; the amount of sunlight filtering through a forest may limit the number of green plants living on the forest floor. Some other specific limiting factors include the intensity of light, the temperature range in the environment, minerals that are available in the water or soil, the type of rock or soil in the ecosystem, and the relative acidity (measured according to the pH scale).

An important biotic factor that limits population sizes is the relationship between **predators,** which kill and eat other organisms, and **prey,** which are killed for food. As predators kill and eat their prey, they limit the growth of the prey population. If too many prey animals are killed, predators begin to starve, and their population is reduced. With fewer predators, the size of the prey population begins to recover.

The number of organisms of any single species that an ecosystem can support is referred to as its **carrying capacity.** It is determined not only by the available energy, water, oxygen, and minerals (and the recycling of such minerals), but also by the interactions of its organisms. For example, a field's carrying capacity for a population of foxes is affected not only by the climate, but also by the number and kinds of other populations present. If there are many mice for the foxes to eat, the fox population may boom. If there are many viruses affecting the health of the foxes, their population may crash. Figure 6-3 shows the population increase that normally occurs until the carrying capacity is reached.

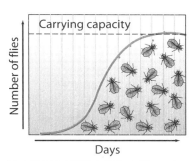

Figure 6-3. Carrying capacity: This population of insects increased until it neared its carrying capacity. Then the population became approximately stable.

Review Questions

Set 6.1

1. All of Earth's water, land, and atmosphere within which life exists is known as

   (1) a population
   (2) an ecosystem
   (3) the biosphere
   (4) a biotic community

2. In the biosphere, what are some of the major abiotic factors that determine the distribution and types of plant communities?

   (1) temperature, sunlight, and rainfall
   (2) humidity, location, and humans
   (3) soil type, soil bacteria, and soil water
   (4) insects, carbon dioxide, and nitrogen in the air

Base your answers to questions 3 and 4 on the two graphs below and on your knowledge of biology. The first graph shows the number of days of snow cover from 1940–1960. The second graph shows the percentage of white mice in a population that was sampled during the same period.

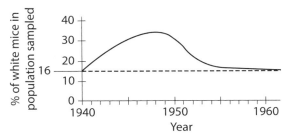

3. The appearance of the greatest percentage of white mice occurred

   (1) before the maximum number of days of snow cover
   (2) at the same time as the maximum number of days of snow cover
   (3) after the maximum number of days of snow cover
   (4) both before and after the maximum number of days of snow cover

4. Which statement is supported by the data in the graphs?

   (1) The percentage of brown mice was greatest during the years of longest snow cover.
   (2) The percentage of mice with white fur was greatest during the years of longest snow cover.
   (3) The actual number of white mice was greatest during the years of least snow cover.
   (4) The actual number of brown mice was greatest during the years of longest snow cover.

5. The fact that an organism cannot live without interacting with its surroundings is a basic concept in the field of study known as

   (1) ecology
   (2) evolution
   (3) behavior
   (4) technology

6. When two different species live in the same area and use the same limited resources, which of the following will occur?

   (1) competition
   (2) succession
   (3) parasitism
   (4) industrialization

7. Which term includes all of the interactions that occur between the organisms and the physical factors in a pond environment?

(1) population
(2) ecosystem
(3) abiotic
(4) competition

8. The amount of salt in the air and water of coastal areas determines which species can exist there. In these areas, salt functions as a

(1) source of energy
(2) biotic factor
(3) food source
(4) limiting factor

9. This graph shows the changes in two populations of herbivores in a grassy field.

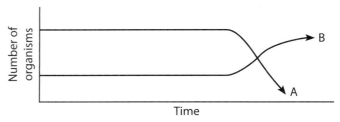

A possible reason for these changes is that

(1) all of the plant populations in this habitat decreased
(2) population B competed more successfully for food than population A
(3) population A produced more offspring than population B
(4) population A consumed members of population B

Population Interactions

There is a wide diversity of interacting species in most ecosystems. Most of the interactions occur as organisms obtain their food. Every population is linked, directly or indirectly, with all of the other populations in the ecosystem. Each population has one or more specific roles in the ecosystem. As a result, maintaining the ecosystem's diversity is essential to its stability.

Roles in the Ecosystem

The role that each species plays in an ecosystem is called its **ecological niche.** Only one species at a time can occupy a particular niche. If two species attempt to fill the same role in an ecosystem, competition results. Usually, one species will be more suited to the niche, which forces the other species to move on or face elimination. Eventually, only one species will occupy each niche.

Figure 6-4. Feeding patterns among warblers: Several warbler species feed in spruce trees, but they actually occupy different niches because each species feeds in a different part of the spruce tree.

Sometimes it appears as if different populations occupy the same niche. For example, deer and moose often live in the same area and seem to eat the same plants. A closer examination reveals that the deer and moose have different food preferences and only compete when food is very scarce. Similarly, several bird species may seem to nest and feed in the same tree. In reality, it is more probable that the birds are nesting in different parts of the tree and eating different insects. For example, the northeastern United States is home to several species of warblers. Five of those species feed on the insects that live in spruce trees. As shown in Figure 6-4, each species feeds in a different part of the tree.

Competition for a particular ecological niche often occurs when a foreign species enters an area. The new species may be more successful than the native species, partly because the newcomer may not have any natural enemies to control its population. Humans frequently bring foreign species into an area either on purpose or accidentally. One example is the zebra mussels that were brought to the Great Lakes on cargo ships. The zebra mussel has become a major problem in New York waterways.

Relationships in an Ecosystem

In every ecosystem, populations of different species are linked together in a complex web of interactions. Sometimes these relationships are competitive; occasionally they are cooperative. For example, termites have one-celled organisms in their intestinal tracts. These unicellular organisms help the termites digest their food. The tiny organisms gain a place to live and plenty of food, and the termites can make use of a food supply that they would not be able to digest without this cooperative relationship.

Other relationships benefit one organism and have no effect on the other. For example, when a shark attacks and eats its prey, small pieces of the food drift downward. Smaller fish swimming below the shark feed on these scraps. The small fish benefit, but the shark is unaffected.

Food Chains Among the most common relationships in any ecosystem are the predator-prey relationships. **Food chains,** such as those shown in Figure 6-5, illustrate the relationships between prey and predator. In simple terms, the food chain shows what eats what.

Organism's niches are partly defined by how they obtain their food. For example, photosynthetic organisms make their own food and in the process, store the sun's energy. They are known as **autotrophs** (self-feeders) or **producers**. They provide a source of food energy for almost all other living things.

Heterotrophs must acquire food by consuming other organisms. **Herbivores** are heterotrophs that survive on plant tissues; **carnivores** are heterotrophs that eat other animals. Heterotrophs are also known as **consumers**.

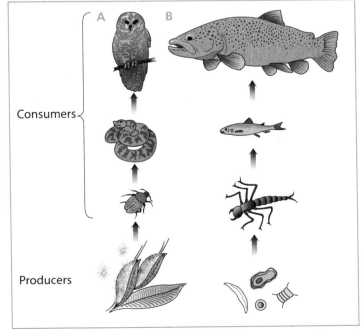

Figure 6-5. Typical food chains: A field ecosystem (A) and a pond ecosystem (B)

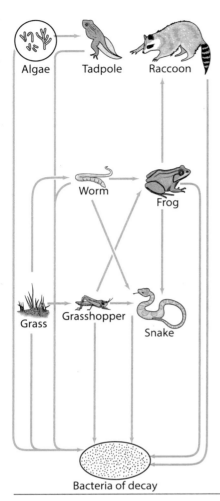

Figure 6-6. **A simplified food web near a pond**

The wastes and dead bodies of all these organisms are consumed by the **decomposers.** The decomposers recycle materials that can then be reused by producers.

Two other feeding relationships between organisms do not fit into the typical predator-prey categories. These organisms are similar to predators in that they feed on other organisms, but different in that they do not kill the organisms for food. **Scavengers,** such as vultures, are consumers that eat dead organisms. They are nature's "clean-up crew." Scavengers, however, are not decomposers. Dead bodies and wastes still have to be broken down by decomposers. **Parasites** are organisms that attack other live organisms (called **host** organisms), but rarely kill them. Parasites usually live on or in the body of their host. Ticks, for example, may live on a dog and also feed on its blood.

Notice in Figure 6-5 that both food chains begin with autotrophs—the photosynthetic producers—and end with consumers. The intermediate heterotrophs (the herbivores and carnivores that rely on others for food) are often, but not always, part of food chains. All of the organisms in a food chain, if not eaten by others, are eventually consumed by decomposers. So a food chain may be as simple as: grass → decay bacteria.

Decomposers may be included at the end of a food chain, but it is important to remember that they actually consume and break down the chemical materials in all dead organisms and in the wastes of all living organisms.

Food Webs Normally, each organism feeds on more than one kind of organism. Because organisms normally have more than one food source, food chain diagrams are oversimplified. **Food webs,** as shown in Figure 6-6, are diagrams that show the more complex feeding relationships among producers, consumers, and decomposers. The food web shows the many interconnected food chains that exist in the ecosystem. Because organisms have several food choices, ecosystems often remain stable even when one population shows a major decline in numbers. The organisms that feed on the declining population simply rely more heavily on one of their other food choices until the declining population recovers.

Review Questions
Set 6.2

10. The diagram below illustrates the feeding areas of two populations in the same ecosystem during the summer and fall. Both populations feed on oak trees.

Summer

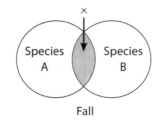

Fall

The portion of the diagram labeled X most likely indicates that

(1) these populations compete for food in the fall, but not in the summer
(2) the species are separated by a geographic barrier in the summer
(3) the supply of oxygen is greater in the summer than in the fall
(4) mating occurs between the species in the fall, but not in the summer

11. An earthworm lives and reproduces in the soil. Through its feeding, excretion, and tunneling activities, the worm adds nutrients and allows air to enter the soil. Together, these statements describe the earthworm's

(1) habitat (3) niche
(2) nutrition (4) environment

12. Among the populations of any natural community, the basic food supply is always a critical factor because it is

(1) produced by all organisms
(2) synthesized from oxygen
(3) a means of transferring energy
(4) present in surplus amounts

13. A consumer–producer relationship is best illustrated by

(1) foxes eating mice
(2) leaves growing on trees
(3) rabbits eating clover
(4) fleas living on a cat

Base your answers to questions 14 through 16 on the food chain below and on your knowledge of biology.

rosebush→aphid→beetle→spider→toad→snake

14. Which organism in this food chain can transform light energy into chemical bond energy?

15. At which stage in this food chain will the population with the smallest number of organisms probably be found?

(1) spider (3) rosebush
(2) aphid (4) snake

16. If all of the aphids were killed off due to the spraying of pesticides, what would happen to the number of toads this ecosystem could support?

17. Which group of organisms is *not* represented in the food web below?

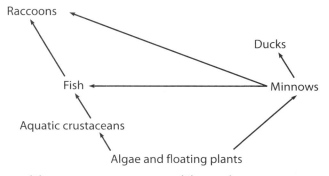

(1) consumers (3) producers
(2) carnivores (4) decomposers

18. Which organisms are chiefly responsible for the recycling of dead matter?

(1) parasites (3) decomposers
(2) viruses (4) producers

19. In a natural community in New York State, the producer organisms might include

(1) bacteria, fungi, and viruses
(2) deer, rabbits, and squirrels
(3) grasses, maple trees, and weeds
(4) trout, peas, and earthworms

20. Which sequence illustrates a generalized food chain in a natural community?

(1) autotroph → herbivore → carnivore
(2) autotroph → herbivore → autotroph
(3) heterotroph → herbivore → carnivore
(4) consumer → autotroph → carnivore

21. In a food chain consisting of photosynthetic organisms, herbivores, carnivores, and organisms of decay, the principal function of the photosynthetic organisms is to

(1) capture energy from the environment
(2) provide material for decay
(3) prevent erosion of the topsoil
(4) release energy from organic compounds

22. A characteristic shared by both predators and parasites is that they

(1) feed on decomposing plant material
(2) capture and kill animals for food
(3) live inside their hosts
(4) attack a living food source

23. As you drive down the highway, you may see crows feeding on dead animals. As a result of this nutritional pattern, crows may be classified as

(1) scavengers (3) herbivores
(2) predators (4) producers

24. When the food relationships in a habitat are illustrated by means of a diagram, the result is always a complicated weblike pattern. This is due to the fact that

(1) many consumers are adapted to use more than one food source
(2) producer organisms always outnumber the consumer organisms
(3) matter is lost in an ecosystem as it moves from producers to consumers
(4) both producers and consumers require oxygen for metabolic processes

25. Although three different butterfly species all inhabit the same flower garden in an area, competition between the butterflies rarely occurs. The most likely explanation for this lack of competition is that the butterflies

(1) occupy different niches
(2) have a limited supply of food
(3) share food with each other
(4) are able to interbreed

26. In the diagram below, which organisms are components of the same food chain?

(1) trees, mountain lion, snake, and hawk
(2) trees, rabbit, deer, and shrubs
(3) grasses, cricket, frog, and mouse
(4) grasses, mouse, snake, and hawk

27. In the diagram of a food chain below, what do the arrows indicate?

(1) the direction in which organisms move in the environment
(2) the direction of energy flow through a series of organisms
(3) the order of importance of the various organisms
(4) the return of chemical substances to the environment

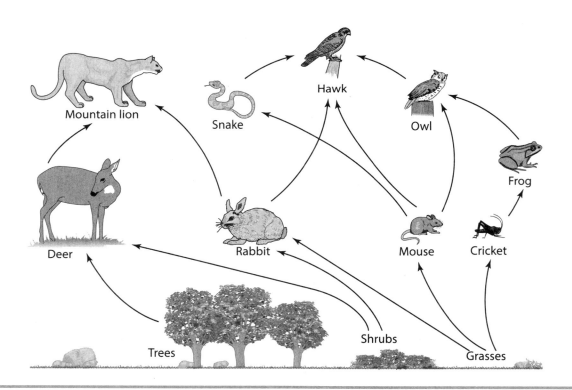

Energy Flow Through an Ecosystem

Almost all organisms use the solar energy stored in food to power their life processes. That energy, however, does not remain in the organism forever. Every second of every day, an animal that is not eating has less energy in its tissues than it had a few seconds before. This energy loss occurs because the organism is continually breaking the chemical bonds in food to use the energy to live. As it is released to make ATP and then used in the cells, much of the energy is converted to heat and is lost to the environment. Only a small amount can actually be used by the cells. As a result, each next step in the food chain has less of the original solar energy available to it.

Figure 6-7 shows how the energy is lost. Only the energy stored in the body tissues of each organism is passed to the next consumer in the chain. Because of the energy loss described above, most of the original stored energy is lost in just a few steps of the food chain. For this reason, food chains are usually quite short.

An **energy pyramid,** shown in Figure 6-8, is a diagram that illustrates the transfer of energy through a food chain or web. Each block of the energy pyramid represents the amount of energy that was obtained from the organisms below it. Only this amount of energy is available to the organisms in the next higher block. Notice that each level is smaller due to the loss of heat as the organisms carry on their life activities.

A continual input of energy, typically from the sun, is required to start the process and to keep it going. Producer organisms capture this energy and store it in the chemical bonds of the food molecules they make. The flow of energy that accompanies the transfer of the food shown in food chains and webs is essential to life on Earth. In spite of this constant drain of energy to the environment, life continues because the sun continues to provide energy.

Figure 6-7. As energy is transferred, much of it is lost to the environment as heat.

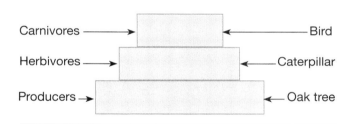

Figure 6-8. An energy pyramid: Each block in the energy pyramid illustrates the amount of energy available for use by organisms at the next level above it. (Energy for decomposers actually comes from organisms at all the levels, so they are not shown in this simplified pyramid.)

Recycling and Reusing Materials

The parts of dead organisms that are not consumed during one of the other steps in the food chain are not wasted. Decomposers extract the last bit of energy contained in the dead organisms (as well as the energy in the waste products from living organisms) and use it to sustain their life processes. As they do so, they return the raw materials contained in the once-living matter to the soil. This process of breaking down dead organisms, as well as the wastes produced by living organisms, into their raw materials and returning those materials to the ecosystem is known as <u>decomposition</u>.

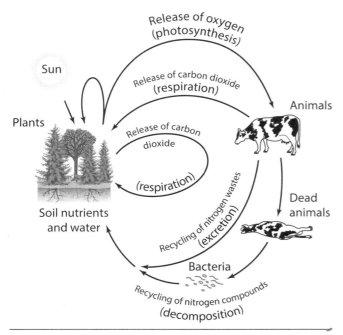

Release of oxygen (photosynthesis)

Sun

Release of carbon dioxide (respiration)

Plants

Animals

Release of carbon dioxide

(respiration)

Dead animals

Soil nutrients and water

Recycling of nitrogen wastes (excretion)

Bacteria

Recycling of nitrogen compounds (decomposition)

Figure 6-9. **The recycling of materials in ecosystems:** Dead organisms and wastes must be recycled in ecosystems so that their raw materials can be made available for re-use by producer organisms. The gas exchanges of photosynthesis and respiration, along with the action of decomposers, are crucial to the recycling process.

Two examples of organisms that fill the role of decomposers are bacteria and fungi. Because of the actions of decomposers, the atoms and molecules in living things cycle through both the nonliving and living parts of the biosphere. As they do, chemical elements, such as carbon, hydrogen, oxygen, and nitrogen, that make up the bodies of living things pass through food webs and are combined and recombined in different ways in different living organisms. For example, plants trap carbon dioxide and water molecules in energy-rich compounds (such as glucose and starch) during photosynthesis. When plants need energy to power their cell processes or are eaten by a consumer, these molecules may be broken down and used by the organism. During respiration, energy is released by the cells and molecules of carbon dioxide and water returned to the environment.

Much of the cycling of materials in ecosystems is carried out by decomposers. Figure 6-9 shows some of the ways matter cycles throughout the ecosystem.

Review Questions

Set 6.3

28. Decomposition and decay of organic matter are accomplished by the action of

(1) green plants
(2) bacteria and fungi
(3) viruses and algae
(4) scavengers

29. Which statement best describes energy transfer in a food web?

(1) Energy is transferred to consumers, which convert it to nitrogen and use it to make amino acids.
(2) Energy from producers is converted into oxygen and transferred to consumers.
(3) Energy from the sun is stored in green plants and transferred to consumers.
(4) Energy is transferred to consumers, which use it to produce food.

30. Organisms that eat goats obtain less energy from the goats than the goats obtain from the plants they eat. This is because the goats

(1) pass on most of the energy to their offspring
(2) convert solar energy to food energy
(3) store all of their energy in milk
(4) use energy for their own metabolism

Base your answers to questions 31 and 32 on the energy pyramid below and on your knowledge of biology.

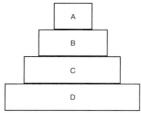

31. If birds eat insects that feed on corn, which level on this pyramid would birds occupy?

(1) A   (2) B   (3) C   (4) D

32. Which statement concerning the energy in the pyramid is correct?

(1) The producer organisms contain the least amount of energy.
(2) Stored energy decreases as it is passed from consumer to consumer.
(3) Consumers contain more energy than producers.
(4) Decomposers are the source of energy for this pyramid.

33. Most green algae are able to obtain carbon dioxide from the environment and use it to synthesize organic compounds. This activity is an example of

(1) cellular respiration
(2) autotrophic nutrition
(3) heterotrophic nutrition
(4) heterotrophic respiration

Base your answers to questions 34 through 37 on the activities described in the paragraphs below and on your knowledge of biology.

A tomato plant was placed under a sealed bell jar and exposed to light. Carbon dioxide containing radioactive carbon was introduced into the bell jar as shown in the following diagram. After an hour, the inlet valve was closed. Later, the entire plant was removed from the soil and cleaned by rinsing it in water.

A Geiger counter indicated radioactivity in the roots. These roots were then dried and chopped into very small pieces. The chopped roots were sprinkled into an aquarium containing a very hungry goldfish that was *not* radioactive.

Four days later, the fish was removed from the aquarium and a tissue section of the fish was tested with the Geiger counter. The counter indicated an above-normal level of radioactivity in the fish tissues.

34. Which cycle is primarily being studied by means of this investigation?

(1) oxygen   (3) nitrogen
(2) carbon   (4) water

35. A control setup for this investigation would be identical to the one described except for the replacement of the

(1) tomato plant with a geranium plant
(2) goldfish with a tadpole
(3) radioactive carbon dioxide with atmospheric carbon dioxide
(4) soil with distilled water

36. By which process was the radioactivity incorporated into the material that was transported to the roots?

(1) growth   (3) photosynthesis
(2) mitosis   (4) respiration

37. This investigation suggests that when plants are eaten by animals, some of the plant materials may be

(1) changed to animal tissue
(2) separated into smaller molecules before being digested
(3) eliminated by the animal in a form that allows the plant to grow again
(4) used in regulating the animal's digestive processes

38. A cycling of materials is represented in the diagram below.

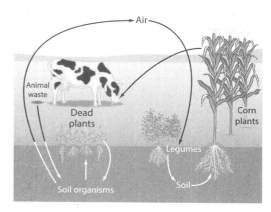

Which statement is supported by the events shown in the diagram?

(1) Materials are cycled between living organisms only.
(2) Materials are cycled between heterotrophic organisms only.
(3) Materials are cycled between the living and nonliving components of the environment only.
(4) Materials are cycled between autotrophic organisms only.

39. Which ecological principle is best illustrated by the diagram below?

(1) In an ecosystem, material is cycled among the organisms and the environment.
(2) In an ecosystem, the number of producers and consumers is equal.
(3) Competition within a species results in natural selection.
(4) An ecosystem requires a constant source of energy.

Diversity Benefits Species and Habitats

As a result of evolution, there is a great diversity of species on Earth. Almost every ecosystem is populated by many species, each occupying its own special niche. The interrelationships and interdependencies of these species help to keep ecosystems stable, and the diversity of species increases the chance that at least some organisms will survive in the face of large environmental changes.

Biodiversity is a measurement of the degree to which species vary within an ecosystem. There is a strong connection between biodiversity and the stability of an ecosystem. A natural forest, for example, contains many different species of trees. If disease or insects attack one population, nearby trees of another species are likely to survive. The mix of species in the ecosystem also makes it difficult for the disease organisms to move quickly through this environment. Here, biodiversity serves as a barrier to the spread of disease or insect attack. In contrast, on a tree farm where all of the trees are planted and are of a single species, the entire population could be seriously damaged by a single disease or insect attack.

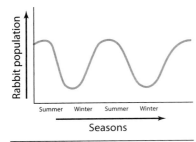

Figure 6-10. Rabbit populations: Rabbit populations may rise and fall over the course of a year, but from year to year they follow the same pattern if the environment is stable.

The interactions between organisms may allow an ecosystem to remain stable for hundreds or thousands of years. In established, stable ecosystems, populations tend to increase and decrease in size in a predictable pattern. Over time, however, the size of the population remains relatively stable. For example, when the prey population increases, a large food supply causes the size of the predator population to rise. Because each predator requires many prey to meet its energy needs, the prey population rapidly decreases. Soon, with the decline in a prey population, some of the predators begin to starve. When only a few predators remain alive, the prey population reproduces and greater numbers of prey survive. The cycle begins anew. Figure 6-10 illustrates the seasonal change in a rabbit population.

The loss of biodiversity in an ecosystem upsets its stability. Removing species from an environment often causes instability due to the loss of organisms that were filling critical ecological niches.

Many species may be lost when natural disasters or human activities cause large-scale destruction to habitats. Clearing large areas of tropical rain forest, for example, has disrupted many ecosystems; some may never recover. Although some species may be able to return to a damaged ecosystem, others with critical roles may be totally lost. The interdependencies between populations in the original ecosystem may have been so great that if biodiversity is lost, the ecosystem may never be restored to its original state.

Species can also be lost when humans do not consider the environmental impact of their actions. For example, offering bounties for the removal of predatory mountain lions from some environments sounded like a good idea at one time, but it led to population explosions of deer herds. Soon the deer overpopulated the area, and their overgrazing reduced the food supply so much that many deer starved. The overgrazing also led to soil erosion that caused permanent environmental damage.

When humans clear land for agricultural purposes, the loss of biodiversity may also lead to an unstable environment. Disease and insect pests present major problems to farmers whose crops are genetically similar. For these farmers, any disruption threatens to affect the entire crop. Farmers are constantly in search of ways to control insect pests and diseases in their crops, because they have created an environment that is always in danger of serious disruption. In natural ecosystems, the diversity of species provides no such concentration of one kind of food, making it far less likely that any single pest or disease will cause problems.

Biodiversity Benefits Humans

Biodiversity also represents one of the greatest resources known to humans. It ensures the availability of a rich variety of genetic material, some of which may prove valuable to humans. Though still largely untapped, the genetic diversity found in rain forests has provided humans with medicines, insecticides, and other useful resources. If we destroy ecosystems, we lose much of the biodiversity they hold. As diversity is lost, potentially valuable resources are lost with it.

Review Questions

Set 6.4

Base your answers to questions 40 and 41 on the information and graph below and on your knowledge of biology.

During the 1970s, Canadian forests in New Brunswick were heavily sprayed to control the spruce budworms that were damaging the spruce trees. Ecologists discovered that, along with the budworm, bees of many species—including sweat bees and bumblebees—had also been killed. All of the bees were important for pollinating flowers so the plants could produce fruit. Miles away from the spruce forests, blueberry growers were devastated when their blueberry yield declined by 75 percent over the same time period as the spraying was taking place. The graph shows the biodiversity present in the Canadian spruce forests prior to, during, and after the spraying.

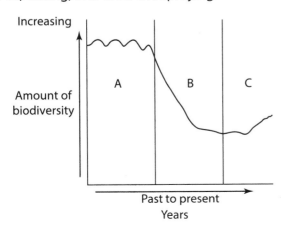

40. As the number of insect species declined due to spraying, the blueberry production decreased. Explain how these two events might be related even though the pesticide did not land directly on the blueberry plants. [1]

41. On the graph provided below, draw a line that shows the relationship of ecosystem stability to changes in biodiversity. [1]

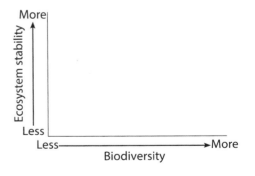

42. Explain why medical researchers are concerned when the biodiversity of an ecosystem decreases. [1]

43. The color, taste, and juiciness of a particular variety of strawberry makes it very popular. Growers are able to plant hundreds of acres of this variety, and all the plants are exactly the same, since they reproduce asexually. Explain why this lack of diversity in the strawberry field could prove to be a problem for the growers. [1]

44. The graph shows the biodiversity present in four different species living in the same area.

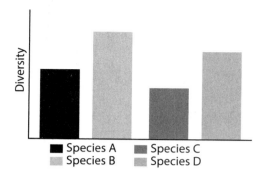

If the environment were to change dramatically or if a new plant disease were to be introduced, which plant species would be the most likely to have individuals that could survive the disease?

(1) Species A
(2) Species B
(3) Species C
(4) Species D

45. A forest community is made up of thousands of species of organisms and can exist practically unchanged for hundreds of years. This stability is due to the

(1) diversity of organisms present
(2) abundance of insects that feed on plants
(3) changes in the climate of the area
(4) lack of decomposers in the forest

Environmental Changes

Many environments, such as the bare rock on a mountaintop, have few resources that can provide homes for living organisms. Through natural processes, these environments will change over long periods of time to become habitats for many diverse species. The series of changes by which one habitat changes into another is called **ecological succession.**

In the process of ecological succession, each community causes modifications to its environment. The modifications result in changes that make it more suitable for another community. The original species that lived there may find it harder to adapt to these changes, while the new species coming in may be able to compete more successfully for the new niches.

For example, as grasses grow in an area with very shallow soil, they add organic matter, making the soil deeper and more fertile. Shrubs are then able to live in this modified environment and will eventually produce enough shade to eliminate the grasses growing below them. Over a period of many years, these gradual changes may result in the formation of a stable forest community that can last for hundreds or even thousands of years. (In dry or cold climates, succession may not advance to the forest stage, but the final stage will be a stable ecosystem that can last for many years.)

Climatic changes, natural disasters, and the activities of animals (including humans) can alter stable ecosystems. These changes may occur rapidly, perhaps due to a forest fire or flood, or slowly, as when a long-term drought or climate change occurs. Altered environments undergo a slow series of successional changes that return them to a point where long-term stability is possible. In this process, an existing community of organisms is replaced by different communities over a period of time ranging from a few decades to thousands of years.

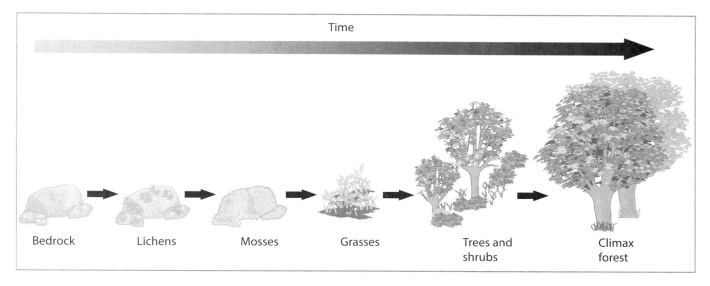

Figure 6-11. Succession from bare rock to a forest: As the depth of the soil increases, it can support the root systems of larger plants.

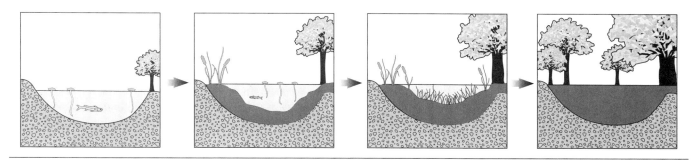

Figure 6-12. Succession from a lake to a forest

There are two commonly observed patterns of succession. A community of mostly bare rock will gradually accumulate soil, leading to a progression of vegetation types from grasses to shrubs, and eventually a forest. This process is seen in Figure 6-11.

Another commonly observed example of ecological succession is the change from a lake community to a forest. The lake will gradually accumulate sediments from erosion and the buildup of organic debris from plants and dead organisms. As the lake fills in, it becomes shallower. After many years, it may become a swamp. The filling-in continues, and eventually a mature forest may result. Successional changes from lake to forest are shown in Figure 6-12.

Base your answers to questions 46 through 49 on the sequence of diagrams below and on your knowledge of biology.

1840

1870

1900

1930

1960

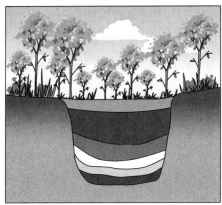

1990

46. This sequence of diagrams best illustrates
(1) succession
(2) evolution
(3) the effects of acid rain
(4) a food chain

47. If no human intervention or natural disaster occurs, by the year 2050 this area will most likely be a
(1) lake   (3) desert
(2) swamp   (4) forest

48. The natural increase in the amount of vegetation from 1840 to 1930 is related to the
(1) decreasing water depth
(2) increasing amount of sunlight
(3) presence of bottom-feeding fish
(4) use of the pond for fishing

49. Describe what would happen over the fifty years following 1990 if a fire burned off all of the vegetation in the area. [1]

Base your answers to questions 50 and 51 on the information below and on your knowledge of biology.

If you travel inland from the shores of the present Lake Michigan, which was once much larger than it is today, you would travel through the following areas:

1. the present sandy beach
2. grasses
3. a cottonwood forest
4. a pine forest
5. an oak forest
6. a beech-maple forest (where the original shoreline was located)

50. The sequence of plant growth is an illustration of

(1) succession
(2) a food chain
(3) evolution
(4) an autotroph pyramid

51. Describe why the plants growing in the area of the old shoreline are beech and maple trees and no longer the grasses observed near the new shoreline. [1]

_____

52. When a stable forest community is destroyed by fire, the community usually is

(1) not restored
(2) restored in a series of successive changes
(3) restored only if humans reforest the area
(4) changed into a permanent grassland

53. The conditions that existed in a forest before a fire will be established mainly by

(1) the water cycle
(2) the carbon cycle
(3) succession
(4) evolution

54. Which statement accurately describes ecological succession?

(1) The lack of animals in an altered ecosystem speeds up the process of natural succession.
(2) Abrupt changes in an ecosystem only result from human activities.
(3) After a major disaster, stable ecosystems can never become established again.
(4) An abrupt change in an ecosystem can lead to a long-term gradual change.

55. When Mount St. Helens erupted in 1980, a portion of the surrounding area was covered by lava, which buried all of the vegetation. Four months later, _Anaphalis margaritacea_ plants were found growing out of lava rock crevices. The beginning of plant regrowth in this area is a part of the process known as

(1) species preservation
(2) evolution
(3) biotic competition
(4) succession

Base your answers to questions 56 through 58 on the diagram below, which represents the changes in an ecosystem over a period of 100 years, and on your knowledge of biology.

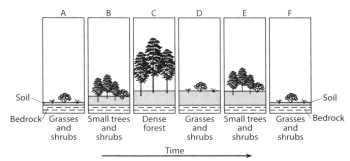

56 State one biological explanation for the changes in types of vegetation observed from *A* through *C*. [1]

57 Identify one human activity that could be responsible for the change from *C* to *D*. [1]

58 Predict what would happen to the soil and vegetation of this ecosystem after stage *F*, assuming no natural disaster or human interference. [1]

_____

59 The diagrams below show some changes in an environment over time.

Which phrase best describes this sequence of diagrams?

(1) the path of energy through a food web in a natural community
(2) the altering of an ecosystem by a natural disaster
(3) natural communities replacing each other in an orderly sequence
(4) similarities between an aquatic ecosystem and a terrestrial ecosystem

Directions

Review the Test-Taking Strategies section of this book. Then answer the following questions. Read each question carefully and answer with a correct choice or response.

Part A

1 The members of an animal community are usually similar in
   (1) size
   (2) structure
   (3) food requirements
   (4) environmental requirements

2 Which is a biotic factor that affects the size of a population in a specific ecosystem?
   (1) the average temperature of the ecosystem
   (2) the number and kinds of soil minerals in the ecosystem
   (3) the number and kinds of predators in the ecosystem
   (4) the concentration of oxygen in an ecosystem

3 In order to be self-sustaining, an ecosystem must contain
   (1) a large number of organisms
   (2) a warm, moist environment
   (3) a constant source of energy
   (4) organisms that occupy all of the niches

4 An overpopulation of deer in a certain area will most likely lead to
   (1) a decrease in the number of predators of the deer
   (2) an increase in the number of autotrophs available for food
   (3) a decrease in the incidence of disease
   (4) an increase in competition between the deer

5 For a natural ecosystem to be self-sustaining, many essential chemical elements must be
   (1) converted to energy
   (2) changed into fossil fuels such as oil and coal
   (3) permanently removed from the environment
   (4) cycled between organisms and the environment

6 A food chain is illustrated below.

Seaweed ⟶ Small fish ⟶ Large fish ⟶ Shark

The arrows represented as ∿⟶ most likely indicate
   (1) energy released into the environment as heat
   (2) oxygen produced by respiration
   (3) the absorption of energy that has been synthesized
   (4) the transport of glucose away from the organism

Part B

Base your answers to questions 7 and 8 on the information and graph below and on your knowledge of biology.

The Effect of pH on Survival Rates of Selected Species in Certain Adirondack Lakes

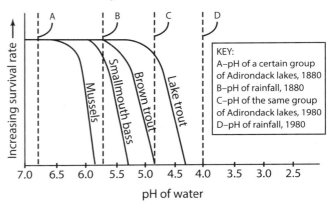

KEY:
A–pH of a certain group of Adirondack lakes, 1880
B–pH of rainfall, 1880
C–pH of the same group of Adirondack lakes, 1980
D–pH of rainfall, 1980

–National Geographic (adapted)

7 State how the pH of these Adirondack lakes changed between 1880 and 1980. [1]

8 State the effect that the pH change in these Adirondack lakes had on lake trout, brown trout, smallmouth bass, and mussels. [1]

9 Which types of organisms must be present in an ecosystem if the ecosystem is to be maintained?
   (1) producers and carnivores
   (2) producers and decomposers
   (3) carnivores and decomposers
   (4) herbivores and carnivores

10 Although three different bird species all inhabit the same type of tree in an area, competition between the birds rarely occurs. The most likely explanation for this lack of competition is that these birds
(1) have different ecological niches
(2) eat the same food
(3) have a limited supply of food
(4) are unable to interbreed

11 Identify one abiotic factor that would directly affect the survival of the fish shown in the diagram below. [1]

12 Which pair of terms would most likely apply to the same organism?
(1) heterotroph and herbivore
(2) heterotroph and autotroph
(3) autotroph and parasite
(4) producer and predator

13 A food chain is represented below.

corn plants → field mice → garter snakes → red-tailed hawks

The most abundant organisms in the food chain would be the
(1) corn plants
(2) field mice
(3) garter snakes
(4) red-tailed hawks

Base your answers to questions 14 through 16 on the food web and graph and on your knowledge of biology. The graph represents the interaction of two different populations, A and B, in the food web.

Food Web

Graph

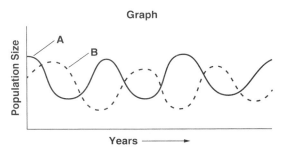

14 Population A is made up of living animals. The members of population B feed on these living animals. The members of population B are most likely
(1) scavengers   (3) predators
(2) autotrophs   (4) parasites

15 Identify one heterotroph from the food web that could be a member of population A. [1]

16 An energy pyramid is shown below.

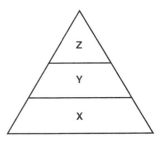

Identify one organism shown in the food web that would be found at level X. [1]

Base your answers to questions 17 through 20 on the graphs below that show data on some environmental factors affecting a large New York lake.

17 Which relationship can be correctly inferred from the data present?

(1) As sewage waste increases, the oxygen content decreases.
(2) As sewage waste increases, the oxygen content increases.
(3) As oxygen content decreases, the carp population decreases.
(4) As oxygen level decreases, the trout population increases.

18 The greatest change in the lake's whitefish population occurred in the years between
(1) 1950 and 1955   (3) 1960 and 1965
(2) 1955 and 1960   (4) 1965 and 1970

19 Identify the fish species that appears to withstand the greatest degree of oxygen depletion. [1]

20 Explain the impact of increased sewage levels on the biodiversity of the lake ecosystem. Support your answer with specific examples from the graph. [1]

Base your answers to questions 21 through 24 on the information below and data table.

A field study was conducted to observe a deer population in a given region over time. The deer were counted at different intervals over a period of 40 years. During this period, both ranching and the hunting of deer and their predators increased in the study region. A summary of the data is presented in the table.

Deer Population Changes 1900-1940

Year	Deer Population (thousands)
1900	3.0
1910	9.5
1920	65.0
1924	100.0
1926	40.0
1930	25.0
1940	10.0

Using the information in the data table, construct a line graph on the grid following the directions below.

Deer Population Changes 1900-1940

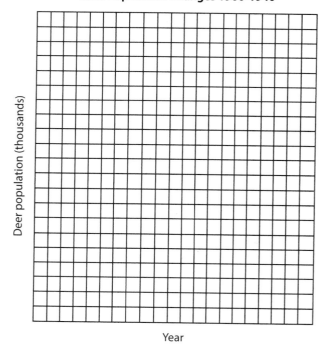

21 Mark an appropriate scale, without any breaks in the data, on each labeled axis. [1]

22 Plot the data for the deer population on the grid. Connect the points and surround each point with a small circle.

Example:

23 During which 10-year period did the greatest increase in the deer population occur?
(1) 1900–1910　　(3) 1920–1930
(2) 1910–1920　　(4) 1930–1940

24 State one possible action that could have been taken to help maintain a more stable population of deer in the area. [1]

Base your answers to questions 25 through 28 on the information below and on your knowledge of biology.

For 25 years, hay was cut from the same 10 acres on a farm. During these years, shrews, grasshoppers, spiders, rabbits, and mice were seen in this hayfield. After the farmer retired, he no longer cut the hay, and the field was left unattended.

25 Which description best matches the events in the former hayfield over the next few decades?
(1) The plant species will change, but the animal species will remain the same.
(2) The animal species will change, but the plant species will remain the same.
(3) Neither the plant species nor the animal species will change.
(4) Both the plant species and the animal species will change.

26 The grasshoppers, spiders, shrews, and other organisms, along with the soil minerals, amount of rainfall, and other factors, constitute
(1) an ecosystem　　(3) a biosphere
(2) a species　　　(4) a food web

27 Just before he retired, the farmer determined the population size of several of the field species during the months of May, July, and August. The results are recorded in the table below.

Field Species	Number of Organisms		
	May	July	August
Grasshoppers	1,000	5,000	1,500
Birds	250	100	100
Grasses	7,000	20,000	6,000
Spiders	75	200	500

Draw a food chain that represents the most likely feeding relationships among four of the organisms (grasshoppers, birds, grasses, and spiders) that live in the field. [1]

28 Which graph best represents the relative population size of the field species for May?

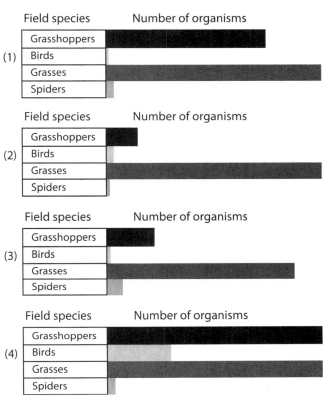

Base your answers to questions 29 and 30 on the information below and on your knowledge of biology.

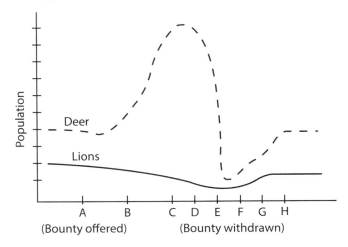

The graph shows the relative populations of mountain lions and deer in a certain geographic area that is generally favorable to both animals. At the time indicated by point A, hunters were offered a bounty payment for each mountain lion killed. Later, at the time indicated by point E, these bounties were withdrawn and hunting mountain lions was discouraged.

29 Which explanation best accounts for the fact that, according to the graph, the deer population is always higher than the mountain lion population?
   (1) The geographic location is more favorable for deer than for mountain lions.
   (2) Hunters are likely to kill more mountain lions than deer.
   (3) The organism serving as the food supply is normally more numerous than its predator.
   (4) Mountain lions usually produce more offspring than deer.

30 The graph is an illustration of the principle that
   (1) predators serve an important purpose in a balanced ecosystem
   (2) human intervention has little permanent impact on the survival of animal species
   (3) deer need the protection of humans in order to survive the attacks of their natural enemies
   (4) mountain lions do not pose the greatest danger to deer in their struggle for survival

Part C

31 State *two* reasons why it is important to preserve biodiversity. [1]

32 Explain the difference between a habitat and a niche. [1]

Base your answers to questions 33 through 35 on the information below and on your knowledge of biology.

The last known wolf native to the Adirondack Mountains of New York State was killed over a century ago. Several environmental groups have recently proposed reintroducing the wolf to the Adirondacks. These groups claim there is sufficient prey to support a wolf population in this area. These prey include beaver, deer, and moose. Opponents of this proposal state that the Adirondacks already have a dominant predator, the Eastern coyote.

33 State one effect the reintroduction of the wolf may have on the coyote population within the Adirondacks. Explain why it would have this effect. [1]

34 Explain why the coyote is considered a limiting factor in the Adirondack Mountains. [1]

35 State one ecological reason why some individuals might support the reintroduction of wolves to the Adirondacks. [1]

Base your answers to questions 36 and 37 on the information and graph below and on your knowledge of biology. The graph contains information about an ecosystem.

The graph below shows the carrying capacities of an ecosystem for three different species, 1, 2, and 3, that inhabit an area and the actual population sizes of these three different species in the area.

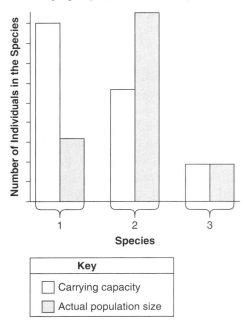

Carrying Capacities of an Ecosystem

36 Identify which species population would most likely have the greatest competition among its members. Support your answer using information from the graph. [1]

37 Explain how an ecosystem can have three different carrying capacities. [1]

Human Impact on Ecosystems

What do **YOU** *Think?*

Global Warming

The hole in the ozone layer is the cause of global warming since it lets in more heat from the sun and warms the polar regions of the Earth.

Global warming is really a natural process. The Earth was first very cold and it has been getting warmer ever since.

Plants are a major cause of global warming since they give off so much carbon dioxide.

Global warming is partly the result of our burning so much fossil fuel like coal and gasoline.

Human Impact on Ecosystems

Vocabulary

carrying capacity	global warming	pollution
deforestation	industrialization	renewable resource
direct harvesting	nonrenewable resource	technology
energy flow	nuclear fuel	trade-off
fossil fuel	ozone shield	water cycle

Topic Overview

All living things affect the environment around them. Porcupines chew the bark from trees; squirrels break twigs as they leap from branch to branch. Generally, the changes to the environment are small. Humans, however, have made impressive technological achievements in the past few hundred years. As a result, we are now making significant changes in Earth's diverse environments. As the human population grows and our need for the resources to sustain our technology expands, the possibility that we will harm Earth's ecosystems increases. Our decisions about how to use—or misuse—Earth's resources will have a profound impact on all the organisms that depend on those resources.

Need for Awareness and Understanding

Human activities can create ecological problems that must be avoided or corrected. If we are to find solutions to those problems, we must encourage everyone to become environmentally literate. That means people need to understand the causes and effects of environmental problems as well as the possible solutions that could lead to environmental stability. Because environmental issues often concern many countries, resolving environmental issues frequently requires global awareness, cooperation, and action.

Our Environment

Like all living things, humans are part of Earth's natural ecosystems. We depend on our ecosystem to supply the food we eat, the water we drink, and the air we breathe. As long as our ecosystem functions normally, those essential resources will be available. We can continue to depend on the plants in the ecosystem to provide food and oxygen and to recycle the carbon dioxide we exhale. We will also be able to rely upon our ecosystem to maintain the quality of our water.

Limited Resources

Earth has a finite supply of resources. Some of Earth's resources, such as our food supply and solar energy, are renewable. Given sufficient time,

renewable resources can be replaced. Other resources, such as fossil fuels and minerals, are **nonrenewable resources.** Once they're used, they cannot be replaced. Decisions we make today and tomorrow will determine whether or not we increase our consumption of Earth's limited resources. One way to reduce our use of resources is to control the growth rate of our population. An ever-increasing human population accelerates the use of Earth's limited resources. Making the right decisions about these issues will affect you as well as the future generations of all the organisms that share the biosphere.

Figure 7-1. **A commercial fishing trawler**

Renewable Resources Although many resources are renewable, they must be used carefully. Increased consumption can stress the natural processes that renew some resources. As a result, the resource might be unable to renew itself. For example, the fish we eat are a renewable resource. Even if many fish are captured, over time the fish populations can reproduce and recover their losses. Today, however, modern, commercial fishing (see Figure 7-1) can remove so many fish so quickly that specific populations may not have time to recover. In some cases, the reduction can be so severe that the fish population may fail to reproduce. At that point, the fish would no longer be a renewable resource.

Nonrenewable Resources Our increasing consumption of resources that cannot be replaced naturally is becoming a serious problem. Most metals, such as the aluminum we use for packaging, and other minerals, such as the silicon we use for computer chips, are nonrenewable resources. Fossil fuels, such as the gas that runs our cars and the coal that powers many factories, are also nonrenewable resources. Using too many nonrenewable resources will cause their <u>depletion</u> (serious reduction) within a relatively short time.

Preserving Our Resources Individuals can help maintain our supply of both renewable and nonrenewable resources by practicing the three R's: Reduce, Reuse, and Recycle. Suggestions are included in Table 7-1.

Natural Processes in Ecosystems

Several natural processes that occur in ecosystems affect the life and health of humans as well as all the other organisms that rely on the ecosystem. Some activities of humans affect these processes, and most of the changes are likely to be <u>detrimental,</u> or damaging, to the ecosystems. For example,

Table 7-1. How Individuals Can Preserve Resources		
The 3 R's	**Action**	**Example**
Reduce	Avoid using the resource.	Use energy efficiently; walk, bike or carpool instead of driving.
Reuse	Use the same product over and over, instead of throwing it away after one use.	Use dishes rather than paper plates. Instead of discarding your paper lunchbag, take it home and use it again.
Recycle	Don't throw it in the trash. Instead, discard the product in a way that it can be used again, or to make another product.	Paper, metal, plastic, and glass are all easily recycled. Donate unwanted clothing, books, and furniture to charitable organizations.

if **pollution**—a harmful change in the chemical makeup of the soil, water, or air—spreads to a particular habitat, some of the species that live in that habitat will suffer. The stability of the ecosystem and the variety of species that live in it might be threatened.

Maintaining Atmospheric Quality Throughout the biosphere, animals take in oxygen during respiration and release carbon dioxide. Plants and algae take in carbon dioxide during photosynthesis and release oxygen. Through the biotic processes of respiration and photosynthesis, the levels of carbon dioxide and oxygen in the atmosphere are kept in the range that is suitable for life.

Abiotic factors also help maintain the quality of the atmosphere. For example, as it falls, rain cleans the air of particles and soluble gases. The rainfall also helps maintain humidity in the atmosphere.

Soil Formation Soils form when weathering breaks down rocks and when organic materials from decaying plants and animals accumulate. Such soils support the growth of many producer organisms and serve as a habitat for decomposers. The root systems of plants hold the soil in place. If the vegetation that covers the ground is removed, the soil can be washed away by rain or blown away by wind. Soil erosion sometimes occurs during a drought when many plants die, leaving bare soil.

The Water Cycle Water continuously evaporates from the surface of the land and water and from the leaves of plants. The water vapor rises into the atmosphere and collects as clouds that can move long distances. Eventually, the vapor condenses as precipitation, which is distributed over many areas of Earth. The water collects as runoff or groundwater or evaporates. The process by which water continually moves from Earth's surface to the atmosphere and back is called the **water cycle,** and is shown in Figure 7-2. Many ecosystems maintain a supply of fresh water, which is available to all organisms, including humans.

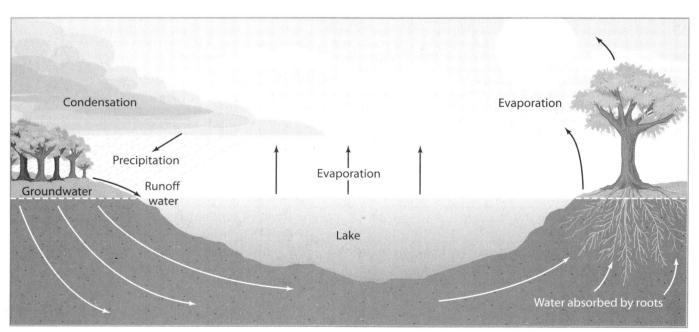

Figure 7-2. The water cycle

Waste Removal and the Recycling of Nutrients Plants that live in the soil use the soil's minerals as they grow. Nutrients are transported from one organism to another through the food chains in the ecosystem. Those that are not released into the atmosphere are eventually contained in the dead bodies and wastes of organisms. Decomposers break down the wastes and the dead bodies of organisms, removing the nutrients in the process. The nutrients are then restored to the soil, where they can then be used by other plants, continuing the cycle.

Without this natural recycling, much of the abiotic materials needed by living organisms would remain "locked up" in the bodies of dead organisms. Minerals and other nutrients would not be available for new organisms. In tropical forests, where heavy rains are frequent, decomposition and the recycling process must take place rapidly. Otherwise, the frequent rains strip the land of minerals before new plants can absorb and use them. In areas where the Amazon rain forest has been cleared and burned for planting, many nutrients have been washed away, leaving the soil unfertile.

Humans sometimes make use of this natural recycling process when they mix decaying lawn and garden wastes to make compost, which is a natural fertilizer and soil conditioner. Adding compost to the soil recycles wastes naturally and reduces the need for chemical fertilizers. It also reduces the amount of waste material in landfills and eliminates the need to burn yard waste, which pollutes our atmosphere.

The Flow of Energy Food chains, food webs, and energy pyramids illustrate the **energy flow** through ecosystems. Each organism has a role in the process and contributes to the overall stability of the ecosystem. As a result, losing all or most of the members of any species of an ecosystem could upset the stability of the whole ecosystem.

Energy is passed through the environment, but unlike nutrients, it does NOT recycle. Instead, at each feeding level in an energy pyramid, organisms lose large amounts of energy (as heat) to the environment. This energy cannot be recaptured by living things. Because of this constant energy loss, ecosystems need a constant source of new energy. That energy source is usually the sun.

People and the Environment

Because humans are part of Earth's ecosystems, they affect the way ecosystems function. They also are affected by changes in the ecosystem. Once the ecosystem is damaged, people may suffer from that damage just like any other species.

Population Growth

Most species in new environments can have a period of rapid population growth. The population increase levels off as it approaches the ecosystem's **carrying capacity,** which is the number of individuals of a species the environment can support. For example, as rabbits move into a field, their population may boom. Eventually, the food supply dwindles, and the scarcity of food leads to a reduction in the population of rabbits. Those that do not get enough to eat may become too weak to escape predators or

Figure 7-3. A population growth curve: In a new environment, the population usually increases quickly, but it stabilizes when it reaches the carrying capacity of that environment.

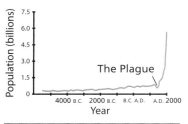

Figure 7-4. Growth curve for the human population worldwide

recover from diseases. Some may even die of starvation. The population growth levels off when the number of rabbits is balanced by the availability of food and the presence of limiting factors, such as predators. The relationship between population and the carrying capacity of an environment is shown in Figure 7-3.

Earth can only support a certain number of people. Our planet has a carrying capacity for humans just as it does for other species. The more people there are, the more resources they need. These resources come from the environment. More people also produce more waste, which must be disposed of or recycled. Overcrowding and lack of food also become problems when populations are very large.

For thousands of years, the human population grew slowly. Then about 300 years ago, our food supply began to increase, and improvements in health care and hygiene led to dramatic increases in our population. At present, the population curve inclines steeply upward. To many population scientists, the sharp increase suggests that the human population is growing at a dangerously fast rate. Compare Figure 7-4, the growth curve for the human population, with Figure 7-3, the growth curve typical for animals in an ecosystem.

If the human population continues to grow at the rate shown in Figure 7-4, Earth's carrying capacity could be reached soon. That result could be catastrophic. With no controls, the human population might even overshoot Earth's carrying capacity for our species. There might not be enough food, water, space, and/or oxygen. The resulting deaths from famine, disease, or wars over resources could reduce the human population to a small fraction of its present level. Finding ways to slow our population growth so that the growth rate levels off before Earth's carrying capacity is reached could save future generations from suffering the consequences of unlimited population growth.

Review Questions

Set 7.1

1. Which of these resources is renewable?
   (1) wood
   (2) oil
   (3) iron
   (4) coal

2. The best way to ensure that there will be enough aluminum for all future needs is to
   (1) dig more mines and process more aluminum ore
   (2) buy more aluminum from other countries and save our own
   (3) recycle and reuse aluminum
   (4) increase space exploration and search for new sources of aluminum

3. Some ecologists are concerned that the human population has outgrown the capacity of many of Earth's ecosystems. The natural limiting factor that will most likely prevent further human population growth in many parts of the world is
   (1) habitat destruction
   (2) political intervention
   (3) food supply
   (4) social intervention

4. Which of these human activities is quite often responsible for the other three human activities?
   (1) increasing demand on limited food production
   (2) rapid increase of loss of farmland due to soil erosion
   (3) rapid increase of human population
   (4) increasing levels of air pollution

5. The graphs on the right show the size of the human population in relation to food production per acre in four different countries over the same period of time.

Which country's population appears to have reached—and is now maintaining—its population close to its carrying capacity? Explain how you can tell. [1]

Key ———————— Population size
- - - - - Food production/acre

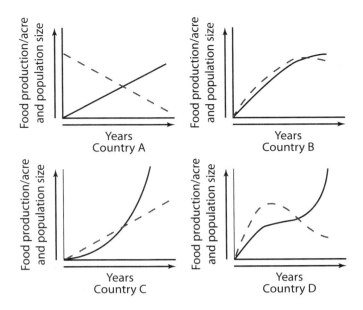

Human Activities and the Loss of Diversity

Some human activities that destroy habitats and degrade ecosystems do far more than damage individual organisms. They also destroy diversity in both the living and nonliving parts of the environment. For example, when humans use land to build a parking lot, the organisms that lived on that land are likely to die. Other organisms that ate the plants, burrowed through the ground, or nested in the nearby trees are also affected. There will be fewer resources available for a variety of species.

Many deliberate human activities, such as clearing land to plant a single crop, can change the equilibrium in an ecosystem. So can some accidents, such as inadvertently or unknowingly adding a species to an ecosystem.

Direct Harvesting The destruction or removal of species from their habitats is known as **direct harvesting.** It can sometimes lead to the extinction of a species. For example, some species that live in distant parts of the world (rain forests or deserts) are removed from their native habitats and sold to people who want them as unusual pets, ornaments, or house or garden plants. That cute monkey or beautiful parrot in the pet shop may not have been born in captivity. Instead, it may have been captured in the wild and shipped here. Many animals die in the process.

Other organisms are killed to collect a specific body part. For example, baby harbor seals are killed for their pelts, and elephants are killed for the ivory in their tusks, which people carve into jewelry or other trinkets. Direct harvesting can threaten the existence of the entire population of a species. Due to over-harvesting, some species of plants and animals have been taken from their native habitats in such large numbers that those species are now endangered. So many whales have been slaughtered that some species are now in danger of extinction.

In the past, humans have caused the extinction of several species. For example, in the early 1800s, billions of passenger pigeons lived in

Figure 7-5. **The passenger pigeon:** The passenger pigeon, once present in huge numbers, is now extinct because of uncontrolled hunting.

Estimated Area of Rain Forest

Figure 7-6. **Habitat destruction:** The destruction of rain forests, an example of deforestation, eliminates many ecosystems.

North America. (See Figure 7-5.) Each year hunters shot millions, until the population was greatly reduced. By the time people realized that the species was endangered, it was too late to save it. The last passenger pigeon died in a zoo in Cincinnati, Ohio, in 1914. Today, some endangered species are protected by law. However, because there may be a demand for products made from endangered species, poaching (illegally capturing or killing an organism) is a continuing problem.

Land Use As human populations grow, we use more resources to make the things we need or want, such as clothes, homes, refrigerators, MP3 players, and cars. We also need more space for places to live. More land is needed to grow food, to build roads and factories, and even to provide parks and recreational areas. As human populations and needs increase, our use of land decreases the space and resources available for other species.

Habitat Destruction Many people think that when a habitat is destroyed, the organisms simply find a new home. However, because other parts of the ecosystem are already occupied, displaced animals seldom find a new place to live. Habitat destruction occurs when people take over land for their own use. It is an important way that species can become endangered. They simply have nowhere to live! As habitats are destroyed, whole ecosystems can be damaged and entire species may become extinct. For example, pandas are endangered today because humans have greatly reduced the size of their habitat.

Deforestation, or the destruction of forests resulting from human activity, is a land use decision that causes widespread habitat destruction. People clear the forest by burning or cutting down the trees. Deforestation can provide people with land for farming and places to live. It also provides resources to use in building or manufacturing. Due to deforestation, the area covered by the world's rain forests is only about half as large as the area covered 150 years ago. (See Figure 7-6.) The wetlands, fields, and forests of New York are also threatened by development.

Biodiversity When a wide variety of different species live together in an ecosystem, it is said to have biodiversity. A reduction in biodiversity occurs when species are lost. This lost biodiversity can affect the health of whole ecosystems and food webs. It can even affect the proportion of gases in the atmosphere. Our future ability to find new medicines for treating diseases or to discover new sources of genes that could be genetically engineered into more productive and pest-resistant crops is threatened when biodiversity is lost.

Habitat destruction, such as deforestation, can lead to loss of biodiversity, but it is not the only way that human activities threaten biodiversity. For example, a farmer might plow under a meadow that is home to many species. Then the farmer might plant a single crop, such as corn or wheat, on many continuous acres of land. This practice greatly reduces the biodiversity of the area. (See Figure 7-7.) In addition, it creates an ideal environment for insects that feed on that crop. To control the insects, the farmer may need to use pesticides, which could harm other organisms living in the same or nearby environments.

Figure 7-7. Loss of biodiversity: The corn in this field provides habitats for only a few species. The meadow that once grew here was home for hundreds of species of flowers, shrubs, trees and small animals such as insects, mice, and birds.

Imported Species Biodiversity is often reduced when people import and release a species from one environment into another. The release may be inadvertent or intentional. For example, before 1859, there were no rabbits in Australia. Then two dozen rabbits were released in Australia. By 1953, more than a billion rabbits occupied 1.2 million square miles of the continent. These rabbits ate massive amounts of vegetation ordinarily available to the native species.

Many species become pests when they are added to a new environment. Because the new organisms are not part of an existing food web in the area, they often have no natural enemies in their new environment and rapidly overpopulate the area. They then crowd out, feed on, or otherwise eliminate native species. Two examples are Japanese beetles and gypsy moths, which were accidentally released in the U.S. (See Figure 7-8.) Now they are serious pests in New York.

Once an imported species becomes a pest, it is very difficult to solve the problem. If another species is imported to control it, the second species may choose to feed on native organisms, adding another problem. Using pesticides or poisons can kill other organisms in addition to the imported one. Sometimes scientists find a disease organism that only affects the imported species. The rabbits that overran Australia were eventually controlled by a disease organism. However, there is always a risk that the species may become resistant to the disease and overpopulate again.

Because imported species are such a problem, many states and countries have laws to restrict the transport of fruits and vegetables. The goal of these laws is to avoid introducing diseases or insects that might damage local crops. Some countries require the <u>quarantine</u> (confined isolation) of certain animals and plants until officials are sure they are free of any pests that could escape into the new environment.

Scientists are working to find safer methods of pest control. One safe pest control method is setting traps that use chemical scents to attract insects. With this method, no other species are harmed and the population of the pest species can be reduced to a safe level. Breeding and releasing native predators of a pest species has also sometimes been used successfully and without harm to other species.

Figure 7-8. Imported species: (A) During the larval stage, the gypsy moth consumes vast quantities of leaves. (B) The adult moth lays hundreds of eggs, continuing the problem.

6. Ladybugs were introduced as predators into an agricultural area of the United States to reduce the number of aphids feeding on grain crops. This action is an example of

(1) preservation of endangered species
(2) conservation of natural resources
(3) protection of watershed areas
(4) use of a nonchemical means of pest control

7. An example of a human activity that has had a positive effect on the environment is the

(1) disruption of natural habitats through deforestation
(2) capture and sale of rare South American birds
(3) use of reforestation to control erosion in the mountains
(4) hunting of endangered species of animals

8. The trees in a forest aid in reducing flood damage chiefly because their

(1) branches store water in the form of sap
(2) leaves absorb moisture from the air
(3) root systems hold the soil in place
(4) stems serve to store food

9. The creation of wildlife refuges and the enforcement of game laws are conservation measures that promote increased

(1) use of chemicals to control pests
(2) preservation of species
(3) use of natural controls to limit pest populations
(4) exploitation of wildlife species

10. When land is cleared for agriculture or home construction, small isolated sections of the original habitat may remain. Explain how this reduction in habitat size and the isolation of small sections of habitat might lead to species endangerment. [1]

11. A method of agriculture presently used throughout the world where one crop is grown on many acres of land has created serious insect problems. This is primarily because this method

(1) increases soil erosion
(2) provides concentrated areas of one kind of food for insects
(3) increases the effectiveness of insecticides used over long periods of time
(4) involves the growing of crops in former desert areas

12. The least ecologically damaging method for controlling the mosquitoes that spread the diseases malaria and encephalitis is by

(1) draining the swamps where mosquitoes breed
(2) spraying swamps with chemical pesticides
(3) spreading oil over swamps
(4) introducing local fish species to the swamps where mosquitoes breed

13. Many people place bat boxes on their property to provide housing that attracts insect-eating bats. Explain how this activity has a positive effect on the environment. [1]

14. In 1859, a small colony of 24 rabbits was brought to Australia. By 1928 it was estimated that there were 500 million rabbits in a 1-million square mile section of Australia. Which statement describes a condition that probably contributed to the increase in the rabbit population?

(1) The rabbits were affected by many limiting factors.
(2) The rabbits reproduced by asexual reproduction.
(3) The rabbits were unable to adapt to the environment.
(4) The rabbits had no natural predators in Australia.

15. Humans are responsible for some of the negative changes that occur in nature because they

(1) have controlled the use of many pesticides and other environmentally damaging chemicals
(2) have passed laws to preserve the environment
(3) are able to preserve scarce resources
(4) are able to modify their physical environment to provide for human needs

16. Which of the following human activities would be the most likely to prevent certain species from becoming extinct?

(1) Pass laws to place all endangered species in zoos.
(2) Increase the hunting of predators.
(3) Increase wildlife management and habitat protection.
(4) Mate organisms from different species to create new and stronger organisms.

17. In the Cochella Valley in California, much of the desert has been converted into golf courses, housing developments, and hotels. The habitat of the Cochella Valley fringe-toed lizard is rapidly being lost. This lizard is adapted to life on fine, windblown sand. Environmentalists want to save the lizard, and developers want to continue construction. Which action would be the best long-term solution?

(1) Land in the Cochella Valley should be purchased and set aside as a preserve for the lizards.
(2) The fringe-toed lizards should be crossed with a species adapted for survival in a different habitat.
(3) The land should be developed as planned and the lizards relocated to a different valley.
(4) The land should be developed as planned and the lizards monitored to see if they can adapt to the new conditions.

18. Refer to the chart below, which illustrates some methods of pest control.

Methods of Insect Pest Control
Insect pests can be repelled or attracted with sex hormones.
Insect populations can be controlled by releasing males sterilized with X-rays.
New plant varieties can be produced and grown that are resistant to insect pests.
Insect pests can be controlled by introducing their natural enemies.

One likely effect of using these methods of pest control will be to

(1) prevent the extinction of endangered species
(2) increase water pollution
(3) reduce pesticide contamination of the environment
(4) harm the atmosphere

The Impact of Technology and Industrialization

Humans modify ecosystems through population growth, consumption, and technology. As human populations grow, they take up more space, consume more resources, and produce more wastes. The expansion of **technology** (using scientific knowledge and technical processes to meet human needs) also increases the quantity of resources people use. All these activities lead to changes in ecosystems, including the way they function. The equilibrium of stable ecosystems can be upset by human actions.

Industrialization

Industrialization is the development of an economy in which machines produce many of the products people use. These products may add to the quality of life, but their manufacture can harm the environment. In addition to contributing to pollution of the air and water, industrialization increases the demand for energy, water, and other resources, including fossil and nuclear fuels.

Higher energy demands in an industrialized society mean that more power plants must be built. Additional power plants—especially those that burn coal—add to the pollution of our air and water. **Nuclear fuel** is an energy source that results from splitting atoms. Nuclear power plants do not pollute the air or water with toxic chemicals, but they can cause thermal pollution of waterways. Also, the disposal of radioactive nuclear wastes presents a huge environmental problem.

Another problem with increased industrialization is that most factories use a lot of water. Large wells drilled for factories sometimes dry up the nearby smaller wells that individuals use to supply their homes. In some cases, withdrawing large quantities of water causes the ground to collapse, forming sinkholes. In dry climates, reducing the supply of groundwater can have serious consequences for native plants and the consumers that depend on them for food.

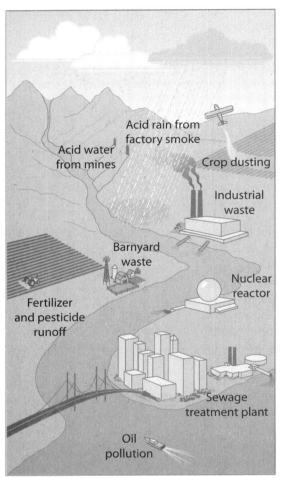

Figure 7-9. **Water pollution:** Water pollution, which can damage an ecosystem, comes from many sources.

Labels in figure:
Acid rain from factory smoke
Acid water from mines
Crop dusting
Industrial waste
Barnyard waste
Nuclear reactor
Fertilizer and pesticide runoff
Sewage treatment plant
Oil pollution

Just as conservation (the three R's) can help preserve our resources, it can also help to limit the negative impact of industrialization. We can REDUCE our demand for energy and manufactured goods that we don't really need. We can REUSE manufactured products rather than discard them, and we can RECYCLE as many products as possible, conserving both energy and resources in the process.

Water Pollution

Rivers, lakes, and oceans are easy places for people to dispose of wastes, including sewage, wastes from homes and factories, and animal wastes from farms. The addition of pollutants to natural environments causes water pollution, which can change the abiotic conditions in ecosystems. For example, sewage and animal wastes can act as fertilizer, increasing the growth of plants, algae, and bacteria in aquatic systems. Plants consume oxygen all the time, day and night. However, photosynthesis, the primary source of oxygen, stops at night because it requires light. As a result, oxygen production also stops. Then, oxygen levels drop and many organisms suffocate. When these organisms die, oxygen-using decomposers begin their decay activity, which further decreases the oxygen supply. Eventually, all the organisms in this oxygen-reduced ecosystem may be lost. Figure 7-9 shows several ways water pollution can affect a natural habitat.

Toxic Wastes Many wastes dumped into waterways from cities, farms, or industries can be toxic (poisonous) to the organisms that use or live in the water. Chemical fertilizers and weed and insect killers can be washed off farmlands into streams or rivers. The chemicals can collect in the cells of organisms living in the water and along the shore. These toxic materials then move through the food chain and eventually damage or kill many kinds of organisms.

Although the level of toxic substances in the water might be low, scientists have learned that the concentration of a toxin increases as it moves through the food chain. For example, small quantities of toxic substances are absorbed into the cells of algae and other producers living in the water. When those producers are eaten by small herbivores, the toxins are stored in the herbivore's fatty tissue. There it stays until the herbivore is eaten by the next consumer in the food chain. At each level of the chain, larger and larger amounts of toxic material collect in the fatty tissue. Organisms at or near the top of the food chain are most likely to accumulate enough of these chemicals in their bodies to cause them harm. (See Table 7-2.)

For example, farmers used to spray the pesticide DDT on their crops. Rain washed some of the DDT off the land and into streams and rivers. In the water, the DDT moved up through the food chain. Soon, fish-eating birds at the top of the food chain produced eggs with very thin shells. The shells were so thin that they broke easily, which killed the next generation of birds before it even hatched.

Table 7-2. Accumulation of a Toxic Substance by Organisms in a Food Chain				
Food Chain Organisms	Plant —>	Herbivore —>	Carnivore 1 —>	Carnivore 2
Relative concentration of the toxic substance	.000003	0.04	0.5	2.0
Magnification factor (compared to the amount in the plant)	0	1,333 times as much	16,667 times as much	66,667 times as much

Thermal Pollution Some power plants and industries use water to cool their machines or materials. The warmed water is then released into a river or lake, and the water temperature in the river or lake rises. Because warm water cannot hold as much dissolved oxygen as cold water, the oxygen level in the river or lake drops as the water temperature rises. Some species may suffocate as a result of <u>thermal</u> pollution; others may be forced to try to find a new home.

The solution to most of these problems is to find better ways to deal with wastes and to reduce the need for power. Sewage can be treated before it is discharged into waterways. Toxic wastes can be separated from other materials and either recycled or stored safely. People could conserve energy by using less power. Methods could be developed for cooling industrial processes that would reduce their damage to the environment.

Air Pollution

Just as wastes dumped into rivers and oceans cause water pollution, harmful substances released into the air cause air pollution. Early in the industrial age, people thought that burning wastes just disappeared into the atmosphere, and that they didn't have to worry any more about the wastes. We now know this is not true! Most of the pollutants released into the atmosphere eventually wind up in the water cycle and return to the water or land. Like water pollution, air pollution can damage habitats and harm the organisms that live in them. Figure 7-10 shows how air pollution can affect a natural habitat.

Burning Fossil Fuels Fuels such as the coal and gas that formed from the remains of organisms that lived millions of years ago are known as **fossil fuels.** Factories, cars, and most electrical power-generating plants burn fossil fuels. When fossil fuels are burned, carbon dioxide and other gases—some containing sulfur and/or nitrogen—are added to the air.

Acid Precipitation Sulfur and nitrogen compounds that are produced when fossil fuels burn can combine with moisture in the atmosphere. When this moisture falls to Earth as <u>acid rain</u>, snow, or other precipitation, it has a low pH level and is much more acidic than normal precipitation. Some acid precipitation can be as acidic as lemon juice. When highly acidic rain or snow touches plants, it may damage them and disrupt the way they function. The damaged plants may be more susceptible to attacks by fungi or insects.

Acid precipitation can also fall into lakes and streams or run off the land into the water. In lakes, the lower pH levels can be deadly to algae, the eggs of some fish, and other organisms. Producer organisms, such as algae, are killed. Without algae suspended in it, the water looks crystal clear and pure. However, the food chains in the ecosystem have been disrupted, and

Figure 7-10. Air pollution: Trees can be damaged—or killed— by polluted air.

populations of fish and other organisms have died. Some lakes have become so acidic that nothing can live in them.

Smog Other air pollutants are produced by automobile exhaust and by industrial processes. Some of these pollutants can be toxic when inhaled. This kind of pollution becomes more serious when weather conditions trap the gases in an area for hours or even days. Smog is a kind of air pollution that results when certain pollutants react with sunlight. It looks like a gray or brown haze and contains many airborne pollutants. People with respiratory diseases are especially sensitive to air pollution and may be in danger when air pollution is intense.

Global Atmospheric Changes

Some pollutants in the air harm living things directly, like the trees in Figure 7-10. Others can cause worldwide atmospheric changes that threaten many habitats and the organisms that live in them.

Global Warming Sunlight passes through the gases in the atmosphere to reach Earth. But some of these atmospheric gases, called greenhouse gases, also trap and absorb the infrared radiation that bounces off Earth's warmed surface. For thousands of years, this process—called the greenhouse effect—has kept Earth warm. In recent years, however, the amount of greenhouse gases in the atmosphere has increased. As Figure 7-11 shows, the increased amount of greenhouse gases in Earth's atmosphere traps some of the heat that would normally radiate into space. The result is that Earth's average temperature is rising. This increase in temperature, called **global warming,** could lead to changes in climate patterns and even to the melting of the ice caps at the North and South Poles. Most of the recent increase in greenhouse gases has been caused by burning fuel for transportation and industry.

Carbon dioxide, a major greenhouse gas, is released when fossil fuels are burned. (See Figure 7-12.) If the greenhouse effect causes climate change, the world's food supply may suffer. Another effect could be that the ice

Figure 7-11. Global warming: Pollution caused by human activity is increasing the amount of greenhouse gases in the atmosphere. This increase can intensify the greenhouse effect, causing global warming.

caps could melt, leading to a rise in sea level and flooding in many coastal habitats.

Finding and using energy sources that do not add carbon dioxide to the atmosphere is one way to prevent further global warming. Because trees remove large quantities of carbon dioxide during photosynthesis and store it in their tissues as carbon compounds, growing more long-lived trees could also help solve the problem.

Ozone Depletion Ozone depletion is another atmospheric problem that we must solve. Like global warming, ozone depletion is a worldwide problem, and international cooperation is needed to find an effective long-term solution.

The release of certain industrial gases into the atmosphere has led to destruction of much of the **ozone shield,** the layer of ozone gas in the upper atmosphere that protects Earth from some of the sun's radiation. (See Figure 7-13.) The thinning "hole" in the ozone shield allows above normal amounts of ultraviolet radiation from the sun to reach Earth's surface. Ultraviolet radiation can cause genetic mutations and can kill cells that are exposed to it. An increase in ultraviolet radiation at Earth's surface could result in more cases of skin cancer. It could also destroy many of the producer organisms in the oceans. This would disrupt food chains and reduce the amount of oxygen released by the producers.

The main cause of ozone depletion is the release of gases called chlorofluorocarbons, or CFCs, into the atmosphere. CFCs have been used as coolants in refrigerators and air conditioners, as propellants in aerosol cans, and in the manufacture of plastic foam. Some steps have been taken to reduce the release of these gases. Researchers have found alternatives to the products that cause the most damage, and international agreements to reduce emissions of the harmful gases have been made.

Individual Choices and Societal Actions

Many people hope technology will help solve some of our environmental problems. In fact, technology has led to some improvements. For example, advances in technology have allowed farmers to greatly increase the crop yield of an acre of land. Larger crop yields mean a greater supply of food. However, some kinds of technology, such as pesticides and fertilizers, can cause pollution and have other harmful effects on the environment.

If technology cannot solve all our environmental problems, people will need to take some difficult steps to save our ecosystem. For some problems, solutions are now available, but they affect our quality of life. For example, we know how to reduce the air and water pollution caused by factories, power-generating plants, and automobiles, but the solutions are expensive and would make the

Figure 7-12. Carbon dioxide in the atmosphere from 1750 to 2000: The amount of carbon dioxide in the atmosphere has increased greatly since the beginning of the Industrial Revolution. The dots are data from ice core samples; the solid line represents direct measurements.

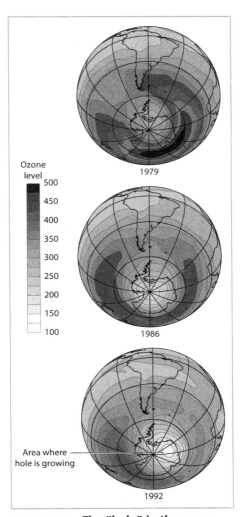

Figure 7-13. The "hole" in the ozone shield: These satellite maps show how much the "hole" in the ozone shield above the South Pole grew in just over a decade.

Figure 7-14. **CFCs:** Aerosol cans no longer use ozone-destroying CFCs as propellants. Safer alternatives have been found.

Figure 7-15. **Public hearings:** Discussion can be held to consider environmental issues and the trade-offs involved.

Figure 7-16. **Recycling:** Decisions on recycling are made by individuals and their communities.

products we buy cost more. We also know how to conserve energy, but many people are unwilling to give up their large cars, brightly lit neighborhoods, and air-conditioned comfort and to turn off their radios, computers, and televisions.

For each environmental problem, people must learn to assess the risk to the ecosystem. For each solution, they must learn to analyze the costs and benefits. Then they must determine which **trade-off,** or compromise, is acceptable and which is simply too dangerous to the welfare of future generations.

The Impact of New Technologies

New laws restrict the introduction of certain new technologies or major construction projects. The individual or company seeking permission to make a change that affects the environment must prepare a statement known as an environmental impact statement. This statement includes an analysis of how the project or technology will affect the environment and is usually discussed at public hearings. Then members of the public or their elected representatives vote on whether or not to allow the new technology or construction project to go forward. Appropriate decisions can be made only if the public is environmentally literate and has a clear understanding of the ecological issues. If an incorrect decision is made, it may be impossible to undo the damage that might result.

Today's Decisions Affect the Next Generation

The decisions we make today can have a huge impact on our environment. Those decisions, right or wrong, will affect the people living today as well as future generations.

The loss of some species may seem unimportant. However, the loss of that single species might have a huge impact on the ecology of an area. If the loss of species continues, large-scale destruction of natural environments will result, with serious consequences for the future. For example, the destruction of large forests or the loss of algae in ocean waters affects not only the organisms that live in those ecosystems but organisms elsewhere too. Those losses may compromise Earth's ability to produce enough oxygen and remove enough carbon dioxide to maintain an atmosphere that meets the needs of all of its inhabitants, including humans.

Many important decisions about the environment are made by states and nations, but a surprising number of important decisions are made each day by individuals. For example, individuals decide whether to burn their garden waste or turn it into compost, whether to toss the soda can into the trash or recycle it, whether to grab a fresh sheet of paper or write a note on an old envelope.

Much of the impact of our technology and population growth on Earth's ecosystems has been detrimental. If our environmental problems are not recognized and solved, the long-term damage will be irreversible and severe. On the other hand, cooperation by individuals and nations can help maintain the stability of the ecosystems upon which all life depends. Making people aware of the successful results of the collective actions of many separate individuals may be the most promising approach to solving ecological problems.

19. Car exhaust has been blamed for increasing the amount of carbon dioxide in the air. Some scientists believe this additional carbon dioxide in the air may cause

(1) global warming
(2) increased biodiversity
(3) habitat preservation
(4) ozone destruction

20. Deforestation will most directly result in an immediate increase in

(1) atmospheric carbon dioxide
(2) atmospheric ozone
(3) wildlife populations
(4) renewable resources

21. Which human activity has probably contributed *most* to lake acidification in the Adirondack region of New York State?

(1) passage of environmental protection laws
(2) reforestation projects in lumbered areas
(3) production of chemical air pollutants by industry
(4) use of biological insect controls to eliminate pests

22. A major reason that humans can have such a significant impact on an ecological community is that humans

(1) can modify their environment through technology
(2) reproduce faster than most other species
(3) are able to increase the amount of finite resources available
(4) remove large amounts of carbon dioxide from the air

23. Explain how the runoff waters from farm land and golf courses might be dangerous to organisms living in ponds, rivers, or streams. [1]

24. Explain why water shortages occur frequently in parts of New York State even though the water supply is nearly constant. [1]

25. The number of industries along New York State's rivers is increasing. What is the most likely consequence of increased industrialization?

(1) a decrease in the amount of water needed by industry
(2) a decrease in the amount of water pollution
(3) an increase in the destruction of natural ecosystems
(4) an increase in the amount of water available for recreational use

26. Which statement illustrates how human activities can most directly change the dynamic equilibrium of an ecosystem?

(1) A hurricane causes a stream to overflow its banks.
(2) Increased wind increases water evaporation from a plant.
(3) Water pollution causes a decrease in fish populations in a river.
(4) The ozone shield helps prevent harmful radiation from reaching the surface of Earth.

27. Which illustrates the human population's increased understanding and concern for ecological interrelationships?

(1) importing organisms in order to disrupt existing ecosystems
(2) allowing the air to be polluted only by those industries that promote technology
(3) removing natural resources from the Earth at a rate equal to or greater than the needs of an increasing population
(4) developing animal game laws in order to limit the number of organisms that may be killed each year

28. When living organisms obtain water and food from their environment, they may also take in toxic pesticides. Low concentrations of some pesticides may not kill animals, but they may damage reproductive organs and cause sterility. The data table below shows concentrations of a pesticide in tissues of organisms at different levels of a food chain.

Concentration of Pesticide in Tissues	
Organisms	**Pesticide Concentration** (parts per million)
producers	0.01 — 0.03
herbivores	0.25 — 1.50
carnivores	4.10 — 313.80

What does this information suggest to a person who is concerned about health and is deciding on whether to have a plant-rich or an animal-rich diet? Support your answer using the information provided. [1]

Directions

Review the Test-Taking Strategies section of this book. Then answer the following questions. Read each question carefully and answer with a correct choice or response.

Part A

1 Today's lifestyles have led to increased demands for disposable products. The packaging of these products has caused environmental problems most directly associated with
   (1) food web contamination
   (2) atmospheric depletion
   (3) solid waste disposal
   (4) the use of nuclear fuels

2 Some modern agricultural methods have created serious insect problems, primarily because these methods
   (1) increase soil loss
   (2) provide concentrated areas of food for insects
   (3) aid in the absorption of water
   (4) grow crops in areas where formerly only insects could live

3 The decline and extinction of many predatory animal species is most probably the result of
   (1) an overabundance of prey species
   (2) the introduction of a new species of animal into an area
   (3) the disruption of natural food chains
   (4) the decreased use of chemical pesticides

4 Modern methods of agriculture have contributed to the problem of soil depletion because many of these methods
   (1) require smaller amounts of mineral and fertilizer application
   (2) interfere with the natural cycling of elements
   (3) use many varieties of cloned plants
   (4) depend on the practice of planting and harvesting

5 Which action that humans have taken in attempting to solve an ecological problem has had the most negative effect?
   (1) seeking better means of birth control in the human population
   (2) applying scientific farming techniques to oceans
   (3) producing stronger and more effective pesticides
   (4) developing new techniques for the disposal of sewage and industrial and chemical wastes

6 Japanese beetles, a major insect pest in the United States, do relatively little damage in Japan because they
   (1) are kept in check by natural enemies
   (2) are kept in check by effective pesticide sprays
   (3) hibernate during the winter months
   (4) have gradually adapted to the environment

7 Gypsy moths were accidentally introduced into North America. The most probable reason these insects have become serious pests in North America is that they
   (1) were bred by research scientists and are resistant to all pesticides
   (2) are protected by environmental laws and feed on other insect species
   (3) have few natural enemies and reproduce successfully
   (4) are affected by natural controls and feed on plants

8 The survival of many plants and animals has been aided most by
   (1) increasing the height of industrial smokestacks to spread air pollutants away from the immediate vicinity of combustion
   (2) reduction in the number of restrictive pollution control laws
   (3) heavy use of pesticides to kill all of the insect pests that compete with humans for food sources
   (4) development of research aimed toward the preservation of endangered species

9 DDT is an insecticide that accumulates in the fatty tissues of animals and is transferred through food chains. Its concentration increases at each link of a food chain. Which organism in a food chain is most likely to accumulate the highest concentration of DDT?
(1) rabbit (a herbivore)
(2) corn (a producer)
(3) field mouse (a consumer)
(4) owl (a predator)

10 What is the most likely cause of the change in life expectancy shown in the graph below?

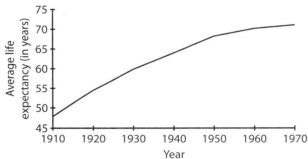

(1) poor land-use management that has affected the quality of the topsoil
(2) technological oversights that have had an impact on air quality
(3) a decrease in natural checks, such as disease, on the population
(4) widespread use of pesticides, such as DDT, in water supplies

11 As water flows downhill, its energy can be used to generate electricity. Later, this water may evaporate, fall as rain, and be used again to generate electricity in the same way. This explains why electricity generated with water is considered
(1) a source of water pollution
(2) a renewable form of energy
(3) more expensive than nuclear energy
(4) responsible for global warming

Part B

Base your answers to questions 12 through 15 on the passage below and on your knowledge of biology.

Keystone Species

A keystone species is one whose presence contributes to the diversity of life and whose extinction would lead to the extinction of other forms of life. A keystone species helps to support the ecosystem of which it is a part.

An example of what can happen when a keystone species is removed occurred when fur hunters eliminated sea otters from some Pacific Ocean kelp beds. Otters eat sea urchins, which eat kelp. With its major predator gone, sea urchin populations exploded and consumed most of the kelp. Fish, snails, and other animals associated with the kelp beds disappeared.

The grizzly bear is another example of a keystone species. Grizzlies transfer nutrients from the ocean ecosystem to the forest ecosystem. The first stage of this transfer is performed by salmon that swim up rivers, sometimes for hundreds of miles. Salmon are rich in nitrogen, sulfur, carbon, and phosphorus. The bears capture the salmon and carry them onto dry land, scattering nutrient-rich feces (wastes) and partially eaten salmon carcasses. It has been estimated that the bears leave up to half of the salmon they harvest on the forest floor.

12 One action humans can take that might ensure that these sea otters will continue their function as a keystone species in their environment is to
(1) establish a sea otter wildlife refuge in the Atlantic Ocean
(2) pass laws to regulate the hunting of sea otters
(3) plant kelp in the Pacific Ocean
(4) destroy sea urchins found living in the kelp beds

13 Some people feel the grizzly bear should be eliminated from parts of its natural range. Describe the impact of this proposed action on the forest ecosystems in these areas if the bears are eliminated. Support your answer with information from the passage. [1]

14 Which organism is most likely *not* functioning as a keystone species in its ecosystem?

(1) beaver — transforms its territory from a stream to a pond or swamp, maintaining the habitat for a variety of native species

(2) elephant — destroys trees, making room for grass species and preventing the environment from becoming a woodland

(3) black-tailed prairie dogs — burrows act as homes to other creatures, including burrowing owls, badgers, rabbits, snakes, salamanders, and insects

(4) zebra mussels — compete with native species, reducing the biodiversity of the Great Lakes ecosystem

15 Which sequence best represents the feeding relationships in a kelp ecosystem that has not been disturbed by humans?

(1) sea urchins → kelp → fish
(2) kelp → sea urchins → sea otters
(3) kelp → sea otters → sea urchins
(4) sea urchins → snails → kelp

Base your answers to questions 16 through 19 on the diagram below and on your knowledge of biology. The diagram represents the growth rate of a mouse population introduced into an abandoned field ecosystem.

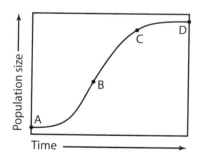

16 At what points is food most likely a limiting factor in the rate of mouse population growth?

(1) A and B   (3) C and D
(2) B and C   (4) B and D

17 At what point is the rate of population growth the greatest?

(1) A   (2) B   (3) C   (4) D

18 At what point would the mouse population be the greatest in the ecosystem?

(1) A   (2) B   (3) C   (4) D

19 Compare the growth rate of the mouse population in the abandoned field to the growth rate of the human population. In your comparison be sure to identify

- how it is similar [1]
- how it is different [1]

Base your answers to questions 20 and 21 on the information and graph below and on your knowledge of biology.

The screw-worm fly is a destructive parasite of livestock. The graph shows the results of an experiment in which one population of screw-worm flies was treated with pesticides and another group of equal size was treated with ionizing radiation, which made the male flies sterile.

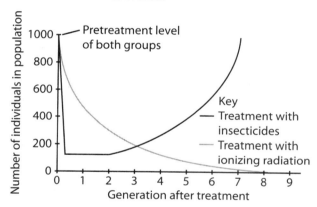

20 At what point after treatment will the group treated with pesticide probably reach its pretreatment population?

(1) first generation   (3) third generation
(2) seventh generation   (4) eighth generation

21 At what point after treatment will the sterility method be more successful against screw-worm flies than the pesticide method?

(1) immediately   (3) third generation
(2) second generation   (4) sixth generation

Base your answers to questions 22 and 23 on the information in the paragraph below and on your knowledge of biology.

A single protist (a one-celled organism) was placed in a large test tube containing nutrient broth. The tube was kept at room temperature for 24 hours. Samples from the tube were observed periodically during the 24 hours, using the low power of a compound light microscope. The data are summarized in the table below.

Age and Number of Protists in Culture	
Age of the Population in Hours	**Number of Protists in the Population**
0	1
6	2
8	3
10	4
13	8
16	16
18	32
20	64
22	128
24	256

22 Which graph best represents the data given in the table?

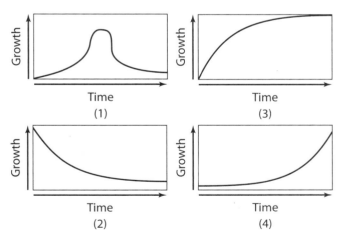

23 Which graph most resembles the growth of the human population at the present time?
(1) 1   (2) 2   (3) 3   (4) 4

Base your answers to questions 24 and 25 on the graph below which shows pollution from nitrogen-containing compounds (nitrates) in a brook flowing through a deforested and a forested area between 1965 and 1968.

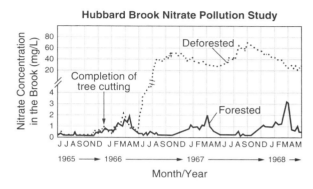

24 State how nitrate pollution in the brook changed after the brook flowed through the deforested area. [1]

25 Explain how deforestation contributed to this change. [1]

Part C

Base your answers to questions 26 through 29 on the information and graphs below, and on your knowledge of biology.

For over 100 years scientists have monitored the carbon dioxide concentrations in the atmosphere in relation to changes in the atmospheric temperature. The graphs below show the data collected for these two factors.

Concentration of Carbon Dioxide in the Atmosphere

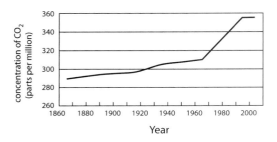

Average Atmospheric Temperature Change per Year

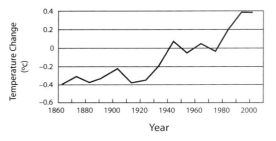

26 State the overall relationship between the concentration of carbon dioxide and changes in atmospheric temperature. [1]

27 State one way in which humans have contributed to the increase in atmospheric carbon dioxide. [1]

28 Identify one specific *negative* effect the continued rise in temperature would be likely to have on an ecosystem. [1]

29 Describe one way humans could try to reduce the problem of global warming. [1]

Base your answers to questions 30 and 31 on the information below and on your knowledge of biology.

Cattail plants that grow in freshwater swamps in New York State are being replaced by an imported species of plant called purple loosestrife. The two species have very similar environmental needs.

30 Since cattails and loosestrife occupy the same niche, it is predicted that eventually only one of the two species will exist in New York freshwater swamps. State one reason why loosestrife will probably out-compete the cattails and be more successful. [1]

31 Explain why loosestrife plants replacing the native cattails could potentially cause a decrease in many swamp wildlife populations and perhaps even lead to the elimination of some species from New York State. [1]

---

32 Describe two ways in which the destruction of the rainforest in South America could affect a hospital patient in New York State? [1]

Base your answer to questions 33–35 on the information below, and on your knowledge of biology.

Human activities continue to place strains on the environment. One of these strains on the environment is the loss of biodiversity.

33–35 Explain what this problem is and describe some ways humans are involved in both the problem and the possible solutions. In your answer be sure to:
- state the meaning of the term *biodiversity* [1]
- state one *negative* effect on humans if biodiversity continues to be lost [1]
- suggest one practice that could be used to preserve biodiversity in New York State [1]

Base your answers to questions 36 and 37 on the information below and on your knowledge of biology.

Plankton is the name given to the algae and microscopic life that grow in great numbers on and near the surface of the ocean. Plankton serve as the basis of food chains for oceanic life. Scientists have become concerned with the increase in ultraviolet (UV) radiation reaching the surface of the Earth in recent years. They fear that UV rays may negatively impact the plankton.

36 Explain why the amount of UV radiation reaching the surface may be on the increase, especially near the North and South Poles. [1]

37 Describe the effect any large-scale plankton destruction will have on larger species living in these same areas of the ocean where the UV levels have been increasing. [1]

38 Destruction of the ozone shield is generally considered a negative aspect of human involvement with the ecosystem. Explain how solving this problem will require increasing global awareness and cooperation [1]

Base your answers to questions 39 and 40 on the diagram below and on your knowledge of biology. The diagram represents a part of a food web in a Long Island ecosystem.

The numbers in the diagram show the concentration of the insecticide DDT in parts per million (ppm) in the body tissues of the various organisms.

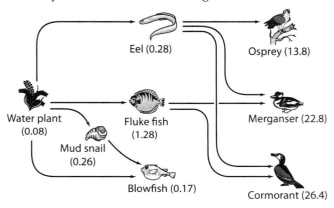

Eel (0.28)

Osprey (13.8)

Water plant (0.08)

Fluke fish (1.28)

Merganser (22.8)

Mud snail (0.26)

Blowfish (0.17)

Cormorant (26.4)

39 Explain why the water plant contains the pesticide DDT. [1]

40 Explain why the amounts of DDT in the three bird species are so much higher than in the other organisms of this food web. [1]

Base your answers to questions 41 through 43 on the information below and on your knowledge of biology.

The planning board of a community held a public hearing in response to complaints by residents concerning a waste-recycling plant. These residents claim that the waste-hauling trucks were polluting air, land, and water and that the garbage has brought an increase in rats, mice, and pathogenic bacteria to the area. The residents were insistent that the waste-recycling plant be closed permanently.

Other residents recognized the health risks but felt that the benefits of waste recycling outweighed the health issues.

41 Identify *two* specific health problems that could result from living near the waste recycling plant. [1]

42 State *one* cause of a health problem that can be associated with the presence of the waste recycling plant. [1]

43 State *one* ecological benefit of recycling wastes. [1]

Base your answers to questions 44–45 on the information below and on your knowledge of biology.

44–45 Ladybugs were introduced as predators into an agricultural area of the United States to reduce the number of aphids (pests that feed on grain crops). Describe the positive and negative effects of this method of pest control. Your response must include at least:
- *two* advantages of this method of pest control [1]
- *two* possible dangers of using this method of pest control [1]

Base your answers to questions 46 through 48 on the information below and on your knowledge of biology.

In the 1980s, global deforestation was estimated at 17 to 20 million hectares per year, an area the size of Great Britain. Today, the area affected by deforestation has decreased significantly in some regions of the world through the use of sustainable forest management. However, there are still regions of the world affected by wide-scale deforestation, because of the short-term economic benefits. The harmful effects of deforestation on regional and worldwide climate and ecology continue as forest areas are destroyed.

46 State one short-term economic benefit of deforestation. [1]

47 Explain how deforestation decreases biodiversity. [1]

48 Explain how wide-scale deforestation may contribute to global warming. [1]

Base your answer to questions 49 through 52 on the information below and on your knowledge of biology.

Zebra mussels have caused several major changes in the ecosystem in the Hudson River. Native to Eurasia, zebra mussels were accidentally imported to the Great Lakes in ships during the late 1980s and first appeared in the Hudson in 1990.

In regions of the Hudson north of West Point, zebra mussels have depleted the levels of dissolved oxygen to the point where many native organisms either die or move to other waters. In addition, large amounts of phytoplankton (small photosynthetic organisms) are consumed by the zebra mussels.

Before the introduction of zebra mussels, one typical food chain in this part of the Hudson was:

phytoplankton → freshwater clams → other consumers

49 As a result of the introduction of zebra mussels into the Hudson River, state one likely change in the population of each of two different species (other than the zebra mussels) found in the river. [1]

50 Identify one gas in this ecosystem and state how a change in its concentration due to the effects of zebra mussels would affect organisms other than the zebra mussels. [1]

51 State how the death of many of the native organisms could affect the rate of decay and how this would affect the amount of material being recycled. [1]

52 Explain why the size of the zebra mussel population would decrease after an initial increase. [1]

Base your answer to questions 53–56 on the information and graph below and on your knowledge of biology.

At an observatory in Mauna Loa, Hawaii, scientists have been measuring and collecting data related to changes in the atmosphere since the 1950s. The remote location of the observatory makes it ideal for studying atmospheric conditions that can cause climate change. One specific measurement taken is the amount of atmospheric carbon dioxide. Information for a 7-year period is shown in the graph below.

Atmospheric Carbon Dioxide – Mauna Loa

Source: www.mlo.noaa.gov

53–56 Analyze the data shown in the graph. In your answer, be sure to:
- state the overall relationship between time and carbon dioxide levels [1]
- state *one* possible cause for the overall change in the carbon dioxide levels shown in the graph [1]
- identify the biological process that might account for the decreases in carbon dioxide levels [1]
- identify *two* actions carried out by humans that could lower carbon dioxide levels [1]

Scientific Inquiry and Skills

What do **You** Think?

Experimental Design

I am doing an experiment to determine the effect of different colors of light on photosynthesis. The dependent variable will be how fast the plants use carbon dioxide.

I am doing an experiment to determine the effect of temperature on the activity of a starch-digesting enzyme. The independent variable will be how fast the enzyme breaks down starch.

I am doing an experiment to determine the effect of different amounts of fertilizer on plant growth. My control group will get the most fertilizer.

Scientific Inquiry and Skills

Vocabulary

assumption	dependent variable	model
bias	evidence	observation
conclusion	experiment	opinion
control	hypothesis	peer review
controlled experiment	independent variable	research plan
data	inference	scientific literacy

Topic Overview

Science is both a body of knowledge and a way of knowing things. Through intellectual and social activities, human thinking is applied to discovering and explaining how the world works. Science originates when people ask questions. Scientists use scientific inquiry and skills to seek answers to questions about the world. This involves formulating hypotheses, designing and conducting experiments, collecting data, and analyzing the data to form conclusions. Scientists also rely on peer review by other scientists to confirm the validity of their results.

What Is Science?

At one time, "scientific" knowledge was just a collection of opinions and unrelated ideas attempting to explain observations. For example, many people gazing out over the ocean were certain that Earth was flat as shown in Figure 8-1. A few individuals were equally sure that Earth was round. The topic was hotly debated. Those believing that Earth was flat offered for **evidence** (support for the idea that something is true) the fact that some ships never returned home. They believed that these ships had been destroyed when they sailed over Earth's edge. Those who believed that Earth was round also had evidence. They had observed boats approaching land and noticed that the tops of the sails were visible before the hull of the boat.

Another common idea once was that living organisms could come from nonliving things. Some people believed that when conditions were just right, frogs formed from the mud, water, and gases in the bottom of a pond. People also thought that if you left some grain and a dirty shirt in a wooden box, mice would develop after a period of time. Many people were certain that reproduction was not necessary for life to form. This idea, too, was discussed and debated.

Today, scientists do more than debate whether or not a new opinion or idea seems to make sense. They develop explanations using observations as evidence. New information is combined with what people already

Figure 8-1. **Ships at sea:** At one time a flat Earth seemed to make sense.

know. Learning about the historical development of scientific concepts and about the individuals who have contributed to scientific knowledge helps people understand the thinking that has taken place. At first, it might seem silly to believe that Earth is flat, but based on observations made at the time and the tools available at the time, it's not surprising that many people believed in a flat Earth. The emergence of life from pond mud seemed equally reasonable.

Scientific Inquiry

Scientific investigation involves the following:

- questioning
- observing and inferring
- experimenting
- collecting and organizing data
- finding evidence and drawing conclusions
- repeating the experiment several times
- peer review

Questioning is at the heart of science. Progress in science depends on people who not only wonder how the world works but who also take the time to develop questions that can be tested and answered.

Observations and Inferences

Observations are things or events that are made using any of the senses or tools, such as thermometers, graduated cylinders, balances, or rulers. As more and better tools are developed, the ability of scientists to observe the natural world increases. For example, the invention of both the microscope (Figure 8-2) and, later, the electron microscope increased our ability to observe the structure of living organisms. This led to the realization that all living things are composed of cells.

Figure 8-2. **The microscope:** With the invention of the microscope, scientists could finally observe microorganisms.

Inferences Conclusions or deductions based on observations are **inferences.** Inferences may be very subtle. An inference can also be thought of as an idea or conclusion based on the results of an experiment or observation. For example, you may infer that a slug that remains motionless for several hours is dead.

Assumptions A good experiment keeps assumptions to a minimum. An **assumption** is the belief that something is true. Assumptions also may be very subtle, and at first you may be unaware you are making them. For example, when doing a seed germination experiment, you might assume that all 100 seeds planted will germinate when watered and kept under favorable conditions. The idea that 100% of the seeds will grow is an assumption. An assumption that could be made during a slug feeding experiment is that slugs will eat every day if provided with desirable food.

Opinions Ideas people have that may or may not have any basis in fact are **opinions.** Opinions are often **biased,** or influenced by an assumption that may or may not be correct. Although everyone has opinions, which should be respected, a good way to avoid bias is to leave opinions out of data collection and analysis.

The Scientific View Understanding the scientific view of the world is essential to personal, societal, and ethical decision making. To think scientifically, you must critically analyze events, explanations, and ideas. You should use these skills—as well as ideas from other disciplines—to develop personal explanations of natural events. You should also create visual models and mathematical formulations to represent your thinking.

Keep in mind that asking questions to develop an explanation is a continuing and creative process. Sometimes conflicting explanations arise from the same body of evidence. For example, plants seem to grow better when talked to daily. Some explain this by crediting the voice or words. Others point out that simply breathing carbon dioxide on the plant helps it grow. Science is a search for the truth. Scientific thinking can keep you from being misled and making poor judgments.

Review Questions

1. A student performed an experiment involving two strains of microorganisms, strain A and strain B, cultured in various temperatures for 24 hours. The results of this experiment are shown in the data table below.

Microorganism Growth and Temperature		
Temperature (°C)	Microorganism Growth (Number of Colonies)	
	Strain A	Strain B
25	10	11
28	10	7
31	11	3
34	12	0

Based on the results of the experiment, the student inferred that strain A was more resistant to higher temperatures than strain B was. What, if anything, must the student do for this inference to be considered a reasonable conclusion?

(1) nothing, because this inference is a valid scientific fact
(2) repeat this experiment several times and obtain similar results
(3) repeat this experiment several times using different variables
(4) develop a new hypothesis and test it

2. The graph below represents the results of an investigation of the growth of three identical bacterial cultures incubated at different temperatures.

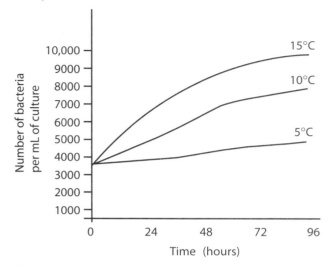

Which inference can be made from the graph?

(1) Temperature is unrelated to the reproductive rate of bacteria.
(2) Bacteria cannot grow at a temperature of 5°C.
(3) Life activities in bacteria slow down at high temperatures.
(4) Refrigeration will most likely slow the growth of these bacteria.

3. A student prepared the following list of steps for performing a laboratory investigation. She omitted one important step for completing the investigation.

Steps to Follow in an Experiment
Define a problem.
Develop a hypothesis.
Select suitable lab materials and perform a controlled experiment to test the hypothesis.
Collect, organize, and graph the experimental data.
?

State the procedure that is missing in the chart. [1]

4. When heavy rains occur while apple orchards are in bloom, the apple crop the following fall is much smaller than normal. This information can best be described as

(1) an inference   (3) a prediction
(2) a hypothesis   (4) an observation

5. Which of the steps listed below would be first in a scientific investigation?

(1) Perform the experiment.
(2) Analyze the experimental data.
(3) Formulate a hypothesis.
(4) Define the problem to be investigated.

Inquiry Skills and Understandings

Everyone needs to understand certain concepts about science and inquiry. **Scientific literacy** involves applying critical thinking skills to everyday life, particularly to claims related to health, technology, and advertising. For example, imagine you are watching a television commercial with your family. The advertiser claims its company has developed a cream that makes hair grow when applied to the scalp. According to the commercial, people with thin hair or no hair have both used the cream with success.

Before rushing out to buy this product, you should think about the claims and begin to question some of what you heard. Next, think about how you can get answers to your questions. Then you should evaluate whether or not the information is to be believed. Here is a way to approach the problem:

1. *Inquiry involves asking questions, and locating, interpreting, and processing information from a variety of sources.*

You may begin by thinking about the following questions:

• How many people were tested?
• What is in the product?
• How long do you have to use it to get results?
• Does it have any side effects?

Next, you ask your friends, and no one knows anything about the product. You also find that your state's consumer product information agency has no information about the company or the hair growth product. Then, you may go to the Internet and find that the company has a Web page that claims 50% of the people using the product grew a full head of hair after ten applications.

Now ask yourself: Are you ready to use the product based on the information you have found? Do you know enough about the product to make an informed decision? You might want to find answers to more questions.

- How many people actually took part in the study? In other words, 50% of how many people grew hair?
- What caused the participants to have thinning hair or to be bald? Did they have a medical condition that needed attention?
- How long has the company been in business?
- Why hasn't the consumer information agency heard of them and their product?
- Was the cream tested scientifically with careful experimental techniques and design?

Keep in mind that careful scientific inquiry involves doing research to find answers to questions and explanations of natural phenomena. Much of the research in the hair product example was done by finding information without actually doing a laboratory investigation.

2. *Inquiry involves making judgments about the reliability of the source and relevance of information: Scientific explanations are accepted when they are consistent with experimental and observational evidence.*

When evaluating evidence and making decisions about how useful your information is, keep the following in mind.

- All scientific explanations are tentative. They can be changed or updated as new evidence emerges. What seems to be true today may be disproved tomorrow.
- Each new bit of evidence can create more questions than it answers. This leads to an increasingly better understanding of how things work.
- Good scientific explanations can be used to make accurate predictions about natural phenomena.
- Beyond the use of reasoning and consensus, scientific inquiry involves the testing of proposed explanations using conventional techniques and procedures. In other words, logic is not enough. Questions should be answered using a good experimental design and thoughtful interpretation.

For example, suppose you read in a magazine about a newly developed HIV vaccine that is said to be effective on monkeys. You should ask:

- Are these results preliminary and tentative, or are they the final results of extensive studies?
- How was the testing done? How many animals were used? For how long have they remained healthy?

- Is HIV in monkeys the same as HIV in humans? Is this the solution to the HIV epidemic in humans or just an early step?

3. *Answers can be found through a research plan and hypothesis testing.*

Developing a Research Plan A **research plan** involves finding background information, developing a hypothesis, and devising an experimental process for testing a hypothesis. Before investing time and resources on research, it is important to find out what others have already learned. (See Figure 8-3.) Most research plans begin with a thorough library search. This search may include the use of electronic information retrieval (the Internet and library databases), a review of the literature (scientific journals), and feedback from the investigator's peers. This background work is done so that the researcher has a thorough understanding of the major concepts being investigated and any similar investigations.

Figure 8-3. Research: A review of the literature must be done before the investigation can be designed. Useful resources include primary science journals, professional Web sites, and library databases.

Making Hypotheses Inquiry involves developing and presenting proposals, including formal hypotheses, to test explanations. A good **hypothesis** attempts to explain what has been observed in a way that can be tested. It is a tentative answer to a question. Experiments cannot prove a hypothesis; they can only either support the hypothesis or fail to support it.

Most hypotheses would make sense if the words "I think that" were added to the beginning of the statement. Try adding "I think that" to the beginning of each hypothesis in the following chart.

A good hypothesis can also help determine the organization of an experiment as well as what data to collect and how to interpret those data. Testing a hypothesis is valuable even when the hypothesis is not supported by experimental results, since new information is gained in the process of testing any hypothesis.

Examples of Hypothesis Statements
This hormone will make plants grow faster.
The presence of this chemical in our drinking water does not harm us.
If this hormone is applied to plant leaves, then the plant will grow faster.
If this chemical is safe, then it will not harm us when it is added to our drinking water.

Designing an Experiment

Once the background work has been done and the hypothesis developed, the actual experiment must be designed. An **experiment** is a series of trials or tests that are done to support or refute (disprove) a hypothesis.

Let's say that you suspect that applying the chemical IAA (a growth hormone) to plant leaves will increase the growth rate of the plant. Your hypothesis might read as follows: *If IAA is applied to the leaves of plants, then the plants will grow more rapidly than those that do not have IAA applied to their leaves.* Once you have written your hypothesis, you must make decisions about variables and experimental techniques.

The Dependent Variable What is it that you will measure? In this experiment, you will measure the effect of IAA on plants. What you will measure is called the **dependent variable,** since it depends on what you do to the plants. Since you asked about how the plants will grow, you will need to measure how large the plants are at the beginning as well as at regular intervals until the conclusion of the experiment. You will also have to decide how to make the measurements. Will you measure only the height of the stem, or will you also measure the size of the leaves? What units will you use?

Independent Variables Factors that might influence the dependent variable are **independent variables.** This is the variable the investigation manipulates. If you are investigating the effect of IAA being applied to the leaves, you must decide on the concentration of IAA. How often will it be applied to the leaves, and how will you apply it? You may even decide to test several concentrations of IAA. In this example, the frequency of applications and the concentration of IAA are independent variables.

Controlling Variables How will you control the independent variables that might affect your interpretation of the results? A **control** is an established reference point used as a standard of comparison. It allows you to make comparisons that generate valid information. For example, you should start with plants that are of the same kind and are about the same age and size as in Figure 8-4. All of the plants should be healthy, grown in the same kind of soil, and provided with the same amount of water and light. If you neglect to control all independent variables, one or more of them may affect plant growth, and you may reach a false conclusion concerning IAA.

A **controlled experiment** is one in which the possible variables have been carefully considered and regulated so the results are due only to the independent variable you are testing.

Figure 8-4. Experimental controls: The control group will have distilled water applied to their leaves in place of IAA. It is important to apply something to the leaves of the control group or they would be treated differently in two ways from the experimental group. The plants will be the same type, size, and age as those in the experimental group. They will be grown in the same soil, with the same amount of light and water.

Keep in mind that there should only be one variable being tested at one time. You can test different concentrations of IAA, or you can test the frequency of applying IAA, but you cannot test both on the same plants at the same time. You also cannot test both the impact of fertilizer AND the impact of IAA on the same plants at the same time.

Developing Experimental Techniques Selecting, acquiring, and building apparatus, as well as considering safety precautions and planning how to avoid bias, are important parts of this stage in the development of the research plan. For example, in the IAA study, you need to decide how many plants to use. Would one plant for each concentration of IAA be enough? Should you use 100 plants for each concentration? Think about these possibilities. With only one plant, genetic differences could cause variations in growth. Could one of the plants have been infected with a fungus while still an embryo? Would using multiple plants help to cancel out this type of problem? How many trials will you need?

Is one trial enough, or would five or six trials be better? Large sample sizes with repeated trials provide much more accurate information, and there is less probability of error due to chance. Large sample sizes and multiple trials are more likely to produce valid results.

When designing an experiment, think of the steps in the following Experimental Design Guide as a way to assist you in your planning. Remember that you should first formulate the question you want to answer or the problem you want to solve. Then review the literature to learn about the topic you are investigating.

Experimental Design Guide	
What is your hypothesis?	The hypothesis is a testable statement. It should suggest a possible answer to the question you are investigating.
What is your dependent variable?	What should change and/or be measured as a result of the experiment? Make a data table to record the data as they are collected.
What is your independent variable?	What is the treatment? Are you only changing one factor at a time to see its effect? Will there be several groups, with each testing one treatment—such as several pH values, colors of light, or temperatures?
Describe how you will control the experiment.	What other possible factors may vary that could also affect the results and make your experiment inconclusive?
What steps will you take to conduct this experiment?	Make a list of procedures and materials needed to conduct the experiment. Be sure to address safety issues.

Review Questions

Set 8.2

6. A drug company tested a new medication before putting it on the commercial market. Pills without medication were given to 500 test subjects in group A, and pills with medication were given to 500 subjects in group B. In this experiment, the individuals in group A served as the

(1) host group
(2) dependent variable
(3) control
(4) hypothesis

7. In order to find the percentage of organic matter in soil from several different locations, a student collected the samples, weighed them immediately, roasted them for several minutes in a flame to burn off organic matter, and weighed them again. The student concluded that the difference between the first and second weights represented the weight of the organic matter in the soil. The most serious mistake that the student made in this experiment was in

Roasting doesn't burn organic matter

(1) taking large samples
(2) weighing the samples before roasting them
(3) failing to dry the samples before first weighing them
(4) assuming that roasting could remove the organic matter

If roasting organic matter would burn it then no plants would survive under the sun all day

8. In an investigation to determine the effects of environmental pH on the germination of dandelion seeds, 25 dandelion seeds were added to each of five petri dishes. Each dish contained a solution that differed from the others only in its pH, as shown below. All other environmental conditions were the same. The dishes were covered and observed for 10 days. The data table the student designed is shown below.

The Effect of pH on Seed Germination		
Petri Dish	pH of Solution	Number of Seeds Germinated
1	9	
2	8	
3	7	
4	6	
5	5	

State the independent variable in this investigation. [1] *The pH of Solution*

Base your answers to questions 9 through 11 on the information below and on your knowledge of biology.

A student placed five geranium plants of equal size in five environmental chambers. Growing conditions were the same for each plant except that each chamber was illuminated by a different color of light of the same intensity. At the end of 20 days, plant growth was measured. *If the type of light the plant has, if changed then the plant*

9. State a possible hypothesis for this experiment. [1] *will grow taller.*

10. What control should be used in this experiment? [1] *Sunlight*

11. Describe one modification you would make in the design of this experiment to make the results more reliable. [1] *I would test sunlight and one other light only.*

12. A new drug for the treatment of asthma is tested on 100 people. The people are evenly divided into two groups. One group is given the drug, and the other group is given a glucose pill. The group that is given the glucose pill serves as the

   (1) experimental group   (3) control
   (2) limiting factor   (4) indicator

13. As part of a laboratory experiment, a thin slice of peeled raw potato weighing 10 grams is placed in an oven at 80°C. After 5 hours, the potato sample is removed from the oven and weighed again. The purpose of this experiment might be to

   (1) test for the presence of starch in living tissues
   (2) isolate cells in various stages of cell division
   (3) determine the water content of potato tissue
   (4) study the rate of photosynthesis in potatoes

14. Describe the function of a control group in an experiment. [1] *A control group is the group that does things the regular way to see if the experimental group is better.*

15. A student wants to shorten the ripening time for tomatoes. He predicts that the more water the seedlings receive, the faster the tomatoes will ripen. To test this prediction, he grows 20 tomato plants in a garden in full sunlight that has dry soil and 20 in a garden in a shadier location where there is greater moisture content in the soil. He then records the time it takes for fruit to develop and ripen on the plants in each garden location.

State a serious error the student made with the design of this experiment. [1] *In order to get reliable results you need to test only one I*

16. In attempting to demonstrate the effectiveness of a new vaccine, a scientist performed these experimental procedures:

   • One hundred genetically similar rats were divided into two groups of 50 rats each (group A and group B).
   • Each rat in group A was given an injection of the vaccine in a glucose-and-water solution.
   • Each rat in group B was given an injection of the glucose-and-water solution containing no vaccine.
   • After several weeks, all rats in both groups were exposed to the disease for which the vaccine was developed.

Identify the dependent variable that was studied in this experiment. [1] *Whether or not the vaccine works.*

17. Scientists breed mice to be as genetically alike as possible to use in experiments. Explain why scientists would want mice that are genetically alike.

In your answer be sure to explain:
   • The advantage of using genetically alike mice [1] *So the results are reliable*
   • Why cloned mice would be even better [1] *Since Cloned mice would be better because then the mice are for sure the same. they are all the same*

Collecting and Organizing Data

In science, **data** generally refers to the results of trials, or tests, completed during experiments such as that in Figure 8-5. Scientific inquiry involves the ability to use various methods of recording, representing, and organizing data. Data can be organized into diagrams, tables, charts, graphs, equations, and matrices. Scientists must then be able to interpret the organized data and make inferences, predictions, and conclusions based on those data.

A data table is an important initial stage in making sense of the information you will collect while doing an experiment. When constructing a table to record your data, keep the checklist in mind.

✓ Title the table in a way that relates the independent variable to the dependent variable. For example: The Effect of Fertilizer Concentration (the independent variable) on Plant Growth (the dependent variable).

✓ Column headings include the dependent and independent variables. They may also include trial or setup numbers or other information.

✓ Column headings need to indicate units of measurement.

✓ The independent variable is typically recorded in increasing order.

✓ The dependent variable is recorded to correspond with the independent variable.

Figure 8-5. Data collection: Making measurements and carefully recording data are important parts of doing an experiment.

The next step is to construct a graph like the one in Figure 8-6 that allows you to see trends or patterns in your mathematical data. Almost every day you interpret graphs. Television, newspapers, and other media often use graphs to illustrate ideas. Advertisers use graphs to convince us to use their pain reliever or allergy medication. They know that a carefully constructed graph can provide us with a large amount of information quickly. Examining columns of numbers in a data table is time consuming and sometimes difficult. Looking at a graph allows us to make comparisons quickly and to draw conclusions.

Graph Construction Checklist

Title

✓ Title your graph so that the reader knows what it is illustrating. You can often use the same title you used on the data table.

Vertical axis

✓ Dependent variable is on the vertical axis.

✓ Vertical axis is labeled, including units of measure.

✓ Scale on the vertical axis is appropriate, without any breaks, and spaced at even intervals.

Horizontal axis

✓ Independent variable is on the horizontal axis.

✓ Horizontal axis is labeled, including units of measure.

✓ Scale on the horizontal axis is appropriate, without any breaks, and spaced at even intervals.

Points

✓ Points are plotted accurately.

Data

✓ Data points are connected, and the line does not go beyond. (You only know what you measured; beyond that is speculation.)

Legend

✓ Legend indicates the meaning of each line if there is more than one. Often you are expected to surround data points with small circles or triangles.

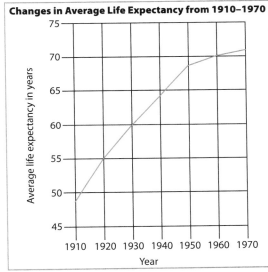

Figure 8-6. Everyday use of graphs: Interpreting graphs like this one is part of everyday life.

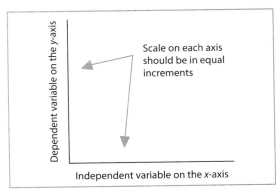

Figure 8-7. Rules for a line graph

There are four basic types of graphs:

- pie or circle graph
- bar graph
- histogram
- line graph

A scientist must decide which type of graph will be the most effective for presenting data so that the conclusion will be clear. Different rules are used in drawing each type of graph. However, there are a few rules common to all line and bar graphs.

Rule 1: The dependent variable is plotted on the vertical, or y-axis. Remember that the dependent variable is what you find out as a result of doing the experiment. It is what you measure during the experiment.

Rule 2: The independent variable is plotted on the horizontal, or x-axis. This is the factor you varied to find its effect on the test organisms or situation.

Rule 3: The spacing between the numbers on both axes must be in equal increments, without any breaks. Figure 8-7 shows how to apply the three rules to a line graph. Use the Graph Construction Checklist when constructing a graph.

The Results

A careful examination of the experimental results involves the ability to look at relationships between the predicted result contained in the hypothesis and the actual result.

Drawing Valid Conclusions After carefully considering how well the predicted result and the actual result of the experiment correspond, a decision about the outcome—a **conclusion**—can be made. A scientist needs to determine whether the hypothesis has been supported.

Scientists often use statistical analysis techniques to find the likelihood that their results were produced by chance. If the results differ only slightly, errors in measurement, genetic differences among the test organisms, or chance may be the reason. Once a significant pattern or relationship has been discovered as a result of data analysis, a scientist next tries to explain why these results were obtained.

A **model** can often be used to explain the results of an experiment. A model is a way of explaining or demonstrating what might be happening and to predict what will occur in new situations. A model explains how DNA carries the genetic code and how traits are passed from one generation to the next. As more is learned about the structure and function of DNA, parts of the model are confirmed or changed. See Figure 8-8.

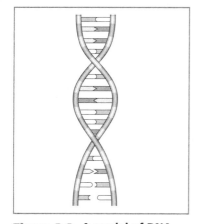

Figure 8-8. A model of DNA

Reporting Results One assumption of science is that other individuals could arrive at the same explanation if they had access to similar evidence. Experiments that cannot be repeated exactly with the same results have little worth.

Research must be shared in such a clear manner that other scientists can repeat the investigation and try to get the same results. When reporting the results of an experiment, a scientist must pay close attention to details. The experimental results may be used by hundreds of other scientists to repeat the experiment. Thus, each step of the experiment must be described accurately and in exact detail.

If you wanted to repeat an experiment done by a friend, would you be able to do it if your friend told you to heat the mixture "for a little while"? Or if you had to add some soap powder to the mixture, would it be acceptable for your friend to tell you to "add two pinches"? If you expect to obtain the same results, your friend must provide precise instructions, such as to heat the mixture at a temperature of 75°C for 5 minutes, and then add 2 grams of a certain kind of soap powder.

Figure 8-9. Peer review: Scientists examine one another's work to ensure that the results are correct.

Scientific inquiry also requires the ability to develop a written report for public scrutiny. Scientists report their findings in scientific journals or during presentations at professional meetings. The report describes the hypothesis, including a literature review of previous studies, the experiment performed, its data and the scientist's conclusion, and suggestions for further study. Based on the results of the experiment and public discussion and review, inquiry may also require the scientist to revise the explanation and think about additional research. A **peer review**, in which several scientists examine the details of an experiment, is an important part of the scientific process. Scientists are expected to question explanations proposed by other scientists. Peers analyze the experimental procedures, examine the evidence, identify faulty reasoning, point out statements that go beyond the evidence, and suggest alternative explanations for the same observations. Peer review is one of the systems of checks and balances in science.

Keep in mind that all scientific explanations are subject to change as more is learned. Scientists know and accept this as a part of the way they work. With new information, they must be willing to change their thinking and, therefore, their explanations.

Evidence is a collection of facts offered to support the idea that something is true. Scientists accept evidence when it is supported by many facts. Until they have a large collection of evidence to support their thinking, scientists must remain neutral.

Sometimes claims are made that are not supported by actual evidence. Scientific claims should be questioned if

- the data are based on samples that are very small, biased, or inadequately controlled
- the conclusions are based on the faulty, incomplete, or misleading use of numbers

For example, enough organisms must be used in an experiment and the difference in data between the control and experimental group must be significant enough so that genetic differences, random chance, and inaccuracies in measurement cannot be responsible for the results. Wherever appropriate, a statistical analysis of the results should be done. This could be something as simple as finding the average, calculating the percentage of difference, or determining the frequency. Claims should also

be questioned if

- fact and opinion are intermingled
- adequate evidence is not cited
- conclusions do not follow logically from the evidence given

Further Science Understandings

Well-accepted scientific theories are supported by many different scientific investigations, often involving the contributions of individuals from different disciplines. In developing a theory, scientists carry out many investigations. They may vary in degree of complexity, scale, and focus. Research by different scientific disciplines can bring to light multiple views of the natural world. The resulting theory can encompass many different aspects of natural events. For instance, the theory of evolution began with the observations of one naturalist. But over the years scientists—including botanists, biologists, geologists, oceanographers, and others—researched numerous aspects of the theory to reach one general scientific idea.

Review Questions   Set 8.3

18. A student conducted an original, well-designed experiment, carefully following proper scientific procedure. In order for the conclusions to become generally accepted, the experiment must

(1) contain several experimental variables
(2) support the original hypothesis
(3) be repeated to verify the reliability of the data
(4) be conducted by a scientist

19. A student tossed a coin five times and observed results of four tails and one head. He concluded that when a coin is tossed, there is an 80% chance of getting a tail and a 20% chance of getting a head. The conclusion would be more valid if

(1) only two tosses of the coin had been used
(2) the weight of the coin had been taken into consideration
(3) a greater number of tosses had been used
(4) the surface the coin landed on had been taken into consideration

Base your answers to questions 20 through 22 on the experiment described below and on your knowledge of biology.

After watching the behavior of earthworms in soil, a biology student suggested that the penetration of air into the soil promotes the root development of plants. The student then set up the following experiment.

20. The important data to be recorded in this experiment will come from the observation of the increase in

(1) leaf size   (3) number of leaves
(2) stem size   (4) number of roots

21. State the hypothesis being tested in this experiment. [1]

22. State one way this experiment could be improved to make the results more reliable. [1]

Base your answers to questions 23 through 25 on the experiment described below and on your knowledge of biology.

A group of 24 frogs was separated into two equal groups. Group A was placed in an environment in which the temperature was a constant 35°F. Group B was placed in a similar environment, except the temperature was a constant 65°F.

Equal amounts of food were given to each group at the start of the experiment and again every 24 hours. Immediately before each daily feeding, the excess food from the prior feeding was removed and measured. This allowed the scientist to determine the daily amount of food each group of frogs consumed. Each day, the heart rate and breathing rate of the frogs were checked. At the end of the experiment, the following bar graphs were prepared:

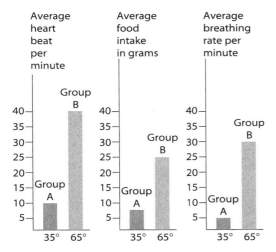

23. Using one or more complete sentences, state the hypothesis the scientist was most likely investigating in this experiment.

24. After examining the graphs, the scientist could reasonably assume that at a low temperature the frogs would

    (1) become more active
    (2) produce less carbon dioxide
    (3) eat more food
    (4) use more oxygen

25. The independent variable in this experiment was

    (1) heart rate
    (2) breathing rate
    (3) amount of food consumed
    (4) temperature of the environment

Base your answers to questions 26 through 29 on the information below and on your knowledge of biology.

A student was working on an investigation to measure the relative activity of an enzyme at various pH values. He collected the following data: pH 2, enzyme activity 10; pH 8, enzyme activity 50; pH 12, enzyme activity 10; pH 4, enzyme activity 20; pH 6, enzyme activity 40; pH 10, enzyme activity 40

26. Identify the independent variable in this experiment. [1]

27. Organize the data by filling in the data table provided. Follow these directions when completing your data table.

    • Provide an appropriate title for the data table. [1]
    • Fill in the first box in each column with an appropriate heading. [1]
    • Arrange the data so that pH values are in increasing order. [1]

Title:	

28. Using the information in the data table, construct a line graph on the grid provided, following the directions below:

    • Provide an appropriate title for the graph. [1]
    • Make and label an appropriate scale, without any breaks, on each axis. [1]
    • Plot the data on the grid. Surround each data point with a small circle and connect the points. [1]

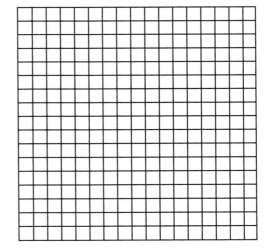

29. According to the data, this enzyme would probably work best at what pH values?

    (1) 7 and 8   (3) 6 and 7
    (2) 2 and 12   (4) 4 and 10

Directions

Review the Test-Taking Strategies section of this book. Then answer the following questions. Read each question carefully and answer with a correct choice or response.

Part A

1 One ounce each of protein, carbohydrate, and fat are burned separately in a calorimeter to determine Caloric content. The results are shown in the data table.

Caloric Content of Substances	
Organic Compound	Number of Calories Produced
Protein	147
Fat	271
Carbohydrate	152

Which statement represents a valid conclusion based on the data?
(1) An ounce of fat contains about twice as many Calories as an ounce of protein.
(2) Protein is a better energy food than carbohydrate.
(3) Carbohydrates, fats, and proteins all yield approximately the same number of Calories per unit of weight.
(4) Proteins and carbohydrates provide the most Calories per ounce.

2 Which laboratory procedure would be best for demonstrating the effect of light intensity on the production of chlorophyll in pea plants?
(1) using 10 plants of different species, each grown in the same intensity of light
(2) using 10 plants of different species, each grown in a different intensity of light
(3) using 10 plants of the same species, each grown in the same intensity of light
(4) using 10 plants of the same species, each grown in a different intensity of light

3 In an early trial of the Salk vaccine for polio, 1,830,000 school children participated. This original trial was an attempt to determine whether the Salk vaccine was effective in preventing polio. Of the 1,830,000 children involved, only 440,000 received the vaccine. The remainder were not given the vaccine because they
(1) had a natural immunity
(2) already had polio
(3) served as a control
(4) were allergic to the vaccine

4 A scientific study showed that the depth at which some microscopic plants were found in a lake varied from day to day. On clear days, the plants were found as far as 6 meters below the surface of the water but were only 1 meter below the surface on cloudy days. Which hypothesis would these observations support?
(1) Light intensity affects the growth of microscopic plants.
(2) Wind currents affect the growth of microscopic plants.
(3) Nitrogen concentration affects the growth of microscopic plants.
(4) Precipitation affects the growth of microscopic plants.

5 A scientist tested a hypothesis that white-tailed deer would prefer apples over corn as a primary food source. The findings of the test, in which the scientist claimed that the deer preferred apples, were published. Which research technique, if used by the scientist, might result in this claim being questioned?
(1) The scientist observed four deer in different locations at various times of the day.
(2) The scientist observed a total of 500 deer in 20 different locations at various times of the day.
(3) The scientist observed 200 deer in various natural settings, but none in captivity.
(4) The scientist observed 300 deer in various locations in captivity, but none in natural settings.

6 Conclusions based on an experiment are most likely to be accepted when
(1) they are consistent with experimental data and observations
(2) they are derived from investigations having many experimental variables
(3) scientists agree that only one hypothesis has been tested
(4) hypotheses are based on one experimental design

Part B

Base your answers to questions 7 through 10 on the information below, and on your knowledge of biology.

The list represents different procedures involved with a scientific experiment and are in no special order. For statements 7 through 10, identify the procedure being described by the appropriate letter.

Experimental Procedures
A. *Test the hypothesis with an experiment.*
B. *State the results.*
C. *Draw a conclusion from the results.*
D. *Form a hypothesis.*

7 Beans will grow faster if you fertilize them at regular intervals than if you only fertilize the ground once before you plant them. [1]

8 If I add more catalyst to the reaction, the reaction will speed up. [1]

9 A scientist took saliva from his dog's mouth and mixed it with a solution of starch and warm water. He took the same amount of saliva from his own mouth and mixed it with the contents of a second tube of starch and warm water. One hour later, the contents of both tubes were checked for sugar. [1]

10 In an experiment, caterpillars consumed 8 grams of lettuce leaves and 0.4 grams of tomato leaves. [1]

11 The data table below shows an effect of secondhand smoke on the birth weight of babies born to husbands and wives living together during the pregnancy.

Effect of Secondhand Smoke on Birth Weight

	Wife: Nonsmoker Husband: Nonsmoker	Wife: Nonsmoker Husband: Smoker
Number of Couples	837	529
Average Weight of Baby at Birth (Kg)	3.2	2.9

Based on these data, a reasonable conclusion that can be drawn about secondhand smoke during pregnancy is that secondhand smoke
(1) is unable to pass from the mother to the fetus
(2) slows the growth of the fetus
(3) causes mutations in cells of the ovaries
(4) blocks the receptors on antibody cells

12 A student studied how the amount of oxygen affects ATP production in muscle cells. The data for amount X are shown in the graph below.

If the student supplies the muscle cells with less oxygen in a second trial of the investigation, a bar placed on the graph to represent the results of this trial would most likely be
(1) shorter than bar X and placed to the left of bar X
(2) shorter than bar X and placed to the right of bar X
(3) taller than bar X and placed to the left of bar X
(4) taller than bar X and placed to the right of bar X

13 A student studied the location of single-celled photosynthetic organisms in a lake for a period of several weeks. The depth at which these organisms were found at different times of the day varied greatly. Some of the data collected are shown in the table below.

Data Table	
Light Conditions at Different Times of the Day	Average Depth of Photosynthetic Organisms (cm)
Full light	150
Moderate light	15
No light	10

A valid inference based on these data is that
(1) most photosynthetic organisms live below a depth of 150 centimeters
(2) oxygen production increases as photosynthetic organisms move deeper in the lake
(3) photosynthetic organisms respond to changing light levels
(4) photosynthetic organisms move up and down to increase their rate of carbon dioxide production

Part C

Base your answer to question 14–17 on the information below and on your knowledge of biology.

Help for Aging Memories
As aging occurs, the ability to form memories begins to decrease. Research has shown that an increase in the production of a certain molecule, BDNF, seems to restore the processes involved in storing memories. BDNF is found in the central nervous system and seems to be important in maintaining nerve cell health. Researchers are testing a new drug that seems to increase the production of BDNF.

14–17 Design an experiment to test the effectiveness of the new drug to increase the production of BDNF in the brains of rats. In your answer, be sure to:
• state the hypothesis your experiment will test [1]

• describe how the control group will be treated differently from the experimental group [1]
• identify two factors that must be kept the same in both the experimental and control groups [1]
• identify the dependent variable in your experiment [1]

Base your answer to question 18–21 on the information below and on your knowledge of biology.

An Experimental SARS Vaccine Works in Animals
Scientists reported that they had protected animals from the effects of the SARS virus by using an experimental vaccine. The SARS virus causes an acute respiratory illness in humans and other animals.

This vaccine was sprayed once into the nostrils of each of four African green monkeys. Four weeks later, these monkeys were exposed to the virus that causes SARS. The monkeys showed no sign of the disease in their respiratory tracts. Blood tests confirmed the presence of proteins known as neutralizing antibodies that indicate protection against disease. The scientists also sprayed a placebo (a substance that did not contain the vaccine) into the nostrils of each of four other African green monkeys. After exposure to the virus that causes SARS, all of these monkeys developed symptoms of this condition.

18–21 Briefly explain the nature of a vaccine and some steps that should be taken before a vaccine is available for public use. In your answer, be sure to include:
• a description of what a vaccine is [1]
• an explanation of why one group had a placebo sprayed into their nostrils before exposure to the virus [1]
• an explanation of why scientists used monkeys to test the SARS vaccine [1]
• a statement of what could be done to verify the results [1]

Base your answer to questions 22 and 23 on the information and diagram below, and on your knowledge of biology.

A laboratory setup for a demonstration is represented in the diagram below.

Test tube
Beaker
Meniscus
Water
Starch-water mixture
Dialysis membrane

22–23 Describe how an indicator can be used to determine if starch diffuses through the membrane into the beaker. In your answer, be sure to include:
- the procedure used [1]
- how to interpret the results [1]

Base your answers to questions 24 through 26 on the information below and on your knowledge of biology.

In an investigation, plants of the same species and the same initial height were exposed to a constant number of hours of light each day. The number of hours per day was different for each plant, but all other environmental factors were the same. At the conclusion of the investigation, the final height of each plant was measured.

The following data were recorded:

8 hours, 25 cm; 4 hours, 12 cm; 2 hours, 5 cm; 14 hours, 35 cm; 12 hours, 35 cm; 10 hours, 34 cm; 6 hours, 18 cm

24 Organize the data by completing both columns in the data table provided, so that the hours of daily light exposure increase from the top to the bottom of the table. [1]

Data Table	
Dally Light Exposure (hours)	Final Height (cm)

25 State one possible reason that the plant exposed to 2 hours of light per day was the shortest. [1]

26 If another plant of the same species had been used in the investigation and exposed to 16 hours of light per day, what would the final height of the plant probably have been? Support your answer. [1]

Base your answers to questions 27 and 28 on the information and data table below and on your knowledge of biology.

Trout and black bass are freshwater fish that normally require at least 8 parts per million (ppm) of dissolved oxygen (O_2) in the water for survival. Other freshwater fish, such as carp, may be able to live in water that has an O_2 level of 5 ppm. No freshwater fish are able to survive when the O_2 level in water is 2 ppm or less.

Some factories or power plants are built along rivers so that they can use the water to cool their equipment. They then release the water (sometimes as much as 8°C warmer) back into the same river.

The Rocky River presently has an average summer temperature of about 25°C and contains populations of trout, bass, and carp. A proposal has been made to build a new power plant on the banks of the Rocky River. Some people are concerned that this will affect the river ecosystem in a negative way.

The data table below shows the amount of oxygen that will dissolve in fresh water at different temperatures. The amount of oxygen is expressed in parts per million (ppm).

Data Table	
Temperature (°C)	Fresh Water Oxygen Content (ppm)
1	14.24
10	11.29
15	10.10
20	9.11
25	8.27
30	7.56

27 State one effect of temperature change on the oxygen content of fresh water. Support your answer using specific information from the data table. [1]

28 Explain how a new power plant built on the banks of the Rocky River could have an environmental impact on the Rocky River ecosystem downstream from the plant.

Your explanation must include the effects of the power plant on:
- water temperature [1]
- dissolved oxygen [1]
- fish species [1]

Base your answers to questions 29 and 30 on the information in the newspaper article below and on your knowledge of biology.

Patients to test tumor fighter
Boston—Endostatin, the highly publicized experimental cancer drug that wiped out tumors in mice and raised the hopes of cancer patients, will be tested on patients this year.

"I think it's exciting, but ... you always have the risk that something will fail in testing," said Dr. Judah Folkman, the Harvard University researcher whose assistant, Michael O'Reilly, discovered endostatin.

Endostatin and a sister protein, angiostatin, destroy the tumors' ability to sprout new blood vessels. This makes cancer fall dormant in lab animals, but no one knows if that will happen in humans.

The Associated Press

29 Explain why it is necessary to test these experimental drugs on human volunteers as well as on test animals. [1]

30 State one reason that mice are often used by scientists for testing experimental drugs that may be used by humans. [1]

Base your answer to questions 31–34 on the information below and on your knowledge of biology.

Many people who are in favor of alternative medicine claim that large doses of vitamin C introduced into a vein speed up the healing of surgical wounds.

31–34 Describe an experiment to test this hypothesis. Your answer must include at least:
- the difference between the experimental group of subjects and the control group [1]
- two conditions that must be kept constant in both groups [1]
- data that should be collected [1]
- an example of experimental results that would support the hypothesis [1]

Laboratory Skills

What do You Think?

Laboratory Procedures

When you are looking at cells with a microscope always start focusing with the high power objective lens, then if the cells appear too large, switch to a lower power.

You shouldn't eat food or drink soda in a classroom laboratory unless you make sure you wash your hands first.

Gel electrophoresis is used to cut DNA into smaller fragments.

Paper chromatography is used to separate mixtures of molecules that are of different sizes.

Laboratory Skills

Vocabulary

balance

chromatography

compound light microscope

dichotomous key

dissection

electronic balance

electrophoresis

graduated cylinder

indicator

magnification

mass

metric ruler

microscope

stain

stereoscope

triple-beam balance

volume

Topic Overview

Biologists are always trying to add to our understanding of the world in which we live. To do this, they make observations and do experiments. To help them collect data from these observations and experiments, they rely on a variety of tools and techniques. These tools, like microscopes, extend our senses, allowing us to collect data that would otherwise be unavailable. Scientists have also developed specific techniques that give us valuable information about the cells, molecules, and processes of living organisms.

Tools for Measurement

During laboratory investigations, you are often required to make measurements of length, mass, and volume. You need to know the proper pieces of equipment to select and the appropriate procedures and units to use.

Measuring Length Typically a **metric ruler** is used to determine the length of an object. To measure length, use either centimeters (cm) or millimeters (mm). You should know how to convert millimeters to centimeters and vice versa.

The metric ruler shown in Figure 9-1 is <u>calibrated</u>—or scaled—in centimeters (cm). The lines indicated by the numbers 1, 2, 3, and so on each represent a distance of 1 centimeter. The smaller divisions each equal 1 millimeter (10 mm = 1 cm). A line equal to 5 cm is shown above the ruler in Figure 9-1.

Figure 9-1. **Metric ruler:** The tool used for measuring length in centimeters and millimeters (not shown to scale)

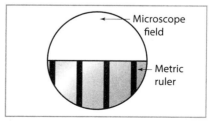

Figure 9-2. **Microscope field with metric ruler** (not shown to scale)

Micrometers (μm), are very tiny units that are used to measure objects through the microscope. One thousand micrometers equal one millimeter.

Figure 9-2 shows a metric ruler as seen under the low-power objective of a microscope. The distance across the field of view is approximately 3.2 millimeters, or 3,200 micrometers (since 1.0 mm = 1,000 μm).

If the cells observed on the slide in Figure 9-3 are being viewed through the same low-power objective, the field of view is still 3.2 millimeters. The approximate length of each cell is therefore about 1 millimeter or 1,000 micrometers, since about 3 cells fit across the diameter (widest part) of the field.

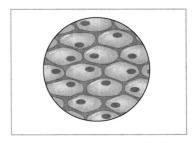

Figure 9-3. Microscope field with cells

Measuring Volume A **graduated cylinder** is often used to measure a liquid's **volume**, or the space it occupies. Liters and milliliters are typically used to indicate volume in the metric system, while quarts and ounces are used in the English system. Graduated cylinders are calibrated in milliliters (mL).

Water and many other fluids form a <u>meniscus</u> (curving surface) when placed in the narrow tube of a graduated cylinder. To correctly read the volume of the liquid, place the cylinder on a flat surface. Then read from the bottom of the curved meniscus at eye level. The volume of liquid in the graduated cylinder in Figure 9-4 is 13 mL.

The correct volume is 13 mL.

Figure 9-4. Graduated cylinder: You can find the volume of a liquid using a graduated cylinder.

Measuring Temperature In the biology laboratory, temperature is often measured in degrees <u>Celsius</u>. The freezing point of water is 0°C; the boiling point is 100°C. Human body temperature is 37°C, which is the temperature indicated on the thermometer in Figure 9-5.

Measuring Mass In the biology laboratory, **mass**—the quantity of matter in something—is often measured with a **balance**, which is a tool that works by comparing an object of unknown mass with an object of known mass. The triple-beam balance or an electronic balance is typically found in a high school laboratory.

A **triple-beam balance** (Figure 9-6) has a single pan and three bars (beams) that are calibrated in grams. One beam, the 500-gram beam, is divided into five 100-gram units. Another beam is divided into ten units of 10 grams totaling 100 grams. The front beam is divided into 10 major units of 1 gram each. Each of these divisions is further divided into 0.1-gram units.

Figure 9-5. Thermometer: This Celsius thermometer shows human body temperature.

Figure 9-6. Triple-beam balance

Before using a balance, make sure that the pan is empty and that the pointer and all of the <u>riders</u> (devices that are moved along the beams) are on zero. To determine the mass of an object, it is first placed on the pan. Then, starting with the 500-gram beam, the masses on the beams are adjusted until the pointer is again pointing to zero. The mass of the object is equal to the sum of the readings on the three beams.

An **electronic balance** measures mass automatically. To use an electronic balance, first turn it on and wait until it shows a zero mass. (This may require using the re-zero button shown on Figure 9-7.) Place the object with the unknown mass on the pan. Read the mass.

Figure 9-7. Electronic balance

Never place a substance directly on a balance pan. Instead, protect the balance with a weighing paper or dish. With a triple-beam balance, first find the mass of the weighing paper. Then find the mass of the substance AND the weighing paper. Subtract the mass of the weighing paper from the total mass of the paper plus the substance. The remainder is the mass of the substance.

For an electronic balance, put the weighing paper on the balance and then use the re-zero button to set the balance to zero. Next, put the substance on the paper and read the mass. The re-zero button automatically subtracts the mass of the weighing paper from the total. The reading on the balance is the actual mass of the substance.

Review Questions
Set 9.1

1. The crab shown in the illustration below has four pairs of walking legs and one pair of pincer legs. The crab is shown in its normal walking position.

In this position, what is the distance between the ends of the front pair of walking legs? (One of the front pair of walking legs is identified with an "X" in the illustration.)

(1) 8.5 cm   (3) 7.5 cm
(2) 85 cm   (4) 75 cm

2. Identify which piece of laboratory equipment you would use to accurately measure 10 grams of glucose. [1]

3. Which piece of laboratory equipment would be used to most accurately measure the volume of a liquid?

(1) beaker   (3) test tube
(2) balance   (4) graduated cylinder

4. A student measured a larva using a metric ruler, as represented in the diagram below.

What is the length of the larva?

(1) 26 cm   (2) 26 mm   (3) 16 cm   (4) 16 mm

5. Which of the graduated cylinders below contains a volume of liquid closest to 15 mL?

(1)   (2)   (3)   (4)

6. Which diagram below shows a correct measurement?

(1)

(2)   (3)

(4)

7. The diagram below shows a triple-beam balance with a mass on the pan.

With the riders in the positions indicated, what is the mass of the object on the pan of the balance?

(1) 9 grams   (3) 249 grams
(2) 200 grams   (4) 942 grams

8. Draw a meniscus to represent a water level of 6 mL on the diagram below of a graduated cylinder. [1]

Microscope Skills

The **microscope** is a tool that uses a lens or a combination of lenses to make an object easier to see. It allows for the examination of objects too small to be seen with the unaided eye. Microscopes also permit the close observation of fine details. For example, without a microscope you can see the legs and wings of a fly. With a microscope you can also see the hairs covering the fly's body, the pads and clawlike structures on its feet, and the framework of its wings. This is possible for two reasons. A microscope magnifies the specimen and also allows you to distinguish between objects that are close together. **Magnification** is the ability of a microscope to make an object appear larger.

Figure 9-8. **A stereoscope**

Figure 9-9. **A compound microscope:** Each part is labeled with a number. The names and functions of the parts are given in Table 9-1.

Types of Microscopes

There are many different types of microscopes. The two most commonly found in a high school laboratory are the compound light microscope and the stereoscope. The primary difference between the two is that with a compound light microscope, light must pass through or reflect off the specimen being examined.

Stereoscopes With a stereoscope (Figure 9-8), light is reflected off the specimen. A **stereoscope**, sometimes called a <u>dissecting</u> <u>microscope</u>, has two <u>ocular</u> eyepiece lenses, one for each eye, and one or more <u>objectives</u> (the other lenses of the microscope). The amount of magnification is low, but the image is three-dimensional and is not reversed as it would be with a compound microscope. Stereoscopes are often used to observe parts of specimens such as insects, worms, or flowers.

Compound Microscopes The typical **compound light microscope** has one ocular lens, at least one objective lens, and a light source. Light passes through the object being examined, through the objective lens, and then through the eyepiece.

The image you see is magnified by both lenses—the ocular lens and the objective lens. The total magnification is calculated by multiplying the magnification of the ocular by the magnification of the objective. For example, if you use a microscope that has a 10x eyepiece and a 40x objective, the magnification of a specimen would be 400x.

Eyepiece × Objective = Total Magnification

10x   × 40x   = 400x

Table 9-1. Names and Functions of Parts of a Compound Microscope	
1 Eyepiece or Ocular Lens	• lens nearest the eye and used to "look through" • usually magnifies 10x
2 Objective Lenses	• lenses located closest to specimen • usually 2 or 3 • commonly magnify at 4x, 10x, and 40x
3 Stage	• flat surface (platform) on which the slide is placed • stage clips hold the slide in place
4 Diaphragm	• located under the stage • controls the amount of light passing up through the specimen
5 Light Source	• might be a mirror or a light bulb • provides light that passes up through the specimen and makes it visible
6 Coarse Adjustment	• used to focus only under low power (up to 100x) • never used when the high-power objective is in place for viewing • usually the larger knob; causes a large amount of movement of the lenses
7 Fine Adjustment	• the only focus you should use with high power • used to sharpen the image under low power • also used to see different layers of a specimen • usually the smaller of the focus knobs; causes a small amount of movement of the lenses

Microscope lenses may get dirty from contact with fingers, specimens, stains, and so on. Do not use paper towels or your shirt to clean them! Only use lens paper to clean the lenses of a microscope. Lens paper will not scratch the soft glass of the lens.

Techniques for Using Microscopes

Due to the action of microscope lenses, there are a number of things you need to remember when viewing objects through a compound light microscope.

- The image will be upside-down and backwards, as shown in Figure 9-10.
- You must move the slide in the direction that is opposite the way the organism appears to be moving. In other words, if the organism appears headed toward the upper right side of your field of view, you must move the slide down and to the left to keep it in view. See Figure 9-11.
- The field becomes darker as you increase the magnification. You will need to increase the amount of light passing through the specimen as you go from low power to high power. The diaphragm, located under the stage, can be used to do this.
- Since the field becomes smaller under high power, center the object you are viewing before switching to a higher power. Otherwise the object may be outside of the field of view.

Focusing When observing specimens through the compound light microscope, first use the low-power objective. Do this even if higher magnification is needed to make your observations.

1. First, place the slide on the stage of your microscope. Position the slide so that the specimen is over the opening in the stage. Anchor the slide with the stage clips.
2. Move the coarse adjustment so that the low-power objective is as close to the slide as you can get it without touching the slide. Some microscopes have a built-in "stop" that prevents you from getting the objective lens too close to the slide. You should look at the objective and the slide while doing this. Never lower the objective while looking through the eyepiece.
3. Look through the eyepiece with both eyes open and turn the coarse adjustment so that the low-power objective and slide move apart. The specimen should come into view.
4. Next, turn the fine adjustment to bring the specimen into sharp focus.
5. To focus the specimen under higher magnification after locating it under low power, move the slide so that what you are interested in seeing is located in the center of your field of view. Remember that as you increase the magnification, the object appears larger, but you see less of its edge. The field of view becomes smaller when you

Figure 9-10. **Microscope view:** The letter "e" as seen on a slide (A) and as seen through the microscope (B). (Only the change in position of the letter is shown, not magnification.)

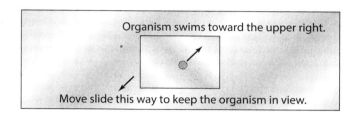

Figure 9-11. **Moving the slide to follow a moving object**

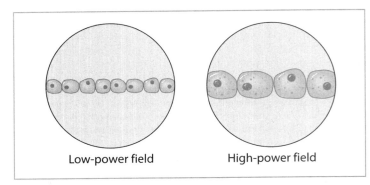

Low-power field   High-power field

Figure 9-12. **Specimen under low and high power:** Note that the high power field is narrower (only 4 cells can be seen), but the cells appear larger, and more detail is visible.

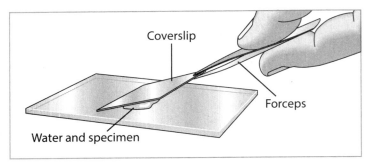

Coverslip

Forceps

Water and specimen

Figure 9-13. **Preparing a wet-mount slide**

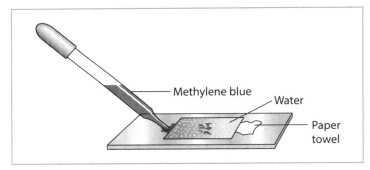

Methylene blue

Water

Paper towel

Figure 9-14. **Staining a wet-mount slide**

switch from low power to a higher power. See Figure 9-12.

6. Watch from the side of the microscope and slowly turn the high-power objective into place. Be sure that the high-power objective is not going to touch the slide. High-power objectives are longer than low-power objectives and can easily hit the slide—be careful.

7. If the objective is not going to hit the slide, click it into position. As you look through the eyepiece, the specimen should be visible. Use the fine adjustment to sharpen the focus. Remember never to use the coarse adjustment when using the high-power objectives. You could damage the microscope lens and break the slide.

Preparing Wet-Mount Slides Only specimens that are small and thin can be seen through a compound light microscope. However, thin slices may quickly dry and shrivel. To avoid this, a temporary wet-mount slide can be prepared by using the following steps:

1. Using a pipette (eye dropper), add a small drop of water to the center of a clean, glass slide.

2. Place the object to be viewed in the water. (It should be lying flat rather than folded over.)

3. Use forceps to position a coverslip, as shown in Figure 9-13. Using forceps will keep you from getting fingerprints on the coverslip. Fingerprints could interfere with your ability to view the image clearly.

4. Lower the coverslip slowly. This technique will prevent the formation of air bubbles under the coverslip.

Staining Specimens When you examine cells and cell parts through a microscope, they often appear to be transparent. You need to adjust the light and the focus so that you can see differences in thickness and density. Although adjusting the amount of light passing through the specimen may help, stains are often used to create greater contrast. Different types of cells and cell parts vary in their ability to soak up various stains. For example, certain cell parts turn darker in the presence of iodine stain. Other parts do not become darker.

To add a stain, such as methylene blue, to a wet-mount slide, place a drop of the stain beside one edge of the coverslip. Next touch a small piece of paper towel to the opposite edge of the coverslip. The towel absorbs water and draws the stain across the slide under the coverslip. This technique allows you to keep the slide on the stage of the microscope. You do not need to prepare a new slide. See Figure 9-14.

Identifying and Comparing Cell Parts It is important to remember that cells have specific structures that perform specific jobs. Many of these structures in Figures 9-15 and 9-16 are visible through a compound light microscope. Some of the parts you can either expect to see or see evidence of are the following:

Figure 9-15. **Typical plant cell:** Structures that can be seen through a microscope

- **Nucleus**—usually observed as a rounded, dense, dark-staining structure. It can be located anywhere in the cell, not just in the middle.
- **Cytoplasm**—typically fills the cell. It appears to be clear in some cells and very grainy in others. Cell organelles, which may or may not be visible, are suspended in the cytoplasm.
- **Cell membrane**—found surrounding the cytoplasm. It is the outer boundary of animal cells and is located between the cell wall and the cytoplasm in plants and some other organisms.
- **Cell wall**—The nonliving cell wall on the outside of the cell membrane in plant cells is a supportive structure. Many bacteria form a different type of protective cell wall.
- **Chloroplasts**—green, oval structures found in the cytoplasm of some plant cells and photosynthetic one-celled organisms.

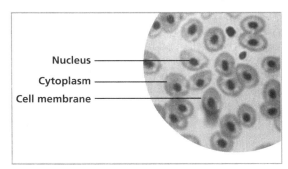

Figure 9-16. **Animal cells:** As seen through a compound light microscope

- **Vacuoles**—often seen as clear areas in the cytoplasm. Plant cells contain very large fluid-filled vacuoles that occupy much of the inside of the cell. Some single-celled organisms may contain specialized vacuoles for digestion and for regulating water balance.
- **Chromosomes**—most easily observed in cells undergoing mitosis or meiosis as in Figure 9-17. They are usually dark-staining and threadlike.

Additional Laboratory Techniques

There are many techniques that are useful in the biology laboratory. Some of the most common are electrophoresis, chromatography, and the application of stains and indicators. Dichotomous keys are especially useful for field research.

Electrophoresis Gel **electrophoresis** is a very powerful tool and is widely used by scientists in many disciplines—not just biologists. It allows scientists to separate mixtures of large molecules according to size. DNA and proteins are the two types of molecules most often separated by gel electrophoresis.

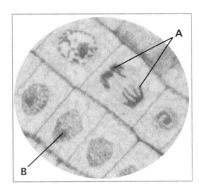

Figure 9-17. **Plant cells undergoing mitotic cell division:** A indicates chromosomes, and B indicates a nucleus before the cell undergoes mitosis.

When setting up a protein gel, a sample of biological material containing proteins is prepared by breaking open the cells in order to release the proteins. Next, the proteins are treated with both chemicals and heat. One of the chemicals used coats the protein molecules and gives them a negative charge. Then, very small amounts of the prepared sample are placed in wells at the top of a special gel positioned in a gel electrophoresis apparatus. (The wells are similar to the holes you would get by pressing the teeth of a comb part way into a block of gelatin dessert.) The gel is placed between two electrodes that are connected to a power supply. This causes one end of the gel to take on a positive charge and the other to take on a negative charge.

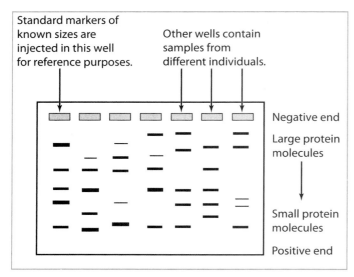

Figure 9-18. **Protein gel electrophoresis:** Protein gels are typically run vertically, with the gel block standing on end.

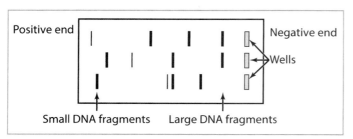

Figure 9-19. **DNA gel electrophoresis:** DNA gels are typically run horizontally, with the gel block lying flat.

Positively charged molecules in the sample move toward the negative electrode, while negatively charged protein molecules move toward the positive electrode. The type of gel used in protein electrophoresis is made up of long molecules that form a tangled mesh. Smaller molecules are able to work their way through the gel more quickly than larger molecules. Therefore, molecules are separated by both their size and electrical charge. See Figure 9-18.

DNA gel electrophoresis is a little different. The analysis of an individual's DNA begins with the use of special enzymes to cut the DNA at specific points in the sequence of bases. This produces fragments of DNA that are of different lengths. These pieces of DNA will vary in size and number from one individual to another due to the uniqueness of each genetic code.

Next, small amounts of the DNA samples are placed in wells located on one side of a semisolid gel. See Figure 9-19. Typically the DNA gel is made of agarose—the same gelatine-like substance used to culture bacteria but without the nutrients. The gel is located between two electrodes that are connected to a power supply. This causes one end of the gel to take on a positive charge and the other to take on a negative charge when the current is turned on. The negatively charged DNA fragments move toward the positive electrode.

As with the protein gel, the smaller the fragment, the more rapidly it moves through the gel. Small pieces of DNA will travel farther and be located farther from the well where they were initially injected. This allows the DNA fragments to form a distinct pattern that becomes visible through staining or a variety of other techniques.

The information provided by both DNA and protein gels looks very much like a bar code. The patterns formed from different protein samples or the DNA of different individuals can provide information about relatedness. DNA has been used to determine who the father and/or mother of a child actually is in paternity cases or in instances where a couple suspects that the child given to them in the hospital is not their child. It has also been used to determine guilt or innocence during criminal investigations. The source of blood, semen, or skin can be identified with this technique. DNA left at a crime scene can be compared to a suspect's DNA to determine if the suspect was at the crime scene.

In the case of endangered species, scientists can use DNA electrophoresis to learn which groups are being devastated by poachers, since skins from members of the same group will have similar DNA patterns. Gel electrophoresis can also be used to determine and to identify the genes responsible for specific genetic diseases such as sickle cell disease.

Chromatography Like gel electrophoresis, **chromatography** is a technique used for separating mixtures of molecules. In one type of chromatography commonly used in the biology laboratory, the mixture being separated is placed on a paper to which it sticks. For example, chlorophyll extract from plant leaves is placed on filter paper or special chromatography paper. It is done by placing a small dot of the concentrated chlorophyll extract near one end of a strip of the paper. Then, the end of the paper nearest the dot of extract is placed in a solvent. In the case of chlorophyll, the <u>solvent</u> could be alcohol. The solvent cannot touch the dot when it is initially set up, or the chlorophyll would simply wash away into the solvent.

As the solvent soaks into the paper and moves upward, substances in the mixture that do not stick tightly to the paper will be picked up by the solvent and moved along quickly. Substances that are more tightly held to the paper and less attracted to the solvent will also be picked up but will move along more slowly. This results in the formation of bands of the different substances on the chromatography paper. If the substances in the mixture are colorless, they can be viewed by combining them with reactive chemicals that will give them color. The chlorophyll extract consists of several plant pigments that are very colorful and easy to distinguish.

In summary, the rate at which a substance moves along the paper in a given solvent can be used to separate it from other substances. By comparing the distances moved with those of known substances in the same solvent, the unknowns can be identified. See Figure 9-20.

Stains and Indicators **Stains** can be used to make cell structures more visible. In fact, chromosomes were so named for the fact that they are easily stained. Commonly used stains are iodine and methylene blue. Iodine darkens certain cell structures. It is especially useful when examining plant cells through the microscope. Methylene blue stains structures in the nucleus. It is useful when observing many types of cells.

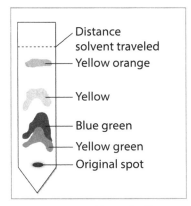

Figure 9-20. Chlorophyll chromatography

An **indicator** is a substance that changes color when it contacts certain chemicals. The examples in Table 9-2 represent only a few of the indicators commonly used in the biology laboratory.

Other indicators can be used to determine how much sugar there is in a solution or the amount of carbon dioxide present. Swimming pool owners use indicators to tell them how much chlorine is in the water. Some of the pregnancy test kits that pharmacies sell also use indicators.

Table 9-2. Indicators Used in the Biology Laboratory	
Indicator	**What It Tests**
pH paper	A piece of pH paper is dipped in the solution to be tested. Its color is then matched to a color scale. Specific colors indicate whether the solution is acidic (pH values from 0 to 6), neutral (pH 7), or basic (pH values from 8 to 14).
Iodine (Lugol's) solution	A color change from golden brown to blue-black indicates the presence of starch in the tested solution.

Dichotomous Keys A key is used to sort, name, and/or classify a particular organism. By working through a series of steps, organisms are eliminated until the one of interest is finally identified. Each step of a **dichotomous key** typically consists of two statements that divide the things being identified/classified into two groups. Each statement is followed by a direction that indicates either what step to go to next or the name of the organism.

To make your own dichotomous key, you would need to start out with two statements that divide the organisms being classified into two groups.

1a	Requires petroleum fuel	go to Step 2
1b	Requires only muscle power	bicycle
2a	Has wings and flies	jet
2b	Has no wings and does not fly	go to Step 3
3a	Has two wheels	motorcycle
3b	Has more than two wheels	car

Figure 9-21. A dichotomous key is used to sort, name, or classify.

Each statement would be followed with a direction about the next step to take. At the next step, you again divide the organisms into two groups that are again followed by directions about the next step to go to or the identity of the organism or object. For example, Figure 9-21 shows how you might construct a key to classify a bicycle, car, jet, and motorcycle.

Pretend that you do not know a motorcycle from a bicycle from a jet, from a car. All you could do is examine each one of the objects, make observations, and determine how they work. Once you did that, you would be ready to place names on each of the four items.

Notice that if you did not work through the key step by step, it would be very easy to misname an object. If you thought about a bicycle as having two wheels and scanned down the list with no attention to following the steps, you could easily mistake the bicycle for a motorcycle. You would spot step 3a, which says, "Has two wheels" and say to yourself, "Yep, that's the bicycle." You would totally miss the fact that the object in step 3a must run on petroleum fuel. Always start at the beginning of a key.

Review Questions

Set 9.2

Base your answers to questions 9 through 11 on the diagram and information below, and on your knowledge of biology.

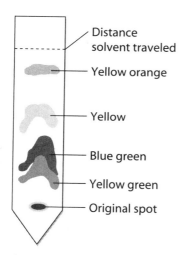

Several drops of concentrated green pigment extract obtained from spinach leaves were placed near the bottom of a strip of highly absorbent paper. When the extract dried, the paper was suspended in a test tube containing solvent so that only the tip of the paper was in the solvent. As the solvent was absorbed and moved up the paper, the various pigments within the extract became visible, as shown in the diagram.

9. A valid conclusion that can be drawn from this information is that spinach leaves

(1) contain only chlorophyll
(2) contain pigments in addition to chlorophyll
(3) contain more orange pigment than yellow pigment
(4) are yellow-orange rather than green

10. The technique used to separate the parts of the extract in the diagram is known as

(1) staining
(2) dissection
(3) chromatography
(4) electrophoresis

11. In which organelle would most of these pigments be found?

(1) nucleus
(2) mitochondrion
(3) ribosome
(4) chloroplast

12. A student observed a one-celled organism in the field of view of a compound light microscope as shown in the adjacent diagram.

On the diagram, draw an arrow to indicate the direction the organism would seem to move if the student moved the slide on the stage to the left and down. [1]

13. To test for the presence of glucose, a student added the same amount of Benedict's solution to each of four test tubes. (Benedict's is a glucose indicator that is a royal blue color when no glucose is present. To determine if glucose is present, Benedict's must be mixed in the unknown solution and heated for several minutes.)

Two of the test tubes contained unknown solutions. The other two test tubes contained known solutions. The chart below shows the color results obtained after the solutions were heated in the four test tubes in a hot water bath.

Data Table		
Tube	Contents	Color After Heating
1	Unknown solution + Benedict's solution	Royal blue
2	Unknown solution + Benedict's solution	Red orange
3	Water + Benedict's solution	Royal blue
4	Glucose + water + Benedict's solution	Red orange

The student could correctly conclude that

(1) all of the tubes contained glucose
(2) tubes 1 and 2 contained glucose
(3) tube 1 did not contain glucose, but tube 2 did
(4) tube 2 did not contain glucose, but tube 1 did

14. A student viewing a specimen under the low-power objective of a compound light microscope switched to high power and noticed that the field of view darkened considerably.

Which microscope part identified on this microscope would the student adjust to brighten the field of view?

(1) A   (2) B   (3) C   (4) D

15. A student studied the upper layer of cells of a tissue sample on a slide, using the high-power objective of the compound microscope shown.

Which part of the microscope should the student adjust to observe the lower layer of the sample?

(1) A   (2) B   (3) C   (4) D

16. State the purpose of using stains in a wet-mount slide preparation. [1]

17. The eyepiece of a compound light microscope has a magnification of 10X and the low-power objective and high-power objective lenses have magnifications of 10X and 30X, respectively. If the diameter of the low-power field measures 1500 micrometers, the diameter of the high-power field will measure either 4500 micrometers or 500 micrometers.

Select the correct diameter. Support your answer. [1]

Base your answers to questions 18 and 19 on the diagram below of some internal structures of an earthworm and on your knowledge of biology.

18. Which laboratory equipment should be used to observe the surface details of structures A, B, and C of the earthworm?

(1) stereoscope
(2) compound light microscope
(3) graduated cylinder
(4) triple-beam balance

19. Structure A has a diameter of 3 millimeters. What is the approximate diameter of the blood vessel indicated by C?

(1) 2.5 mm   (3) 1.5 mm
(2) 2.0 mm   (4) 0.5 mm

Base your answers to questions 20 and 21 on the illustration below and on your knowledge of biology. The image is a representation of an animal cell as it would appear when viewed with compound light microscope

20. Identify the organelle indicated by letter X. [1]

21. What technique could be used to make the organelle indicated by letter X more visible? [1]

22. While focusing a microscope on high power, a student crushed the coverslip. The student probably
    (1) shut the light off
    (2) turned up the light intensity
    (3) rotated the eyepiece
    (4) used the coarse adjustment

23. An experimental setup is shown in the diagram below.

Setup with light

Setup without light

Which hypothesis would most likely be tested using this setup?
    (1) Green water plants release a gas in the presence of light.
    (2) Roots of water plants absorb minerals in the absence of light.
    (3) Green plants need light for cell division.
    (4) Plants grow best in the absence of light.

Base your answers to questions 24 through 27 on the photograph below and on your knowledge of biology. The photograph shows onion root-tip tissue viewed under the high-power objective of a compound light microscope.

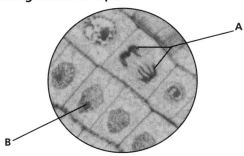

24. The photograph illustrates stages in the process of
    (1) meiosis in root tips
    (2) mitotic cell division in plants
    (3) water conduction in onions
    (4) chlorophyll production in chloroplasts

25. Identify the structure indicated by arrow A. [1]

26. Identify the structure indicated by arrow B. [1]

27. Describe one adjustment that could be made to the microscope to make the field of view brighter. [1]

28. Pieces of pH paper were used to test the contents of three test tubes. The results are shown in the diagram below.

Which statement about the tubes is correct?
    (1) Tube A contains a base.
    (2) Tube B contains a base.
    (3) Tube B contains an acid.
    (4) Tube C contains an acid.

29. When viewed with a compound light microscope, which letter would best illustrate the way in which the microscope inverts and reverses the image?

(1) A   (2) W   (3) F   (4) D

30. Gel electrophoresis is a technique used to

(1) cut DNA into pieces of various sizes
(2) separate DNA fragments by charge and size
(3) move DNA fragments from one species to another
(4) make copies of chromosomes

Observing Plant and Animal Specimens

Classroom experiences involving plants and animals range from observation to dissection. Opportunities to observe plants and animals require consideration and appreciation for the organism. The abuse of any live organism for any purpose is intolerable.

Dissection and Preserved Specimens

The dissection of plant and animal specimens provides a framework upon which to organize biological knowledge. **Dissection** (or the examination of preserved specimens) provides a way to

- observe similarities and differences that exist among species
- understand the relationship between biological form and function
- expose and identify the internal structures of organisms

To dissect a specimen correctly, you need:

- the knowledge of what equipment to use and how to use it properly
- a work area that is clean and well organized both before and after the activity

Equipment commonly used during dissection activities is described in Table 9-3.

Table 9-3. Dissection Equipment

Equipment	Use
Dissecting pan	Resembles a cake pan but has a wax or a rubber-like substance in the bottom. The specimen is placed on the waxy surface.
Dissecting pins	Large pins with a "T" shape used to anchor the specimen during the dissection
Scalpel	A sharp instrument used to slice open the specimen so that the internal parts can be observed
Scissors	Used for cutting open the specimen and to remove parts. May have two sharp points or one blunt and one sharp point.
Probe/ Teasing needle/ Dissecting needle	Used to move structures around while they are still intact. The probe can be used to lift some organs so that others located below them are observable. The probe or dissecting needle is also used to point out different structures when showing specific features to someone else. Another function is to "tease" or gently tear apart structures such as muscle tissue.
Tweezers/ Forceps	Used to lift out small parts, to move structures, and to pry parts open
Safety goggles	Wrap-around shatter-proof glasses used to protect eyes from accidental splashes of preservative when dissecting as well as in other lab situations.

31. State one scientific purpose for dissecting an organism. [1]

32. For what purpose would the equipment in the following illustration most likely be used?

(1) dissecting an earthworm
(2) removing cell organelles
(3) identifying and classifying a single-celled organism
(4) observing mitosis on prepared slides

33. Along with a dissecting pan, which group of equipment would be most useful to a student planning to dissect a preserved specimen?

(1) dissecting pins, compound light microscope, and pH paper
(2) pH paper, eye dropper, and safety goggles
(3) safety goggles, scissors, and compound light microscope
(4) safety goggles, stereoscope, and scissors

34. What is the best use for the dissection instrument illustrated in the diagram below?

(1) cutting through bones
(2) spreading apart muscle tissue
(3) cutting through thick muscles
(4) removing blood plasma

Laboratory Safety

Laboratory investigations are, for some students, the most exciting part of the Living Environment course. However, they sometimes involve potentially dangerous activities and materials. As a result, careful attention to safety procedures is critical.

Using Safety Equipment

You should know how to properly use the safety equipment located in your biology laboratory. It is critical to be aware of the location in your laboratory of each of these:

- fire extinguisher
- safety shower
- eye wash station
- fire blanket
- emergency gas shutoff

Use the safety equipment provided for you. Goggles should be worn whenever a lab calls for the use of chemicals, preserved specimens, or dissection. If indicated by your teacher, you should also wear a safety apron when using chemicals. Some activities, such as those involving chemicals or live or preserved organisms, also require the use of special gloves.

Safety in the Laboratory

Read all of the directions for an investigation before you start to work. If you are unsure about any part of the lab procedures, check with your teacher. As a general rule, do not perform activities without permission; do only what the instructions and your teacher direct you to do.

- Do *not* eat or drink in the laboratory.
- When you are heating a test tube, always slant it so that the open end of the tube points away from you and others. Never heat a closed container, such as a test tube that has been closed with a stopper.
- Never inhale or taste any of the chemicals you are using in a laboratory. This includes the specimens you are dissecting.
- If you spill a chemical or get any on your skin, wash it off immediately. Also, report the incident to your teacher.
- Tell your teacher about any personal injury no matter how minor it may seem.
- Tie back long hair, and keep loose clothing away from laboratory equipment, chemicals, and sources of heat and fire.
- Never expose flammable liquids to an open flame. Use a hot water bath (such as a large beaker of water heated on a hot plate) if you need to heat flammable liquids (such as alcohol). See Figure 9-22.
- Know what equipment to use when handling hot glassware. Do not use bare fingers to pick up hot test tubes or beakers. Use test tube holders and beaker tongs.
- Do not use glassware that has cracks or large chips. Tell your teacher about the damage and get a replacement.
- Do not pour chemicals back into stock bottles or exchange stoppers on the stock bottles.
- Use laboratory apparatus as it is intended to be used. For example, do not stir a solution using a thermometer, plastic ruler, or your pen.
- Do not use electrical equipment around water. If electrical cords seem to have exposed wires or if you get a shock handling electrical equipment, notify your teacher immediately. Do not attempt to disconnect the equipment yourself.

Figure 9-22. Hot water bath: A hot water bath is used to heat test tubes that contain a flammable liquid such as alcohol.

Cleaning Your Work Area

- Turn off the gas and water after you are done with them. Disconnect any electrical devices.
- Clean your work area by returning materials to their appropriate places, washing glassware according to your teacher's instructions, and wiping off the lab surface.
- Dispose of chemicals according to the instructions provided by your teacher.
- Wash your hands thoroughly!

Review Questions

Set 9.4

35. If a student spills nitric acid on her arm, she should *first*
    (1) report the accident to the school nurse
    (2) report the spill to her teacher
    (3) rinse her arm with water
    (4) allow the acid to evaporate

36. When they are not being used during a laboratory investigation, electrical devices should be
    (1) put away
    (2) turned off
    (3) unplugged
    (4) covered

37. A student performing an experiment noticed that the beaker containing the water being heated had a small crack. It was not leaking. What should the student do?

(1) Stop heating the beaker and try to fix the crack.
(2) Stop heating the beaker and report the crack to the teacher.
(3) Stop heating the beaker and immediately take the beaker to the teacher.
(4) Continue heating as long as the liquid does not start to leak out of the crack.

38. The diagram below shows a student conducting a laboratory experiment. Describe one safety procedure the student should be following that is *not* represented in the diagram. [1]

39. The diagram below shows a student heating some test tubes with chemicals in them during a laboratory activity. Describe one error in the laboratory procedure shown in the diagram. [1]

40. An *unsafe* procedure for heating a nutrient solution in a flask would be to

(1) heat the solution at the lowest temperature on a hot plate
(2) stopper the flask tightly to prevent evaporation of the solution
(3) use a Bunsen burner to heat the solution
(4) stir the solution while it is heating

41. Chlorophyll can be removed from leaves by boiling them in alcohol, a flammable solvent. In addition to wearing safety goggles, which is the safest procedure to follow?

(1) A stoppered test tube of leaves and alcohol should be held over the Bunsen burner.
(2) A stoppered test tube of leaves and alcohol should be placed in a large beaker of alcohol and heated on a hot plate.
(3) A beaker of leaves and alcohol should be placed on a tripod over a Bunsen burner.
(4) A beaker of leaves and alcohol should be placed into a larger beaker of water and heated on a hot plate.

42. Which safety procedure should a student follow during a dissection?

(1) The student should wear gloves and hold the specimen in the palm of her hand while cutting the specimen open.
(2) The student should cut the specimen open while holding it under running water.
(3) The student should apply additional preservative to the specimen.
(4) The student should direct the cutting motion away from her body.

Directions

Review the Test-Taking Strategies section of this book. Then answer the following questions. Read each question carefully and answer with a correct choice or response.

Part A

1 The diagram below shows a wasp positioned next to a centimeter ruler.

What is the approximate length of a *wing* of this wasp?
(1) 10 mm   (3) 3.5 cm
(2) 1.4 cm   (4) 35 mm

2 When preparing a wet-mount slide of onion cells, a student put a drop of Lugol's iodine stain on the slide. Lugol's iodine stain was added to
(1) prevent the formation of air bubbles
(2) make cell structures more visible
(3) increase the magnification
(4) increase the rate of photosynthesis in the cells

3 A student views some cheek cells under low power. Before switching to high power, the student should
(1) adjust the eyepiece
(2) center the image being viewed
(3) remove the slide from the stage
(4) remove the coverslip from the slide

4 Bromthymol blue turns yellow in the presence of carbon dioxide. This characteristic makes it possible for bromthymol blue to function as
(1) a measure of volume
(2) an indicator
(3) a catalyst
(4) an energy source

5 Which statement describes two unsafe laboratory practices represented in the diagram below?

(1) The flame is too high, and the test tube is unstoppered.
(2) The opening of the test tube is pointed toward the student, and the student is not wearing goggles.
(3) The test tube is unstoppered, and the student is not wearing goggles.
(4) The beaker has water in it, and the flame is under the tripod.

6 A student sees the image shown below when observing the letter "f" with the low-power objective lens of a microscope.

Which of the four diagrams below most closely resembles the image the student will see after switching to high power?

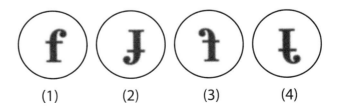

  (1)   (2)   (3)   (4)

Part B

7 The diagram below represents the field of view of a compound light microscope. Three single-celled organisms are located across the diameter of the field.

Knowing that 1 mm = 1000 micrometers, what is the approximate length of each single-celled organism?
(1) 250 micrometers
(2) 500 micrometers
(3) 1000 micrometers
(4) 1500 micrometers

8 Electrophoresis is a method of
(1) separating DNA fragments
(2) changing the genetic code of an organism
(3) indicating the presence of starch
(4) separating colored compounds on a strip of paper

9 A student, not wearing safety goggles, gets some unknown chemical in his eye. What is the most appropriate action he should take?
(1) Put on safety goggles immediately.
(2) Ask his lab partner to see if his eye looks OK.
(3) Go to the eyewash station and use it to rinse his eye thoroughly.
(4) Rub the eye gently and see if it hurts or stings.

10 An indicator for a protein is added to a solution that contains protein and to a solution that does not contain protein. State one way, other than the presence or absence of protein, that the two solutions may differ after the indicator has been added to both. [1]

11 State two safety procedures that should be followed when conducting an experiment that involves heating protein in a test tube containing water, an acid, and a digestive enzyme. [1]

12 Which laboratory procedure is represented in the diagram below?

(1) placing a coverslip over a specimen
(2) removing a coverslip from a slide
(3) adding stain to a slide without removing the coverslip
(4) reducing the size of air bubbles under a coverslip

13 A student is viewing a single-celled organism under the low-power objective of a compound light microscope. Describe an adjustment the student would need to make to see the organism clearly *after* switching from low power to high power. In your description include the name of the part of the microscope that would be used to make the adjustment. [1]

14 What is the volume of the liquid in the graduated cylinder shown below?

(1) 23 mL   (2) 26 mL   (3) 27 mL   (4) 28 mL

15 The diagrams below show four different one-celled organisms (shaded) in the field of view of the same microscope using different magnifications. Which illustration shows the largest one-celled organism?

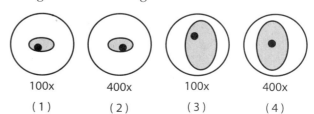

Base your answers to questions 16 through 18 on the information below, the key, and on your knowledge of biology.

Biologists use keys to accurately classify unknown organisms such as the unidentified female mosquito shown in the following diagram. These keys are designed to categorize organisms according to structural characteristics. The key shows various characteristics used to identify the differences among *Anopheles, Deinocerites, Culex, Psorophora,* and *Aedes* mosquitoes.

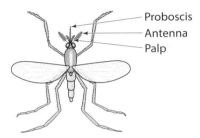

Proboscis
Antenna
Palp

Unknown female mosquito

1a Antennae very bushy —
Male mosquito

1b Antennae not bushy —
Go to 2

2a Palps much shorter than
proboscis — Go to 3

2b Palps as long as proboscis —
Female *Anopheles*

3a Tip of abdomen blunt,
without points — Go to 4

3b Tip of abdomen with
points — Go to 5

4a Antennae much longer
than proboscis —
Female *Deinocerites*

4b Antennae shorter than
proboscis — Female *Culex*

5a Many long scales present
on hind legs —
Female *Psorophora*

5b Hind legs without long
scales — Female *Aedes*

16 According to the key, which feature distinguishes male from female mosquitoes?
(1) palp length
(2) leg scales
(3) abdomen points
(4) antennae appearance

17 According to the key, which characteristics are necessary to identify a female *Anopheles* mosquito?
(1) antennae, palps, and proboscis
(2) wings, proboscis, and scales on legs
(3) eyes, scales on legs, and abdomen tip
(4) palps, abdomen tip, and wings

18 According to the key, the unknown female mosquito belongs to the group known as
(1) *Deinocerites*   (3) *Psorophora*
(2) *Culex*   (4) *Aedes*

Base your answers to questions 19 through 22 on the information and diagram below and on your knowledge of biology. The diagram represents some of the steps in a procedure used in a specific laboratory activity.

Samples of DNA from an eye-color gene of four individuals, W, X, Y, and Z, were cut into pieces using a type of chemical. The results of this procedure are shown below.

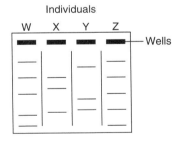

Individuals

W   X   Y   Z

Wells

19 Identify the specific type of chemical used to cut the DNA in this procedure. [1]

20 Which two individuals have DNA base patterns for this gene that are the most similar? Support your answer. [1]

21 The diagram represents the results of the procedure known as
(1) cloning
(2) chromatography
(3) gel electrophoresis
(4) protein sequencing

22 State where the smallest fragments of DNA would be located on the gel in the illustration. [1]

23 A chromatography setup is shown below.

Identify one error in the setup. [1]

Part C

24 Some students did a lab to test the vitamin C content of several fruits. They squeezed the juice from some of the fruits and cut others up and placed them in a blender to obtain a juice sample. Juice for each fruit was kept in a clean, labeled beaker. Pipettes were used to transfer the juices to test tubes for analysis.

During the laboratory cleanup, one student drank some of the juice left in one beaker. State why this was an unsafe procedure. [1]

25 Below is a drawing of a hypothetical electrophoresis gel. Included on the gel are some bands for several different individuals.

- Decribe where the smallest fragments of DNA would be located on the gel in the illustration. [1]
- Discuss two practical applications of information that can be obtained through this process. [1]

Base your answers to questions 26 through 28 on the information and diagram below and on your knowledge of biology.

The diagram below shows the results of a test that was done using DNA samples from three bears of different species. Each DNA sample was cut into fragments using a specific enzyme and placed in the wells as indicated below. The DNA fragments were then separated using gel electrophoresis.

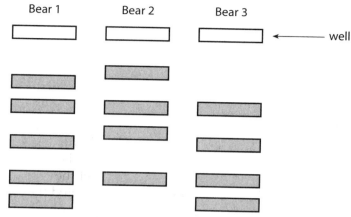

26 Which two bears are most closely related? Support your answer with data from the test results. [1]

27 Identify one additional way to determine the evolutionary relationship of these bears. [1]

28 Identify one procedure, other than electrophoresis, that is used in the laboratory to separate the different types of molecules in a liquid mixture. [1]

29 The dichotomous key begun below should allow users to classify the organisms illustrated. Complete the key using only information shown in the illustration. [3]

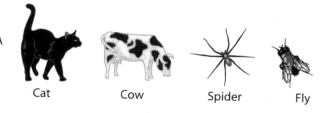

Dichotomous Key
1a. Wings present.....................................Fly 1b. No wings present............................ go to 2

Part D of The Living Environment Regents Examination, is composed of multiple-choice and/or open-ended constructed-response questions, based on the NY State-required laboratory activities.

Questions and Answers About Part D of the Regents Examination

1. **How important are the required laboratory activities?** Everyone taking the Living Environment Regents Examination is expected to have satisfactorily met the laboratory requirement and completed the four laboratory activities. Questions on Part D of the Regents Examination assess content and skills related to these required laboratory activities. Everyone who has completed these activities should have available for review the *Student Laboratory Packet* supplied by the Regents for each of the labs. The packet contains background information, procedures, questions, and answers that were filled in as you carried out the laboratory activity. These packets should be used for review purposes, along with the information provided in this Appendix.

2. **How do the required labs help me in the Living Environment course?** Performing the required laboratory activities accomplishes two basic things. First, you learn and/or practice important laboratory skills associated with the biological sciences. Second, the lab activities are each associated with specific concepts contained in the *Living Environment Core Curriculum*, helping you better learn, understand, and apply those concepts.

3. **How can this Appendix help me prepare for the Part D questions?** To best prepare for the questions on Part D, you need to review your completed *Student Laboratory Packet* for each required laboratory activity along with the information presented here. You should have all four completed packets (with correct answers) available as you work through this Appendix.

4. **What should I know about each of the Required Laboratory Activities?** The most critical thing is that you have actually completed each activity and observed firsthand the results of each part. The next thing is to review the content and skills associated with each activity by working through the rest of this Appendix. In many cases, the content or skills are already found elsewhere in this book. References and notes are provided to show you where to look. Specific information and skills related to each activity is provided in this section.

The questions on Part D may be *applications* of the skills and content associated with the activity. For example, although red onion cells are used in the diffusion laboratory activity, a question involving the basic concepts of diffusion using another kind of plant cell would be appropriate as a Part D question.

It is important to note that you do *not* have to know, for test purposes, all of the content information provided with each activity. Much of it is included in the activity so that you can understand the important concepts. Only a few concepts in the required labs that are not in the Core Curriculum are actually testable. Each of these will be clearly noted in this Appendix.

Laboratory Activity #1: Relationships and Biodiversity

In this activity, you conducted a number of tests to compare various characteristics of a hypothetical "endangered plant species" with 3 other species that were related to it. From the data, you then determined which species might be the most likely to produce the substance "Curol" that has important medical uses. The final segment of the activity focused on biodiversity, both its benefits and how the loss of biodiversity can be an environmental problem.

Skills and/or content associated with the laboratory activity	Procedures and suggestions for review **Note:** Pages noted below are either in *Brief Review in the Living Environment (BR)* or in your *Student Lab Packet (SLP)*.
Making/recording observations of plant tissues	See pages 146–148 and page 179 (BR) for information about observations, inferences, assumptions, and opinions.
Making/recording observations of tissue samples with a microscope	Review focusing and other microscope skills on pages 169–172 (BR). In this activity you examined plant tissues with the microscope to look for similarities and differences.
Comparing samples to determine similarities and differences	You compared the flowers, leaves, seeds, and stem cross-sections in an attempt to determine which one was most closely related to *Botana curus (B. curus)*. If a Regents question illustrates parts of specific organisms, you could be asked to use your observations to determine relationships between them.
Use of paper chromatography	Review what you did during the laboratory activity on pages 2–3 (SLP). Review the process on page 175 (BR). Be prepared to answer questions about why goggles were required or about correct vs. incorrect technique related to chromatography, such as: What if the water (solvent) level was above the pigment spots when the paper was put in the cup? (answer: the pigment would wash away and not go up the paper)
Use of an indicator (to test for enzyme M)	You were testing for an enzyme that was present in *B. curus* to see if any of the other plants also produced it. The presence of this enzyme in any of the other plants might suggest a closer relationship to *B. curus*. Review information about indicators on page 175 (BR).
Use of simulated gel electrophoresis of DNA from plant samples	Review what you did during the laboratory activity on pages 3–4 (SLP), then review the technique of electrophoresis on pages 173–174 (BR). Be prepared to answer questions about how enzymes are used to cut the DNA into fragments as described in the lab activity. Also know how to interpret gel electrophoresis results: e.g., what do the bands represent and what information do they convey, or, where would the smallest fragments be on a gel?
Translating the DNA code to a particular protein sequence	Review what you did during the laboratory activity on page 7 (SLP). You first used the base pairing "rule" for DNA to RNA transcription—G goes with C, and A goes with U (not T) to get the mRNA sequences. Then you used the Universal Genetic Code Table provided by your teacher to look up which amino acid each three-letter mRNA sequence represented. This enabled you to get a particular amino acid sequence for each species, so that you could compare them and determine possible genetic relationships. Similar DNA suggests common ancestry. Review the information on pages 47–48 (BR) regarding proteins and DNA in cells.
Using branching tree diagrams to show relationships	Review question 6 on page 6 (SLP), then review Figure 5–2 on page 81 (BR). Read pages 87–88 (BR). Read the information about Practice Questions 13–14 on pages x–xi (BR).
Human actions and biodiversity	Re-read the passage on page 7 (SLP), then review your answers to questions 8–10. Review pages 110–111 (BR) and pages 127–129 (BR) regarding the benefits of biodiversity, and the section: *Extinction*, on page 91 (BR).

Questions and comments regarding Laboratory Activity #1

After reviewing your *Student Lab Packet* and the sections of this book as noted above, check yourself by answering the following questions found in this book on the pages noted.

p. 49; 8, 9, 13, 16, 17
p. 50; 18, 20, 21, 22
p. 54; 35
p. 55; 1, 6
p. 56; 8
p. 81; 4
p. 82; 5
p. 89; 27, 30
p. 101; 5
p. 111; 40, 41, 42
p. 112; 44, 45

p. 120; 32
p. 143; 36
p. 176; 9, 10, 11
p. 177; 13, 14, 15
p. 178; 22
p. 179; 29, 30
p. 183; 3
p. 184; 12, 13
p. 185; 20
p. 186; 22, 23, 24

You should also be able to:

- explain how you used your lab data to determine which plant species is the closest relative to *B. curus.*
- explain why finding a close relative to *B. curus* is important.
- list several forms of structural evidence that can be used to indicate biological relationships (such as similarities in embryos, flower form, or leaf shape).
- explain why structural evidence is often less useful than molecular evidence to determine biological relationships.
- use a genetic code table to convert a DNA sequence, to a mRNA sequence, to an amino acid sequence. (Ask your teacher for a copy of the table you used in the activity and practice with it.)
- explain why closely related species often share many molecular/biochemical similarities.
- answer questions related to why and how biodiversity may be lost, why such a loss is important, and how human activities often play a role in the loss of biodiversity.
- discuss why tradeoffs must be considered when the destruction of habitats/native species is involved.

Part D Review Questions: Lab 1

Base your answers to questions 1 through 4 on the information below and on your knowledge of biology.

To demonstrate techniques used in DNA analysis, a student was given two paper strip samples of DNA. The two DNA samples are shown below.

Sample 1:
ATTCCGGTAATCCCGTAATGCCGG
ATAATACTCCGGTAATATC

Sample 2:
ATTCCGGTAATCCCGTAATGCCGGA
TAATACTCCGGTAATATC

The student cut between the C and G in each of the shaded CCGG sequences in sample 1 and between the As in each of the shaded TAAT sequences in sample 2. Both sets of fragments were then arranged on a paper model of a gel.

1. The action of what kind of molecules was being demonstrated when the DNA samples were cut? [1]

2. Identify the technique that was being demonstrated when the fragments were arranged on the gel model. [1]

3. The results of this type of DNA analysis are often used to help determine
   (1) the number of DNA molecules in an organism
   (2) if two species are closely related
   (3) the number of mRNA molecules in DNA
   (4) if two organisms contain carbohydrate molecules

4. State one way that the arrangement of the two samples on the gel model would differ. [1]

5. R, S, and T are three species of birds. Species S and T show similar coloration. The enzymes found in species R and T show similarities. Species R and T also exhibit many of the same behavioral patterns.

   Show the relationship between species R, S, and T by placing the letter representing each species at the top of the appropriate branch on the diagram to the right. [1]

Base your answers to questions 6 through 8 on the diagram below and on your knowledge of biology. Letters *A* through *L* represent different species of organisms. The arrows represent long periods of geologic time.

6. Which two species are the most closely related?

(1) J and L   (3) F and H
(2) G and L   (4) F and G

7. Which species was best adapted to changes that occurred in its environment over the longest period of time?

(1) A   (3) C
(2) B   (4) J

8. Which two species would most likely show the greatest similarity of DNA and proteins?

(1) B and J   (3) J and K
(2) G and I   (4) F and L

Base your answers to questions 9 through 11 on the information below and on your knowledge of biology.

Paper chromatography can be used to investigate evolutionary relationships. Leaves from a plant were ground and mixed with a solvent. The mixture of ground leaves and solvent was then filtered. Using a toothpick, twenty drops of the filtrate (material that passed through the filter) were placed at one spot on a strip of chromatography paper.

This procedure was repeated using leaves from three other species of plants. A separate strip of chromatography paper was prepared for each plant species. Each of the four strips of chromatography paper was placed in a different beaker containing the same solvent for the same amount of time. One of the laboratory setups is shown below.

9. State one reason for using a new toothpick for the filtrate from each plant. [1]

10. State one way the four strips would most likely be different from each other after being removed from the beakers. [1]

11. State how a comparison of these resulting strips could indicate evolutionary relationships. [1]

Base your answers to questions 12 through 14 on the information below and on your knowledge of biology.

Scientists found members of a plant species they did not recognize. They wanted to determine if the unknown species was related to one or more of four known species, A, B, C, and D. The relationship between species can be determined most accurately by comparing the results of gel electrophoresis of the DNA from different species.

The chart below represents the results of gel electrophoresis of the DNA from the unknown plant species and the four known species.

Results of Gel Electrophoresis of DNA from Five Plant Species

Unknown Species	Species A	Species B	Species C	Species D

Key
— = Band in the g

12. The unknown species is most closely related to which of the four known species? Support your answer. [1]

13. Identify one physical characteristic of plants that can be readily observed and compared to help determine the relationship between two different species of plants. [1]

14. Explain why comparing the DNA of the unknown and known plant species is probably a more accurate method of determining relationships than comparing only the physical characteristic you identified in question 13. [1]

Laboratory Activity #2: Making Connections

In Part A of this activity, you learned to take your pulse rate. Then you compared pulse rate data for the class. You next experienced muscle fatigue by rapidly squeezing a clothespin. In Part B, you designed a controlled experiment to determine which of two claims about exercise and pulse rate is correct.

Skills and/or content associated with the laboratory activity	Procedures and suggestions for review **Note:** Pages noted below are either in *Brief Review in the Living Environment (BR)* or in your *Student Lab Packet (SLP)*.
Taking pulse rate	You should be familiar with the procedure to find a person's pulse rate on page 2. (SLP) Review the information on human systems on pages 10–13 (BR).
Data tables and graphs	Review the data table and histogram you prepared on page 3 (SLP). Also review the questions and your answers on page 4 (SLP). Review the information about collecting and organizing data on pages 154–156 (BR).
Muscle fatigue	Review the information, questions, and your answers to them on pages 5 and 6 (SLP).
Designing a controlled experiment and a report on the findings	Review the background information on page 7 (SLP) to help you recall how you determined the hypothesis your experiment tested. Review the steps for the design of a controlled experiment and how to organize the final report on pages 8–9 (SLP), then read over your final laboratory report for this activity, noting how you addressed each step of the design and report organization. Review the information on pages 149 through 158 (BR) regarding experimental design and the reporting of results and conclusions.

Questions and comments regarding Laboratory Activity #2

After reviewing your *Student Lab Packet* and the sections of this book as noted above, check yourself by answering the following questions found in this book on the pages noted.

p. 14; 38
p. 16; 15
p. 149; 3, 5
p. 153; 6, 8
p. 154; 9, 10, 11, 12, 14, 15, 16
p. 158; 18, 19
p. 159; 23, 24, 25, 26, 27, 28
p. 161; 7, 8, 9, 10, 11, 12, 13
p. 162; 14

You should also be able to:

- explain what your pulse rate tells you about activities occurring within your body.
- explain why a higher level of activity would affect a person's pulse rate. Be sure to state specifically how the functioning of muscle cells is affected by blood flow through various parts the body including the respiratory and digestive systems.
- explain what muscle fatigue is, what happens to cause it, and how it can eventually be overcome—see page 5 (SLP).

- explain why different individuals may have different resting pulse rates and that not all people experience muscle fatigue with the same amount of muscle activity.
- explain why evidence is important in determining whether or not a claim someone makes is true.
- describe your actual experiment, including the question, hypothesis, independent and dependent variables, and your conclusions. You should also be able to suggest at least one additional experiment that could be done to answer a question that came about as a direct result of the experiment you conducted. (Such a question might involve the effect of more activity on the test subjects, having more test subjects, or choosing a greater variety of test subjects.)

Part D Review Questions: Lab 2

15. On a television talk show, a guest claims that people who exercise vigorously for 15 minutes or more every day are able to solve math problems more rapidly than people who have no vigorous exercise in their daily routine.

Describe a controlled experiment that could be conducted to test this claim. In your description be sure to:

- state the purpose of the experiment [1]
- state why the sample to be used should be large [1]
- describe how the experimental group will be treated and how the control group will be treated [2]
- state the specific data to be collected during the experiment [1]
- state one way to determine if the results support the claim [1]

16. A student measures his pulse rate while he is watching television and records it. Next, he walks to a friend's house nearby and when he arrives, measures and records his pulse rate again. He and his friend then decide to run to the mall a few blocks away.

On arriving at the mall, the student measures and records his pulse rate once again. Finally, after sitting and talking for a half hour, the student measures and records his pulse rate for the last time. Which graph below best illustrates the expected changes in his pulse rate according to the activities described above?

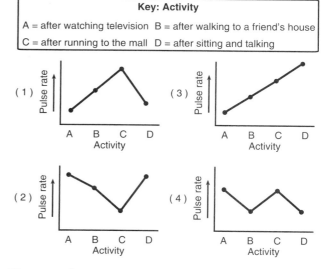

Key: Activity

A = after watching television   B = after walking to a friend's house
C = after running to the mall   D = after sitting and talking

17. A student squeezed a clothespin as many times as possible in a 30-second time period. The student repeated this procedure nine more times in quick succession. The data obtained are in the chart below.

Trial	Number of Squeezes in 30 Seconds
1	32
2	29
3	28
4	27
5	26
6	25
7	23
8	21
9	19
10	17

State one hypothesis that this data would support concerning the relationship between number of trials and number of squeezes in 30 seconds. [1]

Base your answers to questions 18 and 19 on the information below and on your knowledge of biology.

In an investigation, 28 students in a class determined their pulse rates after performing each of three different activities. Each activity was performed three times during equal time intervals. The average results are shown in the graph below.

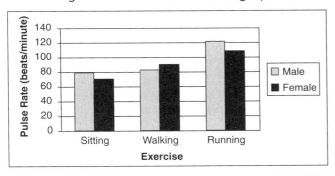

18. Before constructing the graph it would have been most helpful to organize the results of the investigation in
    (1) a research plan
    (2) an equation
    (3) a data table
    (4) a generalization

19. Some students concluded that males always have a higher pulse rate than females. Does the graph support this conclusion? Justify your answer. [1]

Laboratory Activity #3: The Beaks of Finches

The Beaks of Finches lab is a simulation of how natural selection works. Various tools are used in this activity to represent some beak variations that might be present in a population. Competition between participants leads to finding which tool(s) are best suited for obtaining enough food for the individuals with that tool (beak variation) to survive. The activity concludes with data about actual beak variations present today in different species of finches—the result of competition over many years on the Galapagos Islands.

Skills and/or content associated with the laboratory activity	Procedures and suggestions for review **Note:** Pages noted below are either in *Brief Review in the Living Environment (BR)* or in your *Student Lab Packet (SLP).*
Predicting	Review the procedures and questions on page 2 (SLP) to recall why you could expect a particular tool to be useful for the job specified.
Collecting and organizing data, making predictions	Review what you did during the Round One competition on page 3 (SLP). You could be asked to place data in a data table provided, as you did in this activity. Review the information on p. 154–156 (BR).
Analyzing and interpreting data	Review what you did during the Round Two competition on page 3 (SLP). The competition in Round Two was expected to make it harder to collect as many seeds in the same time interval as you had in Round One. State whether or not your results supported this expectation. Include data from the table in your answer. Read the introduction to The Mechanics of Evolution and Overview of Evolution on page 82 (BR) and on pages xiii–xiv (BR) about data table question strategies.
Summarizing results	Review questions 1–9 and your answers on pages 4–6 (SLP). Read the information on page 82 (BR), then on page 83–84 (BR) read the three sections and review the information in figures 5–4 and 5–5. Read pages 99–101 (BR); *Environmental Limits on Population Size.*
Galapagos Island Finches—Interpreting charts	Review the chart on page 6 (SLP), noting the "design" of each beak compared with the way it functions and the preferred food. Review the questions about the chart along with your responses to them. Be prepared to answer similar questions in association with this chart or a similar chart or diagram.

Questions and comments regarding Laboratory Activity #3

After reviewing your *Student Lab Packet* and the sections of this book as noted above, check yourself by answering the following questions found in this book on the pages noted.

p. 84; 6   p. 101; 6
p. 85; 11, 12   p. 102; 9
p. 87; 16   p. 104; 10
p. 93; 1, 3, 5, 7   p. 158; 19

You should also be able to:

- identify a specific procedure or action you carried out in this lab that is directly associated with *each* of the following concepts associated with evolution: variation, competition, survival, adaptation, and the role of the environment as an agent of natural selection. For help, see question #9 on page 6 (SLP).
- describe how being assigned a tool is more like how adaptations occur in nature than being allowed to choose a particular tool for the task.
- predict how the addition of small pebbles to the dish (that could not be used as food) could affect the results as the (food) seeds were being collected.
- explain how the characteristics of a particular bird's beak could affect its survival.
- explain why a bird has no control over the type of beak it has.
- explain how a particular beak could be useful in one environment and nearly useless in another.
- explain why migration to a new environment may enable an individual who cannot successfully compete in its original location to survive.
- explain why an individual with a beak that does not enable it to compete successfully for food cannot simply get a new beak that would make it better adapted.
- describe two characteristics of a bird, other than its beak, that would vary among individuals in the population and be a factor in the ability of individual birds to survive. Select one of these characteristics and state how it would specifically be important to the individual's survival.
- name two species on the beak chart, on page 6 (SLP), that would be likely to compete when food is scarce. Explain the basis for your answer.

Part D Review Questions: Lab 3

20. A hawk has a genetic trait that gives it much better eyesight than other hawks of the same species in the same area. Explain how this could lead to evolutionary change within this species of hawk over a long period of time. In your answer, be sure to include an explanation of:
    - competition within the hawk population [1]
    - survival of various individuals in the population [1]
    - how the frequency of the better-eyesight trait would be expected to change over time within the population [1]
    - what would most likely happen to the hawks having the better-eyesight trait if they also had unusually weak wing muscles [1]

21. In members of a bird species living on a remote island, the greatest number of beak variations in the population would most likely be found when
    (1) there is a high level of competition for limited resources
    (2) homeostasis is limited by a severe climate
    (3) they have a large and varied food supply
    (4) they are prey for a large number of predators

22. The different tools used during the beaks of finches lab represented
    (1) feeding adaptations in finches
    (2) nest construction adaptations
    (3) variations in seed size
    (4) variations in ecosystems

Base your answer to question 23 on the portion of the mRNA codon chart and information below.

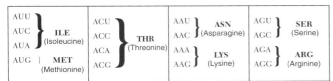

Series I represents three mRNA codons. Series II includes a mutation of series I.

Series I AGAUCGAGU
Series II ACAUCGAGU

23. How would the amino acid sequence produced by the mutant strand (series II) compare to the amino acid sequence produced by series I?
(1) The amino acid sequence would be shorter.
(2) One amino acid in the sequence would change.
(3) The amino acid sequence would remain unchanged.
(4) More than one amino acid in the sequence would change.

Base your answers to questions 24 through 26 on the passage below and on your knowledge of biology.

When Charles Darwin traveled to the Galapagos Islands, he observed 14 distinct varieties of finches on the islands. Darwin also observed that each finch variety ate a different type of food and lived in a slightly different habitat from the other finches. Darwin concluded that the finches all shared a common ancestor but had developed different beak structures.

24. The 14 varieties of finches are most likely the result of
(1) absence of biodiversity
(2) biological evolution
(3) asexual reproduction
(4) lack of competition

25. The second sentence best describes
(1) an ecosystem
(2) a predator/prey relationship
(3) a niche
(4) a food web

26. The different beak structures mentioned in the last sentence were most likely influenced by
(1) selection for favorable variations
(2) environmental conditions identical to those of the common ancestor
(3) abnormal mitotic cell division
(4) characteristics that are acquired during the bird's lifetime

Laboratory Activity #5: Diffusion Through a Membrane

The Diffusion Through a Membrane activity initially focuses on making a model "cell" and determining how certain materials move through the membrane surrounding it. Indicators are then used to test various solutions to determine which materials moved and where they ended up. Red onion cells were treated with salt solution and distilled water to determine the effect of such substances on live cells.

Skills and/or content associated with the laboratory activity	Procedures and suggestions for review Note: Pages noted below are either in *Brief Review in the Living Environment* (BR) or in your *Student Lab Packet (SLP)*.
Making a model "cell"	Review the procedures by which you made a model "cell" out of dialysis tubing (or a plastic bag). The "cell" contained both glucose and starch while the beaker contained starch indicator solution and water—see p. 2 (SLP). Read pages 5–8 (BR) regarding cell organelles, including the cell membrane. Read p. 166–168 (BR), *Tools for Measurement*.
Using starch and glucose indicator solutions	Review the procedures (p. 3 SLP, Table One) for testing for starch and glucose using the indicator. Notice that, in each case, a color change indicated the presence of the substance, and that the glucose test required heating before a result could be observed.

Determining indicator results	Table 2 (p. 3 SLP) summarizes the tests and results for each indicator. Be sure you can explain why it is necessary to test both the substance you want the indicator to "find" and any other substances that are also present. Read p. 175 (BR); *Stains and Indicators*.
Observing and interpreting results	Review your Model Cell Observations (p. 4 SLP) and the diagrams you filled in. Then carefully review your answers to questions 1–7 on pages 4–5 (SLP). Be sure you now understand which molecules moved through the membrane and know how you could tell. Also be sure you know how this information was used to determine the relative sizes of the molecules.
Making a wet-mount slide (of onion cells)	Review the procedures for making a wet mount slide. (p. 6 SLP) Read pages 169–172 (BR); *Microscope Skills*.
Drawing and labeling microscope images	Review the drawings you made for questions 6, 10, and 15. (p. 7 SLP) Note the differences in each drawing and review what you did each time to cause the changes you observed and drew.
Adding liquids to wet-mount slides	Review the procedure for this technique. (p. 6 SLP) You should be able to describe this process and predict the effect a substance being added would have on the cells.
Applying skills and concepts	Review the Analysis Questions and your answers to them. (p. 8–9 SLP) Just as you did for these questions, you should be able to apply the main concepts from this activity to questions like these if they appear on Part D of the Regents examination.

Questions and comments regarding Laboratory Activity #5

After reviewing your *Student Lab Packet* and the sections of this book as noted above, check yourself by answering the following questions found in this book on the pages noted.

p. 6; 11
p. 9; 22, 23, 25, 26, 27, 28
p. 10; 30, 31, 32, 33, 35
p. 15; 4, 5, 6, 7, 8, 9, 10
p. 16; 11
p. 18; 28, 29

p. 168; 3, 4
p. 169; 5, 6, 8
p. 177; 13, 14, 15, 16, 17
p. 178; 22
p. 183; 2, 4

You should also be able to:

- explain why dialysis tubing or a plastic bag could be used to simulate a cell membrane in this activity.
- identify a particular indicator and explain how it is used to indicate whether or not a specific substance is present.
- explain why it was important to keep the onion skin material as flat as possible when making the wet-mount slide.
- describe the direction that particles move during the process of diffusion relative to the concentration of a substance or substances.

- describe how the size of a molecule can affect whether or not it can pass across (through) a membrane.
- provide several examples of cells being affected by the process of diffusion. The effects may be on the appearance of the cell, the contents of the cell, and/or the functioning of the cell.
- provide several specific examples of the process of diffusion occurring within the human body. For each example be able to identify the substance(s) diffusing and the effect of this process on body functioning.
- describe the effect of salt on the water content of cell cytoplasm.
- describe how distilled water can be used to counteract the effect of salt on living cells on a wet-mount microscope slide.
- predict the effect of an error in procedure by students doing this particular laboratory activity, such as putting a substance in the wrong place, using salt solution instead of water, using the wrong indicator, and so on.
- Understand that osmosis, the diffusion of water through a membrane, is a kind of diffusion and therefore follows the same general "rules" as for the diffusion of other substances.

- explain how the process of digestion is related to the process of diffusion—see question 6 on p. 9 (SLP).

Part D Review Questions: Lab 5

27. An investigation was set up to study the movement of water through a membrane. The results are shown in the diagram below.

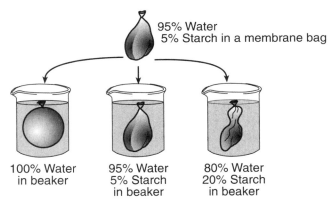

Based on these results, which statement correctly predicts what will happen to red blood cells when they are placed in a beaker containing a water solution in which the salt concentration is much higher than the salt concentration in the red blood cells?

(1) The red blood cells will absorb water and increase in size.
(2) The red blood cells will lose water and decrease in size.
(3) The red blood cells will first absorb water, then lose water and maintain their normal size.
(4) The red blood cells will first lose water, then absorb water, and finally double in size.

28. Molecules A and B are both organic molecules found in many cells. When tested, it is found that molecule A cannot pass through a cell membrane, but molecule B easily passes through. State one way the two molecules could differ, that would account for the difference in the ability to pass through the cell membrane. [1]

29. Elodea is a plant that lives in freshwater. The diagram below represents one Elodea leaf cell in its normal freshwater environment.

Elodea cell in freshwater

Predict how the contents of the Elodea cell would change if the cell was placed in saltwater for several minutes by completing the diagram, "Elodea cell in saltwater" below. Label the location of the cell membrane. [2]

Elodea cell in saltwater

30. The photos below show two red onion cells viewed with the high power of a compound light microscope. Describe the steps that could be used to make cell A resemble cell B using a piece of paper towel and an eyedropper or a pipette without removing the coverslip. [3]

31. An indicator for a protein is added to a solution that contains protein and to a solution that does not contain protein. State one way, other than the presence or absence of protein, that the two solutions may differ after the indicator has been added to both. [1]

Glossary

Glossary items with asterisk are required vocabulary for the Regents Examination.

*abiotic nonliving parts of the environment

acid/acidic a compound that releases hydrogen ions when dissolved in water; a substance, such as vinegar, with a sour taste. Any pH below 7 indicates an acid, the lower the pH, the stronger the acid. The lowest pH possible is pH 0. Strong acids are usually harmful to living cells.

acid rain rain that is more acidic than normal

*active transport the process by which cells use energy to transport molecules through the cell membrane from areas of low concentration to areas of high concentration

*adaptive value any trait that helps an organism survive and reproduce under a given set of environmental conditions

agarose a gel-like substance used in bacterial cultures

*AIDS (<u>a</u>cquired <u>i</u>mmuno<u>d</u>eficiency <u>s</u>yndrome) the disease that results when the HIV virus attacks the human immune system

*allergy a condition in which a person's immune system is overly sensitive to environmental substances that are normally harmless

*amino acid any one of several building blocks of protein

animal a complex, multicellular organism with specialized tissues and organs, but no cell walls; a heterotroph that obtains energy by consuming other organisms

*antibiotic a medicine produced by microorganisms used to destroy pathogens in humans and domestic animals

*antibody (pl. **antibodies**) a protein, produced by the immune system, that either attacks invading pathogens or marks them for killing

*antigen a molecule found on the outer surfaces of cells that the immune system recognizes as either part of the body or an outside invader

antihistamine a substance that reduces the effects of histamines and the symptoms they cause

artificial selection the process of breeding two organisms with desirable characteristics to produce offspring that have the advantages of both parents

*asexual reproduction a method of reproduction in which all the genes passed on to the offspring come from a single individual or parent

*assumption something accepted as true that may or may not actually be true

*ATP (<u>a</u>denosine <u>tri</u>phosphate) a compound that stores energy in cells

*autotroph an organism that produces its own food; the source of energy for all other living things on Earth

*bacterium (pl. **bacteria**) any one of many single-celled organisms without a distinct nucleus

*balance a tool that measures mass by comparing the unknown mass of an object with an object of known mass

base a compound that produces hydroxide ions when dissolved in water, raising the pH above 7; the higher the pH, the stronger the base; strong bases are usually harmful to living cells

*bias a tendency to favor something; prejudice

*biochemical process a chemical process that occurs in a living thing

*biodiversity the variety of species in an area

biome large groups of ecosystems with similar climates and organisms; examples include the tundra, taiga, temperate forest, chaparral, tropical rain forest, desert, temperate grassland, tropical savanna grassland, and polar and high-mountain ice

*biosphere all of Earth's ecosystems, collectively; the biologically inhabited portions of Earth, including all of the water, land, and air in which organisms survive

*biotechnology the combination of technology and biological sciences

*biotic the living parts of the environment

*body cells non-reproductive cells in an individual such as skin, liver, and muscle cells; body cells contain the full number of chromosomes typical of the species

*bond the chemical link between atoms that hold molecules together

calibrate to adjust the scale of a measurement tool

*carnivore an organism that survives by eating animals

*carrying capacity the largest population of any single species that an area can support

*catalyst a substance that can speed up the rate of a chemical reaction without being changed or used up during the reaction

*cell the basic unit of structure and function that makes up all organisms

*cell membrane the thin boundary between the cell and its environment

*cellular respiration the process in which nutrients are broken apart, releasing the chemical energy stored in them

Celsius a temperature scale based on 100 equal units, with 0 as the freezing point of water and 100 as the boiling point of water

*chloroplast the green organelle that contains chlorophyll; where photosynthesis takes place

chlorophyll the molecules in chloroplasts that help convert light energy to chemical bond energy

*chromatography a laboratory technique used to separate mixtures of molecules

*chromosome a thick, threadlike structure that contains genetic information in the form of DNA

*circulation the flow of materials within a cell as well as between parts of a multicellular organism

classify to group things based upon their similarities

climax community a relatively diverse and stable ecosystem that is the end result of succession

*clone an organism that is genetically identical to the organism from which it was produced

*cloning a technique used to make identical organisms

*community a combination of all the different populations that live and interact in the same environment

*competition the struggle between organisms for the same limited resources in a particular area

*compound light microscope a tool that uses more than one lens and a light source to magnify an object

*conclusion the decision made about the outcome of an experiment; usually based on how well the actual result matches the predicted result

*consumer an organism that obtains its energy from producers

*control that group in an experiment in which everything—except the variable to be tested—is identical; the standard of comparison in an experiment

*controlled experiment an experiment in which all variables—except for the one being tested—are exactly the same

coverslip a thin slice of glass that covers the specimen on a slide

*cytoplasm the jellylike substance that is between the cell membrane and the nucleus and that contains specialized structures

*data the results of specific trials or tests completed during experiments

*decomposer an organism, generally a bacterium or fungus, that consumes dead organisms and organic waste

decomposition the process whereby dead organisms, as well as the wastes produced by living organisms, are broken down into their raw materials and returned to the ecosystem

*deforestation forest destruction that results from human activity

*dependent variable the part of an experiment that is changed to test a hypothesis

depletion a serious decline or reduction

detrimental damaging; harmful

*development the changes that occur from the fertilized egg to a complete individual; occurs by mitosis and differentiation of cells

deviation a change from normal circumstances

*dichotomous key a guide that compares pairs of observable traits to help the user identify an organism

*differentiation the process that transforms developing cells into specialized cells with different structures and functions

*diffusion the movement of molecules from areas of high concentration to areas of low concentration

*digestion the process that breaks down large food molecules into simpler molecules that the organism can use

*direct harvesting the destruction of an organism, or the removal of an organism from its habitat

*disease a condition, other than injury, that prevents the body from working as it should

*dissection the act of cutting apart a dead organism to examine its internal structure

*DNA (deoxyribonucleic acid) the material found in all cells that contains genetic information about that organism

*dynamic equilibrium the constant small corrections that normally occur to keep an organism's internal environment within the limits needed for survival

*ecological niche the specific role played by an organism or a population of organisms in the ecosystem

*ecological succession the process by which an existing community is replaced by another community

*ecology the study of how living things interact with one another and with their environment

*ecosystem all the living and nonliving things that interact in a specific area; a subdivision of the environment

*egg a sex cell produced by a female

*electronic balance a balance that measures mass automatically

*electrophoresis a tool that allows scientists to separate mixtures of molecules according to size

*element a substance consisting of only one kind of atom

*embryo an organism in the early stages of development (prior to birth)

endocrine glands various hormone-producing glands that secrete substances directly into the blood or lymph

endoplasmic reticulum an organelle that transports proteins and other materials from one part of the cell to another

*energy flow the movement of energy through an ecosystem

*energy pyramid a diagram showing how food energy moves through the ecosystem

*environment every living and nonliving thing that surrounds an organism

environmental impact statement a statement that includes an analysis of how a new project or technology might affect the environment

*enzymes proteins that speed up the rate of chemical reactions in living things

*equilibrium a state of balance and stability

estrogen a hormone (produced by the ovaries) that controls female sexual development and the reproductive process

*evidence support for the idea that something is true

*evolution the process by which species have changed over time

*excretion the removal of all the wastes produced by the cells of the body

*experiment a series of trials or tests that are done to support or refute a hypothesis

*expressed the way that an unseen gene is seen in an organism as an actual physical trait

*extinction the disappearance of all members of a species from Earth

Fallopian tubes that part of the female reproductive system where the egg cell is fertilized by the sperm cell; also called oviducts

*feedback mechanism a cycle in which the output of a system either modifies or reinforces the first action taken by the system

*fertilization the process that combines a sperm cell and an egg cell

*fetus the unborn, developing young of an animal during the later stages of development

*finite limited; able to be used up; opposite of infinite

flow of energy the movement of energy through an ecosystem

*food chain a representation that identifies the specific feeding relationships among organisms

*food web a representation of many interconnected food chains that shows the feeding relationships among producers, consumers, and decomposers

forceps a tool used mainly during dissection to lift out small parts, to move structures, and to pry parts open

*fossil the preserved remains of ancient organisms

*fossil fuel a fuel, such as coal and gas, that comes from the remains of organisms that lived millions of years ago

*fossil record a collection of fossils used to represent Earth's history

*fungus (pl. fungi) the kingdom of organisms that are mostly multicellular, have cell walls made of chitin, and are heterotrophic

*gamete an egg or sperm cell; a sex cell

*gas exchange the process of obtaining oxygen from the environment and releasing carbon dioxide

*gene (pl. genes) a segment of DNA (on a chromosome) that contains the code for a specific trait

*gene expression see *expressed;* the result of activated genes

*genetic engineering a set of technologies that humans use to alter the genetic instructions of an organism by substituting DNA molecules

*genetic recombination the formation of a new combination of genes during sexual reproduction

*genetic variation the normal differences found among offspring

*geologic time Earth's history as revealed by layers of rock

*global warming a increase in Earth's average surface temperature caused by an increase in greenhouse gases

*glucose a sugar that is a major source of energy for cells

*graduated cylinder a tool used to measure the volume of a liquid

greenhouse effect the trapping of heat by gases in the atmosphere

greenhouse gas an atmospheric gas that traps heat

growth an increase in the size or number of cells

*guard cells specialized cells that control the opening and closing of the pores on the surface of a leaf

*habitat the place where an animal or plant lives

*herbivore an organism that eats only plants

*heredity the passing of traits from parent to offspring

*heterotroph organism that cannot make its own food; a consumer

histamine a chemical that is released as the immune system's reaction to an allergy

*homeostasis the ability of an organism to maintain a stable internal environment even when the external environment changes

*hormone a chemical produced in the endocrine glands

*host the organism in a parasitic relationship that provides a home and/or food for the parasite

hot water bath in the science laboratory, usually a large beaker of water heated on a hot plate; used to heat test tubes that contain a flammable liquid, such as alcohol

humerus the long bone in the upper part of the arm

*hypothesis a statement that predicts a relationship between cause and effect in a way that can be tested

*immune system the body's primary defense against disease-causing pathogens

*immunity the body's ability to destroy pathogens before they cause disease

*independent variable a factor that might influence the dependent variable in an experiment

*indicator a substance that changes color when it encounters certain chemical conditions

*industrialization the process of converting an economy into one in which large-scale manufacturing is the primary economic base

*inference a conclusion or deduction based on observations

infinite without limits or bounds

*inorganic a type of molecule that does not contain both carbon and hydrogen but can contain any other combination of elements

*insulin a hormone that prompts glucose to move from the blood into body cells, resulting in a lower glucose level in the blood

*limiting factor any factor in the environment that limits the size of a population

lipid any one of a group of organic compounds that includes oils, fats, and waxes

*magnification the ability of a microscope to make an object appear larger

*mass a measure of the quantity of matter in an object

*meiosis the process that results in the production of sex cells (sperm and egg)

*meniscus the curved surface at the top of a column of liquid

*metabolism all the chemical reactions that occur within the cells of an organism

*metric ruler a tool used to measure the length of an object

*microbe any microscopic organism

micrometer a unit of length equal to one millionth of a meter

*microscope a tool that uses a lens or a combination of lenses to magnify an object

*mitochondria pod-shaped organelles that contain enzymes used to extract energy from nutrients

*mitosis the process that divides the cell's nucleus into two, each with a complete set of genetic material from the parent cell

*model a representation used to explain or demonstrate a process or structure; also used to predict what might occur in a new situation

molecule a particle in which two or more atoms combine to form a single unit; the smallest unit of a compound

muscular system a body system comprised of tissue that contracts when it is stimulated; the combination of muscles that enables the body to move

*mutation any alteration in the sequence of DNA

*natural selection the process by which the organisms that are best adapted to a specific environment survive and produce more offspring than organisms that are not as well adapted

neutral a solution with a pH of 7 that is neither acidic nor basic; the tissues of many living things maintain a pH within 1 or 2 units of this neutral point

*niche the specific role played by an organism in its ecosystem

nitrogen cycle the movement of nitrogen from the atmosphere to the soil and organisms and then back to the atmosphere

nitrogen fixation the process by which nitrogen forms compounds that can be used by living things

*nonrenewable resource any resource, such as fossil fuels and minerals, that cannot be replaced

*nuclear fuel an energy source that results from splitting atoms

*nucleus a large structure within a cell that controls the cell's metabolism and stores genetic information, including chromosomes and DNA

nucleic acids large, complex organic molecules that contain the instructions cells need to carry out their life processes

nutrient a substance that provides the body with the materials and energy needed to carry out the basic life of cells

objective one of the lenses of a microscope

*observation any information that is collected with any of the senses

ocular the eyepiece lens of a microscope

*opinion ideas people have that may or may not be based in fact

optimum the most favorable condition

*organ a body structure made of different kinds of tissues combined to perform a specific function

*organ system several organs that work together to perform a major function in the body

*organelle a structure within the cell that carries out a specific function

*organic term used to describe molecules that contain both hydrogen and carbon

*organic compound a compound that contains both hydrogen and carbon

*ovary (pl. ovaries) the organ of the human female reproductive system that produces an egg cell, the female gamete

*overproduction the potential for a species to increase its numbers beyond the area's carrying capacity

oviduct the part of the female reproductive system where the egg cell is fertilized by the sperm

oxygen-carbon dioxide cycle the movement of oxygen and carbon dioxide between living things and the environment

*ozone shield the layer of ozone gas in the upper atmosphere that protects Earth from some of the sun's radiation *pancreas an endocrine organ that secretes insulin

*parasite an organism that survives by living and feeding on other organisms

parasitic relationship an arrangement in which one organism lives in or on a host organism, deriving some or all of its nourishment from the host, to the host's detriment

*pathogen an organism that invades the body, causing disease

*peer review the process by which scientists carefully examine the work of other scientists to look for possible flaws in their experimental design or their interpretation of results

*pH a measure of whether a substance is acidic, neutral, or basic

*photosynthesis the process by which some organisms are able to capture light energy and use it to make food from carbon dioxide and water

pioneer species the first organisms to become established in a new habitat

pipette a laboratory tool that looks like a slender tube but works something like an eyedropper

*placenta the organ that enables nutrients and oxygen to pass from the mother's blood to the fetus, and waste products to pass from the fetus to the mother's blood

plant any complex, multicellular organism that obtains energy through photosynthesis and consists of cell walls and specialized tissues and organs

poaching illegally capturing or killing an organism

*pollution a harmful change in the chemical makeup of the soil, water, or air

*population all the individuals of a single species that live in a specific area

*predator an animal that hunts and kills other animals for food

predator-prey relationship the connection between predators and prey that limits the growth of both populations

*prey an animal that is hunted and killed by predators

primary succession the first group of communities that moves into a previously lifeless habitat

*producer an organism that makes its own food from light energy and inorganic materials

*progesterone a hormone associated with sexual development and the reproductive system

proportion the relationship of one thing to another in terms of size, number, amount, or degree

protist a single-celled organism with both its genetic materials and its organelles enclosed in membranes

quarantine confined isolation

radius one of the two long bones of the lower forearm

*receptor molecule certain protein molecules in the cell membrane that can receive chemical messages from other cells

*recombination the additional mixing of genetic material from a sperm and egg which results in a unique combination of genes

refute to disprove

*replicate to copy

*renewable resource Earth's resources, such as our food supply and solar energy, which, given time, can be replaced

*research plan the initial stage of an experiment that involves finding background information, developing a hypothesis, and devising an experimental method for testing the hypothesis

*respiration the process by which the chemical bond energy stored in nutrients is released for use in cells

*reproduction the process by which organisms produce new organisms of the same type

*ribosome one of the tiny structures in the cell that is the site of protein production

rider one of the devices that is moved along the beam of a balance

*scavenger a carnivore that feeds on the bodies of dead organisms

science a way of learning about the natural world and the knowledge gained through that process

*scientific literacy a basic knowledge of the natural world combined with an understanding of the diverse ways that scientists gain knowledge

scientific theory a concept, which has been tested and confirmed in many different ways, that explains a wide variety of observations

secondary succession a type of change that occurs when a disturbance empties an existing habitat without destroying the soil

*selective breeding the process of choosing a few organisms with desirable traits to serve as the parents of the next generation

sensor a structure that reacts to stimuli by sending a nerve impulse to the brain

*   **sex cell** an egg (female) or a sperm (male)

*   **sexual reproduction** a method of reproduction that involves two parents to produce offspring that are genetically different from either parent

sibling a brother or sister

*   **simple sugar** the result of the digestion of starches. Glucose is a simple sugar.

skeletal system the body system that contains the bones, provides shape and support, and protects internal organs

smog a kind of air pollution that results when certain pollutants react with sunlight

*   **species** a group of organisms that share certain characteristics and can mate with one another, producing fertile offspring

sperm the male sex cell

splice to join two things together

*   **stain** a chemical used to make cell structures more visible when viewed under a microscope

steady state the condition in which something remains relatively constant in spite of minor fluctuations

*   **stereoscope** a microscope that uses two eyepieces; often used for dissections; also called a dissecting microscope

*   **stimulus** (pl. **stimuli**) any change in the environment that causes an organism to react

stomata tiny pores found on the underside of most leaves

*   **subunit** the section of a DNA molecule that contains a sugar, a phosphate, and a base

symbiotic a kind of long-term association between members of different species in which at least one species benefits and neither species is harmed

*   **synthesis** a life process that involves combining simple substances into more complex substances

tare button a function on an electronic balance that returns the mass reading to zero

*   **technology** all of the practical scientific knowledge that has been used to meet human needs

*   **template** the pattern for a new molecule

*   **testes** the male reproductive organ that produces sperm and the hormone testosterone

*   **testosterone** a hormone associated with male sexual development and reproduction

*   **theory** an explanation, supported by many observations and/or experiments, that can be used to accurately explain related occurrences

*   **thermal pollution** a kind of water pollution in which the temperature of the water increases

*   **tissue** a group of specialized cells that perform a specific function

toxic poisonous

*   **trade-off** an exchange or agreement made to reach a compromise

*   **trait** a characteristic that is passed from parent to offspring through the genes

transpiration the process whereby plants absorb water through their roots and eliminate it through tiny pores on the undersides of their leaves

*   **triple-beam balance** a tool, with a single pan and three bars calibrated in grams, used to measure mass

tumor a clump of cells that develops when cancerous cells divide uncontrollably

ulna one of the two long bones in the lower forearm

*   **uterus** the organ, in female animals, where the embryo develops into a fetus

*   **vaccine** a substance made of weakened, killed, or partial pathogens and designed to protect the body from future invasions of that pathogen

*   **vacuole** storage sacs within the cytoplasm of a cell that may contain either wastes or useful materials, such as water or food

vertebrate an animal with a backbone

*   **virus** a nonliving particle of protein and genetic material that reproduces by invading the cell of a living organism

*   **volume** the space occupied by something

*   **water cycle** the process by which water continuously moves from Earth's surface to the atmosphere and back

*   **zygote** the cell that results from the joining of the egg and sperm

passenger pigeons 128–129
pathogens 33–34
peer review 157
pest control
    DDT resistance 91
    hormonal 71
pests 129
pH
    of acid rain 133
    effect on enzymes 26–27
    paper 26, 185
photosynthesis 20–22
placenta 69–71, 76
plants
    observing specimens 179
pollution 124, 132
    air 133–135
    thermal 133
    water 132–134
populations 99–100, 110
    and environmental
    limits 100–101
    and evolution 82
    and food chains 104
    growth 125–126
    interactions 102–104
predators 100, 103, 110
pregnancy 69–71, 77
prey 99, 103, 110
producers 103–104, 107
progesterone 69–70
proteins 21, 47–48, 50
    and electrophoresis 173–174
    enzymes 23, 25–26, 47–48
    synthesis 48

rain forests 128
receptor molecules 8
recycling 123–124, 132
    nutrients in ecosystems 125
replication
    of DNA 47
reproduction 12–13, 60–72
    asexual 45, 60–61
    defined 3
    and evolution 82–83

    human 69–70
    sexual 12–13, 45, 60–61
reproductive system 12, 69–70
reproductive technology 71–72
research plans 151–153
resources 122–123, 126
    nonrenewable 123
    renewable 123
respiration 11, 20, 23–24. *See also*
cell respiration
respiratory system 11
results, experimental 155–157
ribosomes 5

safety
    equipment 180
    laboratory 180–181
    with microscopes 172
scavengers 104
science
    definition of 146
    inquiry 146–157
    skills 146–157
scientific literacy 149
selective breeding 52–53, 82
sex cells 61, 63–65
    and evolution 86
sexual reproduction 12–13,
45, 60–61
skeletal system 11
skills
    laboratory 166–168
    microscope 170–171
    in science 146–157
slide preparation 172
smog 134
soil formation 124
species 60, 83, 89
    endangered 71, 88, 174
    extinction 91
    imported 129
    loss 136
    nonnative 129
    roles in ecosystems 102–103,
    136
sperm cell 61, 65, 69, 86

staining slides 172, 175
starch 21, 23
statistics 156
stereoscope 170
stimulus-response 30–31
succession, ecological 112–113
synthesis 3, 8, 22
    as life process 3
    of proteins 48
systems, body
    defined 4
    human 10–13

technology 131, 136
temperature
    body 30–31
    effect on enzymes 26
testosterone 69–70
thermal pollution 133
tissues 4
toxic wastes 132
traits, genetic 44–45, 48
transplants, organ 35

ultrasound 72
ultraviolet radiation 135
uterus 69

vaccines 34–35
vacuoles 5, 13, 173
variables
    dependent 152–153, 155
    independent 152–153, 155
variation, genetic 65, 67
    and evolution 83–84, 86–88, 91
    sources of 86
viruses 3, 33–34

water
    pollution 132–134
    as resource 132
water cycle 124–125
wet mount slides 172
white blood cells 34–35

zygotes 67

Acknowledgments

Photographs:
Every effort has been made to secure permission and provide appropriate credit for photographic material. The publisher deeply regrets any omission and pledges to correct errors called to its attention in subsequent editions.

Unless otherwise acknowledged, all photographs are the property of Pearson Education, Inc.

Photo locators denoted as follows: Top (T), Center (C), Bottom (B), Left (L), Right (R), Background (Bkgd)

Cover Betty Shelton/Shutterstock **i** Betty Shelton/Shutterstock; **66** Comstock Images/Thinkstock; **91** DK Images; **123** DK Images; **173** (B) Comstock Images/Thinkstock, (CR) Duncan Smith/Photodisc/Thinkstock; **178** (R) Comstock Images/Thinkstock, (L) Crestock.

Regents Exams: January 2018: 6 (R) Jerry Shulman/SuperStock; **16 (C)** GK Hart/Vikki Hart/Getty Images; **16 (L)** Alexey Stiop/Shutterstock; **August 2017: 18 (L)** Toby Talbot/AP Images; **18 (R)** Don Ryan/AP Images; **June 2017: 4** Courtesy of the Indiana State Museum and Historic Sites; **22 (L)** Click Candy/Shutterstock; **January 2017 10** Adapted from: U.S. Dept. of Agriculture: Roger A. Morse and Nicholas W. Calderone, Cornell University; **August 2016 22, 24** Pierre Constant; **June 2016 21** markku murto/art/Alamy Stock Photo; **22** ©James Hager/Robert Harding/Getty Images

Text:
Grateful acknowledgment is made to the following for copyrighted material:

164 Excerpt from "Patients to Test Tumor Fighter" by The Associated Press. Used by permission of The Associated Press.

Regents Exams: January 2018: 9 Adapted from Genetic diversity and population structure of the endangered marsupial Sarcophilus harrisii (Tasmanian devil), Figure 2, Webb Miller et al. PNAS 2011;108:30:12348 12353, National Academy of Sciences. Used with permission.; **August 2017: 18** Jeff Barnard, US advances plan to kill barred owls in Northwest, July 24, 2013, Wright's Media o/b/o Associated Press. Used by permission.; **June 2017: 7(R)** Adapted from: Colin R. Roy, H. Peter Gies & Graeme Elliott, Ozone Depletion, Nature volume 347, pages 235–236 (20 September 1990), Springer Nature; **7 (L)** Adapted from University of California Museum of Paleontology, Understanding Evolution. Used with permission.; **12** Data from University of Illinois At Urbana-Champaign. Greater Prairie Chicken Appears on Comeback Trail in Illinois. ScienceDaily. ScienceDaily, 30 November 1998.; **14** Adapted from: Biology: A Community Context, W. H. Leonard and J. Penick, 1998, McGraw-Hill Education; **17** A Catalog of Cancer Genes That's Done, or Just a Start, By Carl Zimmer, Feb. 6, 2014. New York Times.; **22** Based on BenchPrep.com/blog/APBiology-evolution-part-1

Note: Every effort has been made to locate the copyright owner of material reproduced in this component. Omissions brought to our attention will be corrected in subsequent editions.

New York Regents Examinations

The following examinations are actual Regents Examinations prepared by the New York State Education Department. They are provided here to give teachers and students a clear idea of the format and content of the Regents Examination for The Living Environment. The tests were given to students taking The Living Environment Course. The content of this book is designed to provide specifically what you need to review for The Living Environment Regents Examination.

Using the Regents Examinations

The best way to use these examinations is to take the entire test after you have reviewed the course content. Taking these tests as practice before your review may be both discouraging and of little value. Instead, use the tests to determine if you have reviewed enough to do well on the Regents Examination and to determine where further review will be most helpful.

Do not look up any information or answers while you take the examinations. Answer each question just as you would during a real test. As you take the Examination, use the margin of the paper to note any question where you are just guessing. Leave the more difficult questions for last, but be sure to answer each question. Every point counts so do not skip over a long question that is only worth a point or two. A long question could be easier than it looks and may make the difference between an A or a B or between passing or failing.

When you finish, have your teacher score your Examination and help you determine the areas where you need the most work. Also review the "guesses" you noted in the margin to find out what you need to study to ensure that you will be able to answer similar questions on the next test. Once you have determined your weaknesses, you can focus your review on those topics in this book.

Reviewing the areas where you know the least will give you the best chance of improving your final score. Spending time on areas where you are doing quite well will not produce much improvement in your total score, but it is still important if time permits.

Part A

Answer all questions in this part. [30]

Directions (1–30): For *each* statement or question, record on the separate answer sheet the *number* of the word or expression that, of those given, best completes the statement or answers the question.

1 Which organisms and set of characteristics are correctly paired?
 (1) fungi—carry out photosynthesis and heterotrophic nutrition
 (2) plants—carry out respiration and autotrophic nutrition
 (3) decomposers—carry out photosynthesis and autotrophic nutrition
 (4) animals—carry out autotrophic nutrition and heterotrophic nutrition

2 Humans have an effect on ecosystems when they use native grasslands or forested areas for farming or urban use. One *negative* effect of these changes on the ecosystem is that there will be
 (1) less biodiversity
 (2) more homes
 (3) successful economic growth
 (4) increased food production

3 The diagram below represents structures found in the female reproductive system.

If the areas labeled *A* were completely blocked on both sides, the most likely result would be that
 (1) egg and estrogen production would stop
 (2) sperm and insulin production would stop
 (3) fertilization would not occur
 (4) an embryo would develop

4 Scientists have studied oceanic plastic garbage "patches" around the world. These are areas that accumulate plastic garbage from coastal regions. Their environmental effect ranges from killing sea life to blocking sunlight from reaching photosynthetic organisms. Without a change in human plastic usage, new garbage patches will continue to form. Which human activity would most directly *reduce* the amount of plastic garbage that enters the ocean?
 (1) Ban the production and usage of all bags made from recycled plastic.
 (2) Clean up plastic trash from shorelines, rivers, and other waterways that flow into the oceans.
 (3) Manufacture fewer reusable water bottles, so that people will be more likely to use disposable ones.
 (4) Implement a glass bottle deposit system to discourage people from recycling plastic bottles.

5 Monarch butterflies migrate from the U.S. and Canada to Mexico every winter. Over the past 10 years, there has been a drastic decrease in the number of monarch butterflies. Scientists have estimated that the population may have decreased from about 1 billion to 35 million. Which action would *not* be considered a reason for the decline in monarch butterfly populations?
 (1) illegal deforestation
 (2) extreme temperature changes
 (3) decreasing food supplies
 (4) habitat preservation

6 Finches on the Galapagos Islands express a variety of traits. Variability in the offspring of these finches is a result of
 (1) mutation and cloning
 (2) meiosis and mutation
 (3) mitosis and asexual reproduction
 (4) mitosis and genetic recombination

7 Exposure to certain environmental toxins, such as pesticides, may reduce fertility in males by interfering with their ability to produce gametes. These toxins are most likely having an effect on the

(1) testes and progesterone
(2) ovaries and testosterone
(3) ovaries and estrogen
(4) testes and testosterone

8 Which statement best describes an important process carried out by structure *X*?

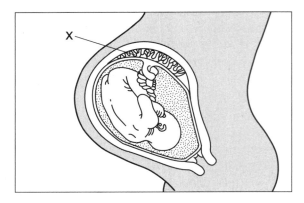

(1) Milk passes from the mother to the fetus.
(2) Materials are exchanged between fetal and maternal blood.
(3) Maternal blood is converted into fetal blood.
(4) Oxygen diffuses from fetal blood to maternal blood.

9 Traditional lightbulbs are only 10% efficient. Ninety percent of the energy they use is converted to heat. Modern lightbulbs are much more efficient, but may cost three times as much as traditional lightbulbs. Consumers who switch to modern lightbulbs are most likely

(1) spending more money for no good reason
(2) trying to stop pollution of the oceans
(3) trading a short-term cost for long-term savings
(4) helping traditional lightbulb factories employ people

10 Many oak trees are cut down and removed from an oak-hickory forest. A likely result of the direct harvesting of the oak species would be the

(1) disruption of natural cycles
(2) conservation of these natural forest resources
(3) recycling of all the nutrients in the forest
(4) prevention of the extinction of animals native to the area

11 A sequence of events is represented in the diagram below.

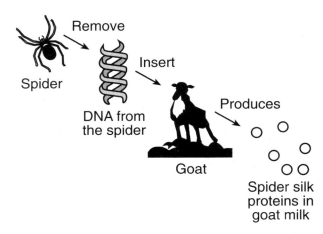

Which statement best describes a result of the process?

(1) The spider from which the DNA sample was obtained can no longer produce spider silk.
(2) The goat milk now contains DNA molecules made of spider silk proteins.
(3) Both the spider and the goat can now produce both spider silk and goat milk.
(4) Spider silk proteins can now be produced in large quantities without killing spiders to obtain them.

12 Which change is an example of a response to a stimulus?

(1) The pupil of an eye decreases in size in bright light.
(2) A leaf absorbs sunlight in the morning.
(3) The water level of a pond rises on a rainy day.
(4) A dead tree decays after many years.

January '18   Regents Examination

13 After feeding at the surface of the ocean during the day, many ocean organisms migrate to deeper waters. While there, they release ammonia in their urine. Many bacteria use the nitrogen from the ammonia as they make amino acids, which eventually end up in food chains on both land and water. These amino acids may even be used in humans. Which statement best explains these observations?

(1) Chemical elements, including nitrogen, pass through food webs and are combined and recombined in different ways.
(2) Chemical elements, including nitrogen, are removed from food webs and eliminated from ecosystems.
(3) Nitrogen is transferred directly from bacteria to humans.
(4) All elements in the ocean remain there and are not transferred to other ecosystems.

14 Which statement describes an event that would most severely disrupt the process of ecological succession in an area?

(1) The season changes from spring into summer.
(2) Native plants are planted in an abandoned field.
(3) Plants and animals begin to colonize a newly formed volcanic island.
(4) A dam is built on a river to form a reservoir.

15 The processes of diffusion and active transport are both used to

(1) break down molecules to release energy
(2) move molecules into or out of cells of the body
(3) bring molecules into cells when they are more concentrated outside of the cell
(4) move molecules against a concentration gradient, using ATP molecules

16 Botulinum toxin is a substance that can cause paralysis in humans. The effects of the toxin are due to the blocking of a signaling molecule that is necessary for communication between nerve cells. The toxin most likely interferes with the normal functioning of a

(1) chromosome   (3) receptor
(2) DNA molecule   (4) digestive hormone

17 The bar graph below shows the number of species in four pond ecosystems.

Number of Species in Four Pond Ecosystems

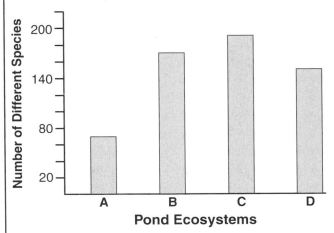

Based on this information, which ecosystem is likely to be the most stable?

(1) A   (3) C
(2) B   (4) D

18 The diagram below represents a marine food web.

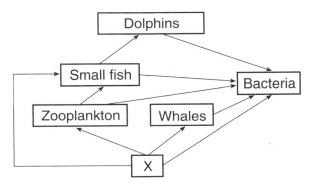

The organisms represented by X are

(1) decomposers   (3) carnivores
(2) producers   (4) scavengers

19 When rain forests are cut down, there is a

(1) loss of fossil fuels that could be used by industry
(2) release of excess oxygen to the atmosphere
(3) release of chemicals which cause helpful mutations
(4) loss of genetic material available for research

20 Scientists who study rock formations in caves describe some of the formations as "living rock" because, under certain conditions, they increase in size. Which statement would best dispute the claim that these rock formations are living?

(1) Rocks are not composed of cells, while living organisms are.
(2) Rocks perform complex metabolic processes, but cannot grow.
(3) Rocks cannot reproduce sexually.
(4) Rocks remain stable in a wide range of physical conditions.

21 Carbon dioxide and oxygen are important resources in ecosystems and are

(1) recycled through the activity of living and nonliving systems
(2) stored in the animals of the ecosystem
(3) lost due to the activities of decomposers
(4) released by the process of photosynthesis

22 Before they can pass from a parent cell to its offspring cells, the inherited instructions that a human cell carries must first be

(1) moved into the nucleus
(2) broken down and made into DNA molecules
(3) used to make specific protein molecules that form genes
(4) accurately replicated

23 Eye color, hair color, and skin color often vary from person to person and even within a family. One explanation is that

(1) the glucose units in a DNA molecule are often rearranged
(2) the genetic material of the female parent has the most influence on offspring
(3) the inherited traits of individuals are determined by different gene combinations
(4) some extra parts of genetic material are often gained during fertilization

24 Organic compounds are used as building blocks for

(1) water, DNA, and starches
(2) water, proteins, and oxygen
(3) proteins, DNA, and carbon dioxide
(4) proteins, starches, and fats

25 Scientists have developed the ability to manufacture hormones, such as human growth hormone, using bacteria. One benefit of this new technology is that

(1) scientists can use only one type of bacteria
(2) bacteria are relatively inexpensive and reproduce quickly
(3) patients can spend more money on their medications
(4) scientists produce drugs that cause more immune reactions

26 Although all of the cells of a plant contain the same genetic material, root cells and leaf cells are *not* identical because they

(1) use different genetic bases for the synthesis of DNA
(2) use different parts of their genetic instructions
(3) select different cells to express
(4) delete different sections of their enzymes

27 During cellular respiration, what is the direct source of the energy used in the cells of consumers in the ecosystem represented below?

(1) the Sun
(2) enzymes
(3) the atoms making up inorganic molecules
(4) the chemical bonds in organic molecules

28 Which dissolved substance do aquatic animals remove from their external environment for use in cellular respiration?

(1) carbon dioxide
(2) ATP molecules
(3) oxygen molecules
(4) nitrogen gas

29 The photographs below are of two Siamese cats.

Cat Kept Outdoors

Source: Http://www.superstock.com/stock-
photos-images/662-220

The Siamese breed has a gene that controls fur color. The cat in the first photograph was kept indoors while the cat in the second photograph was kept outdoors. Which statement best explains the differences in fur color between these two cats?

(1) The cat kept indoors is older than the cat kept outdoors.
(2) The environment influenced the expression of fur color genes.
(3) The environment influenced the production of all the proteins in the cat kept outdoors.
(4) The cat kept outdoors has a gene mutation that prevents it from producing light-colored fur.

30 The diagram below represents a cell.

Which letter indicates the specific structure where most hereditary mutations occur?

(1) A   (3) C
(2) B   (4) D

Part B–1

Answer all questions in this part. [13]

Directions (31–43): For *each* statement or question, record on the separate answer sheet the *number* of the word or expression that, of those given, best completes the statement or answers the question.

Base your answers to questions 31 through 33 on the information and graphs below, and on your knowledge of biology. The diagrams below show the number of fish in a lake and the average water temperature in the lake for the months of May through October.

During certain times of the year, bears feed heavily on a population of fish in a lake. At other times of the year, the bear population feeds primarily on fruits, berries, and insects.

31 During which month would the bears in the area have the most fish available?

   (1) May   (3) August

   (2) July   (4) October

32 One of the best ways to represent the interdependence of all of the organisms in this ecosystem is

   (1) an evolutionary tree   (3) an electrophoresis gel

   (2) a food chain   (4) a food web

33 Within the fish population, variations exist in color, size, gamete production, and swimming speed. A variation that would most likely be passed on to future generations of the species is

   (1) a swimming speed that is less than that of its predators

   (2) the presence of bright, colorful markings that contrast with the lake bottom

   (3) being of a size that enables them to hide among the rocks in the lake

   (4) the production of a small number of gametes during the peak of the breeding season

Base your answers to questions 34 and 35 on the information below, and on your knowledge of biology.

Before conducting an experiment, two students gathered information about the effect of greenhouse gases on global warming. Student A found information in a newspaper article. Student B found information in several peer-reviewed scientific journals and on three websites.

34 Which statement most likely describes the reliability of the students' information?
    (1) Information gathered by student A is more reliable because newspapers are always updated to reflect the most current research.
    (2) Information gathered by student B is more reliable because some of it was gathered from peer-reviewed sources.
    (3) Information gathered by student A is more reliable because it is from a single source without conflicting information.
    (4) Information gathered by student B is more reliable because some of it was found on the internet.

35 After gathering the information, the students presented the information to their class. The class gave the students suggestions about how to continue with their experiment. How does this step benefit the investigation?
    (1) Feedback from the class will help them design a better experiment.
    (2) Feedback creates confusion, and will complicate the investigation.
    (3) The students' investigation will be unaffected because the class is not carrying out the experiment.
    (4) The investigation will be unchanged because students can use information only from published sources to design the experiment.

36 A student wondered if butterflies would show any differences in their wing color if, as caterpillars, they were grown in the dark or grown in bright white light. Which statement would be a possible hypothesis for an experiment to test this idea?
    (1) Caterpillars exposed to bright white light will show more blue and green in their wings when they become butterflies than caterpillars kept in the dark.
    (2) Will caterpillars kept in the dark have brighter wings when they become butterflies than caterpillars exposed to bright white light?
    (3) Ten caterpillars will be kept in the dark and ten caterpillars will be exposed to bright white light and allowed to develop into butterflies.
    (4) Results show that caterpillars kept in the dark and those exposed to bright white light had the same wing color when they became butterflies.

January '18 Regents Examination

37 The chart below shows the number of differences in genetic material between individuals within the same species. Scientists can use this information to determine which populations demonstrate the greatest amount of genetic diversity.

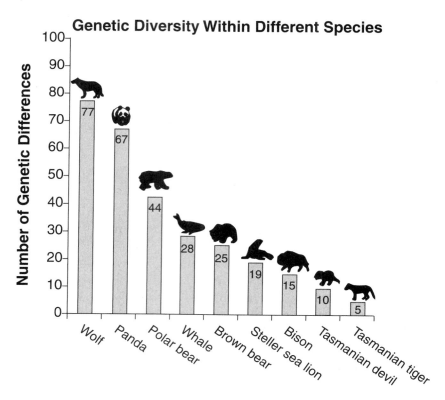

Genetic Diversity Within Different Species

Number of Genetic Differences

Wolf 77 · Panda 67 · Polar bear 44 · Whale 28 · Brown bear 25 · Steller sea lion 19 · Bison 15 · Tasmanian devil 10 · Tasmanian tiger 5

adapted from: www.pnas.org

According to the chart, which two species would be more likely to survive if their environmental conditions changed?

(1) Tasmanian tiger and Tasmanian devil
(2) brown bear and whale
(3) Tasmanian tiger and wolf
(4) panda and wolf

38 Microbeads are tiny, smooth, plastic spheres found in common household products such as facial soap. These beads, measuring from 0.0004 to 1.24 mm, roughly the size of some fish eggs, are too small to be removed by water treatment systems. Thus, they end up in rivers, lakes, and other bodies of water. The accumulation of these microbeads is an environmental concern for aquatic biologists because microbeads

(1) make the lakes and rivers cloudy and dirty, affecting their appearance
(2) may stick to some household water pipes, preventing drainage problems
(3) could be mistaken for food by some species, working their way up the food chain
(4) could clog fishing nets, affecting the ability of fishermen to catch fish

Base your answers to questions 39 and 40 on the diagrams below and on your knowledge of biology. The diagrams represent some of the systems that make up the human body.

System A

System B

System C

System D

39 Which row in the chart below correctly identifies the main function of these systems?

Row	System A	System B	System C	System D
(1)	response	excretion	circulation	digestion
(2)	movement	response	circulation	digestion
(3)	response	circulation	excretion	digestion
(4)	movement	circulation	digestion	reproduction

40 A similarity between these systems is that they all
(1) are made of cells that are identical in structure and function
(2) contain organs that work independently from other organs in that system
(3) work together to maintain a stable internal environment
(4) are separate and do not interact with other body systems

Base your answer to question 41 on the information below and on your knowledge of biology.

In China, farmers switched from growing conventional cotton, which required spraying with insecticides 15 times each year, to a genetically modified cotton variety called Bt cotton. The Bt cotton produces a protein toxic to the insects that destroy the cotton crop. Since the switch to Bt cotton, the use of chemical insecticides has decreased by 60%.

41 An advantage of growing the genetically modified Bt cotton instead of conventional cotton is that growing Bt cotton could
(1) result in an increase in populations of insects that are beneficial
(2) result in an increase in the size of insect populations that are resistant to the Bt protein
(3) lead to an increase in the survival rates of insects that eat cotton
(4) lead to an increase in the use of insecticides that protect cotton from insects

42 The diagram below represents events that occur during sexual reproduction.

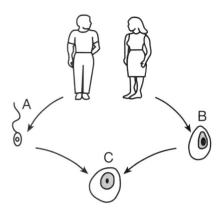

The stages labeled *A*, *B*, and *C* are necessary to ensure that the offspring will inherit

(1) half of their chromosomes from each parent
(2) double the amount of chromosomes from each parent
(3) pairs of chromosomes from each parent
(4) double the amount of chromosomes from one parent

43 A company that produces paint is planning to build a small factory in a rural community. The factory would provide many needed jobs. Before the community agrees to allow the factory to be built, the community should

(1) investigate the use of paint as a method of biological control
(2) consider just the economic advantages of building the new factory
(3) assess the risks of the new factory and compare these to the benefits
(4) insist the factory use finite resources located in the community

Answer all questions in this part. [12]

Directions (44–55): For those questions that are multiple choice, record on the separate answer sheet the *number* of the choice that, of those given, best completes each statement or answers each question. For all other questions in this part, follow the directions given and record your answers in the spaces provided in this examination booklet.

Base your answers to questions 44 through 48 on the information, diagram, and data table below and on your knowledge of biology.

The laboratory setup represented below was used to investigate the effect of light on aquatic plants. Equal amounts of a green water plant were placed in beakers with gas-collecting tubes. The beakers were placed in a temperature-controlled environment. The light source was placed at different distances from the beakers. After an hour, the amount of gas collected from the plants in each tube was measured and recorded in the data table.

Basic Setup

Gas Collected with Light Source at Different Distances from Plant

Distance of Light Source from Plant (cm)	Gas Collected in Tube (mm)
5	85
10	37
15	15
20	8
25	5

Directions (44–46): Using the information given, construct a line graph on the grid following the directions below.

44 Provide an appropriate label for the *y*-axis, including units, on the line provided. [1]

45 Mark an appropriate scale, without any breaks in the data, on each labeled axis. [1]

46 Plot the data on the grid, connect the points, and surround each point with a small circle. [1]

Example:

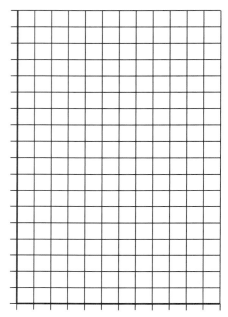

Gas Collected with Light Source at Different Distances from Plant

Distance of Light Source from Plant (cm)

Note: The answer to question 47 should be recorded on your separate answer sheet.

47 Which row in the chart below correctly identifies the variables in this experiment?

Row	Independent Variable	Dependent Variable
(1)	amount of gas collected	distance of beaker from light source
(2)	number of plants in the beaker	temperature of plant
(3)	distance of beaker from light source	amount of gas collected
(4)	minutes of exposure to the light source	rate of gas collection

48 Identify the gas being produced by the plants. [1]

_____

_____

Base your answers to questions 49 through 51 on the information below and on your knowledge of biology.

The Bionic Pancreas

Until recently, diabetics could rely only on regular blood sugar checks, medications, and low-carbohydrate diets in order to maintain their health.

Bioengineers at Boston University are working to create a bionic pancreas. The device includes a sensor implanted just beneath the skin that monitors blood sugar levels. It sends a wireless signal to a smartphone every five minutes. If the phone receives a signal that blood sugar is too low or too high, it then sends a different signal to a separate device also attached to the body. This device releases the appropriate hormone into the bloodstream to return blood sugar levels back to normal.

Note: The answer to question 49 should be recorded on your separate answer sheet.

49 According to the passage, the bionic pancreas makes corrective actions that return blood sugar levels back to normal. This artificial device helps

(1) produce more sugar
(2) break down blood cells
(3) maintain homeostasis
(4) cure their diabetes

Note: The answer to question 50 should be recorded on your separate answer sheet.

50 The corrective actions made by the bionic pancreas on a regular basis in response to changing blood sugar levels are similar to which natural biological process?

(1) a feedback mechanism
(2) an immune response
(3) biochemical digestion
(4) ATP production

51 The bionic pancreas sends a signal to a device to release hormones into the bloodstream to regulate blood sugar. Identify *one* hormone the device would most likely release. [1]

_____

_____

52 Many hormones are proteins used in cellular communication. Each hormone carries a specific message to specific target cells. State why each of these hormones is able to deliver a different message. [1]

_____

_____

53 Two different species occupy the same habitat. Identify *one* reason these two species might *not* compete. [1]

_____

_____

Base your answers to questions 54 and 55 on the diagram below and on your knowledge of biology. The diagram represents the energy in kilocalories (kcal) available at different feeding levels in a food chain.

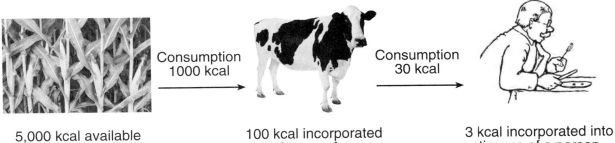

5,000 kcal available in tissues of corn → Consumption 1000 kcal → 100 kcal incorporated into tissues of a cow → Consumption 30 kcal → 3 kcal incorporated into tissues of a person

54 Complete the energy pyramid provided below by writing herbivore, plant, and carnivore in the correct locations. [1]

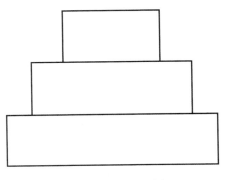

Energy Pyramid

55 Explain why there is a different amount of energy represented at each level of this energy pyramid. [1]

_____

_____

_____

Part C

Answer all questions in this part. [17]

Directions (56–72): Record your answers in the spaces provided in this examination booklet.

Base your answers to question 56–58 on the information below and on your knowledge of biology.

Reindeer Drool

The results of new research highlight interesting findings regarding reindeer and moose saliva. Both reindeer and moose feed on a type of grass called red fescue. Red fescue is usually dangerous to eat due to the presence of a fungus with which it has a mutually beneficial relationship. When the red fescue is eaten, the fungus produces a toxin that decreases blood flow in the legs of the moose and reindeer. This could result in the loss of their limbs.

Since many reindeer and moose successfully feed on red fescue, scientists wondered if their saliva gave them the ability to eat the grass without suffering from circulation problems. Scientists hypothesized that moose and reindeer saliva might detoxify the grass. To conduct their experiment, the researchers smeared reindeer and moose saliva on cut red fescue that contained the fungus. They learned that the saliva slowed the growth of this fungus and detoxified the grass. The results suggest that some animal species have evolved the ability to fight back against a plant's natural defenses.

56–58 Explain the benefit of the ability moose and reindeer have to eat red fescue grass. In your answer, be sure to:

- explain why red fescue plants with the fungus normally have an advantage over red fescue plants without the fungus [1]

- explain how the moose and reindeer saliva protects them from the harmful effects of the fungus [1]

- explain how moose and reindeer (two separate, but related, mammals) could possess the same adaptation that protects them from the toxin produced by the fungus [1]

_____

_____

_____

_____

_____

_____

59 Cancer of the ovary is not common, but when it occurs, the cancer can cause the ovary to malfunction. Identify *one* possible result of an ovary *not* performing its intended function in the body. [1]

_____

60 Several students were diagnosed with strep throat. They were all given the same antibiotic and took it for the time specified. Three weeks later, after finishing all their antibiotic, all the students except one no longer had strep throat. State *one* likely reason why the one student was still infected with strep bacteria. [1]

_____

_____

Base your answers to questions 61 and 62 on the information below and on your knowledge of biology.

Permission to use this third-party content has not been granted to Pearson. View content at nysedregents.org.

61 State *one* reason why the use of sperm from wild elephants, rather than the use of sperm from elephants in zoos in England or Austria, would be more important to the long-term survival of elephants. [1]

_____

_____

62 Identify *one* likely reason, other than poaching and hunting, for the decline of the elephant population. [1]

_____

_____

Base your answers to questions 63 through 65 on the information below and on your knowledge of biology.

Battling Cancer with T-cell Therapy

One reason that cancer is able to spread through tissues and organs is that cancer cells are actually the patient's own cells. The immune system of the patient does not recognize these cancer cells as foreign and, therefore, does not reject and destroy them.

Over the past eight years, immunologists have been developing a treatment for B-cell leukemia that involves using genetically engineered T cells to recognize and destroy B cells, all of which carry a protein, CD19. CD19 is found on the surface of both healthy and cancerous B cells. B cells are immune system cells that produce antibodies.

The procedure used in this treatment is outlined below:

1. T cells are removed from the patient with B-cell leukemia.
2. The T cells are genetically engineered to recognize the CD19 protein.
3. The patient is injected with the engineered T cells, which attach to cells with CD19 and destroy them.
4. The engineered T cells destroy both cancerous and healthy B cells.

This procedure has been successful in several patients. Currently, studies are continuing with more B-cell leukemia patients. It is hoped that the studies will be expanded to include other types of cancer, and that this treatment will be available to treat a variety of cancers in the future.

63 Explain why these specific T cells can be used for B-cell leukemia treatment. [1]

_____

_____

64 Explain why a patient needs treatments of antibodies after being injected with these modified T cells. [1]

_____

_____

65 Explain why the engineered T cells taken from one cancer patient will *not* work as a cancer treatment if injected into another patient with B-cell leukemia. [1]

_____

_____

_____

Base your answers to questions 66 through 68 on the information below and on your knowledge of biology.

Hydrothermal Vent Communities

Scientists discovered a unique hydrothermal ecosystem on the sea floor at hot-water vents thousands of feet below the ocean surface. Organisms in these deep-sea regions have no access to sunlight, so they depend on the heat, methane, and high levels of sulfur-bearing minerals found in the heated fluids in which they live. Scientists were amazed to discover vent communities able to sustain vast amounts of life. The vent organisms depend on bacteria that can use the sulfur-bearing minerals to produce organic materials. These bacteria live on rock surfaces and as free-floating blobs. Some bacteria live within and provide nutrients for an unusual species of giant tubeworms that lacks a digestive system. Snails, shrimp, and clams are among the animals that feed directly on the bacteria. Crabs feed directly on other animals in the vent community.

66 Identify *one* abiotic factor that makes the hydrothermal vent ecosystem different from other ocean ecosystems. [1]

_____

67 State the relationship that exists between the crabs and the other members of the vent community. [1]

_____

_____

68 Describe *one* way the bacteria of the hydrothermal vent community differ from plants in their ability to produce organic materials. [1]

_____

_____

January '18 Regents Examination

Base your answers to questions 69 through 72 on the information below and on your knowledge of biology.

Transgenic Salmon

Transgenic Atlantic salmon have been produced using DNA from other species of related fish. These genetically modified fish have an altered DNA "switch" that causes them to overproduce growth hormone. The transgenic Atlantic salmon grow to normal size, but they reach market size in half the time of conventional Atlantic salmon. As with most of the salmon consumed by people, the transgenic Atlantic salmon would be grown using aquatic farming methods. Scientists have expressed concern that transgenic fish can have undesirable effects on the natural environment. Fish growers would be expected to take steps to ensure that the transgenic salmon do not escape into the wild.

69 State *one* advantage genetic modification has over selective breeding when producing new varieties of animals or plants. [1]

_____

_____

70 State *one* reason the scientists altered the DNA "switch" of the Atlantic salmon to make them produce more growth hormone, rather than directly supplying the Atlantic salmon with more growth hormone. [1]

_____

_____

71 State *one undesirable* effect that escaped transgenic Atlantic salmon could have on the natural environment. [1]

_____

_____

72 State *one* benefit of raising the transgenic Atlantic salmon. [1]

_____

_____

Part D

Answer all questions in this part. [13]

Directions (73–85): For those questions that are multiple choice, record on the separate answer sheet the *number* of the choice that, of those given, best completes each statement or answers each question. For all other questions in this part, follow the directions given and record your answers in the spaces provided in this examination booklet.

Note: The answer to question 73 should be recorded on your separate answer sheet.

73 During periods of vigorous physical activity, a person's breathing and heart rates increase. This enables the cells of the body to perform more efficiently because it helps the cells to

(1) remove waste products faster
(2) store excess glucose in muscles
(3) reduce the amount of ATP produced
(4) convert more oxygen to glucose

Note: The answer to question 74 should be recorded on your separate answer sheet.

74 A step in a procedure used in the *Diffusion Through a Membrane* lab is represented in the diagram below.

Which procedure is represented in the diagram?

(1) adding distilled water to the top of a cover glass on a slide
(2) making an artificial cell
(3) adding salt solution to a specimen under the cover glass
(4) making a thin sample to prepare a slide of red onion cells

75 A student is opening and closing clothespins as part of a lab activity. The student begins to experience muscle fatigue, and the rate at which the student is opening and closing the clothespins slows. Which graph best represents the relationship between time and number of clothespin squeezes?

Base your answers to questions 76 and 77 on the information and diagram below and on your knowledge of biology. The diagram shows an experimental setup using an artificial plant cell.

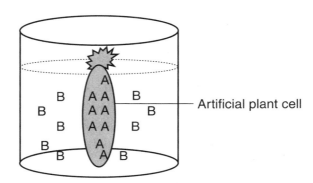

Molecules *A* and *B* are commonly found in plant cells. When tested, it was discovered that molecule *A* quickly passed through the artificial plant cell membrane. Molecule *B* did not pass through.

Note: The answer to question 76 should be recorded on your separate answer sheet.

76 The locations of molecules *A* and *B* at the beginning of the experiment are shown. Which statement best describes what was observed when the setup was examined 20 minutes later?

(1) Molecule *A* remained inside the artificial cell and molecule *B* remained outside.
(2) Only molecule *A* was found both inside and outside the artificial cell.
(3) Only molecule *B* was found both inside and outside the artificial cell.
(4) Both molecules *A* and *B* were found inside and outside the artificial cell.

77 State *one* way the two molecules could differ that would explain the difference in their ability to pass through the artificial plant cell membrane. [1]

_____

_____

_____

Base your answer to question 78 on the information and diagram below and on your knowledge of biology. The diagram shows a plant called hogweed.

Hogweed is highly toxic and has become invasive in New York State. It can cause severe burns and blisters if touched.

Permission to use this third-party content has not been granted to Pearson. View content at nysedregents.org.

78 If you were given packaged samples of hogweed plant parts, describe *one* specific procedure you could use to determine if an unknown plant might be related to hogweed. [1]

_____

_____

_____

Base your answers to questions 79 through 82 on the information and diagram below and on your knowledge of biology.

A human gene contains the following DNA base sequence: ACGCCCACCTTA

The gene mutated. It then contained the following DNA base sequence: ACGCGCACCTTA

Universal Genetic Code Chart
Messenger RNA Codons and the Amino Acids for Which They Code

	SECOND BASE				
	U	**C**	**A**	**G**	
U	UUU ⎱ PHE UUC ⎰ UUA ⎱ LEU UUG ⎰	UCU ⎫ UCC ⎬ SER UCA ⎪ UCG ⎭	UAU ⎱ TYR UAC ⎰ UAA ⎱ STOP UAG ⎰	UGU ⎱ CYS UGC ⎰ UGA ⎬ STOP UGG ⎭ TRP	U C A G
C	CUU ⎫ CUC ⎬ LEU CUA ⎪ CUG ⎭	CCU ⎫ CCC ⎬ PRO CCA ⎪ CCG ⎭	CAU ⎱ HIS CAC ⎰ CAA ⎱ GLN CAG ⎰	CGU ⎫ CGC ⎬ ARG CGA ⎪ CGG ⎭	U C A G
A	AUU ⎫ AUC ⎬ ILE AUA ⎭ AUG ⎬ MET or START	ACU ⎫ ACC ⎬ THR ACA ⎪ ACG ⎭	AAU ⎱ ASN AAC ⎰ AAA ⎱ LYS AAG ⎰	AGU ⎱ SER AGC ⎰ AGA ⎱ ARG AGG ⎰	U C A G
G	GUU ⎫ GUC ⎬ VAL GUA ⎪ GUG ⎭	GCU ⎫ GCC ⎬ ALA GCA ⎪ GCG ⎭	GAU ⎱ ASP GAC ⎰ GAA ⎱ GLU GAG ⎰	GGU ⎫ GGC ⎬ GLY GGA ⎪ GGG ⎭	U C A G

(FIRST BASE on left axis; THIRD BASE on right axis)

79 In the table below, record the mRNA codons coded for by the DNA base sequence of the mutated gene ACGCGCACCTTA. [1]

80 Then, using the Universal Genetic Code Chart, record the amino acid sequence that is coded for by the mRNA codons you placed in the table. [1]

Mutated Gene DNA Base Sequence	ACG	CGC	ACC	TTA
mRNA codons	_____	_____	_____	_____
Amino acid sequence	_____	_____	_____	_____

81 Which type of mutation is represented in the new gene?

  (1) addition   (3) inversion

  (2) deletion   (4) substitution

82 The amino acids bond together to form which type of complex molecule?

  (1) protein   (3) fat

  (2) starch   (4) sugar

83 A certain small population of finches already has an "ideal" beak type for its present environment. Describe *two* specific adaptations, other than beak type, that would contribute to the ability of these finches to survive. [1]

84 In order to determine the effect of muscle fatigue on the ability of students to squeeze a clothespin, five male students did jumping jacks for three minutes and then squeezed a clothespin as many times as possible in a minute. Three other male students ran up and down the stairs for 30 seconds and then squeezed a clothespin as many times as possible for one minute. The results of the two groups were recorded. Identify *one* change that could be made to the experiment to increase the validity of the conclusion made from these results. [1]

85 There is a group of plants, known as halophytes, that has traits that enable them to survive in salty environments. Describe *one* change, other than death, that would be observed in the cells of a plant that did *not* have these traits and was planted in a salty environment. [1]

Part A

Answer all questions in this part. [30]

Directions (1–30): For *each* statement or question, record on the separate answer sheet the *number* of the word or expression that, of those given, best completes the statement or answers the question.

1 A fruit fly is classified as a consumer rather than as a producer because it is unable to
  (1) reproduce asexually
  (2) synthesize its own food
  (3) release energy stored in organic molecules
  (4) remove wastes from its body

2 Which change is an example of maintaining dynamic equilibrium?
  (1) A plant wilts when more water is lost from the leaves than is lost by the roots.
  (2) A plant turns yellow when light levels are very low.
  (3) Insulin is released when glucose levels in the blood are high.
  (4) A person sweats when the environmental temperature is low.

3 Organisms contain compounds such as proteins, starches, and fats. The chemical bonds in these compounds can be a source of
  (1) amino acids   (3) energy
  (2) simple sugars   (4) enzymes

4 Phosphorus is necessary for the growth of healthy plants. Scientists are developing plants that can grow in phosphorus-poor soil. Some of these new varieties, produced in a lab, make extra copies of a protein that helps them obtain more phosphorus from the soil. The process being used to develop these new varieties is most likely
  (1) paper chromatography
  (2) natural selection
  (3) direct harvesting
  (4) genetic engineering

5 Which life function is *not* necessary for an individual organism to stay alive?
  (1) nutrition   (3) regulation
  (2) reproduction   (4) excretion

6 Lobsters prey on sea hares, which are marine animals. The lobsters find their prey through a sense of smell. The sea hares defend themselves by squirting ink at the lobster, as shown in the photo below. The ink sticks to the lobster, interfering with its sense of smell.

Permission to use this third-party content has not been granted to Pearson. View content at nysedregents.org.

The most likely reason the sea hare can escape is because the sea hare ink
  (1) pushes the sea hare away rapidly as the ink is expelled
  (2) blocks a receptor on certain cells in the lobster
  (3) causes the lobster to change its prey
  (4) prevents movement of the lobster

7 Which statement is an accurate description of genes?
  (1) Proteins are made of genes and code for DNA.
  (2) Genes are made of proteins that code for nitrogen bases.
  (3) DNA is made of carbohydrates that code for genes.
  (4) Genes are made of DNA and code for proteins.

8 The bobolink is a small blackbird that nests in fields of tall grass. It breeds in the summer across much of southern Canada and the northern United States. It migrates long distances, wintering in southern South America. The numbers of these birds are declining due to disruption of the areas where they live.

In order to save these birds from extinction, the best course of action would be to

(1) prevent the birds from migrating to South America

(2) encourage farmers to let their hay fields undergo succession

(3) work to protect bobolink habitats in South and North America

(4) capture all the bobolinks and keep them safe in zoos

9 A child with cystic fibrosis has an altered protein in his cells that stops chloride ions from leaving the cells. This protein most likely affects the functioning of

(1) cell membranes   (3) mitochondria
(2) nuclei   (4) ribosomes

10 Which row in the chart below shows a direct relationship that can exist between two living organisms?

Row	Relationship
(1)	producer – carnivore
(2)	predator – prey
(3)	parasite – prey
(4)	carnivore – host

11 Scientists have studied the return of plant life on Mount St. Helens ever since the volcano erupted in 1980. Wildflowers began colonizing the area, followed by shrubs and small trees. Scientists predict that it will likely take hundreds of years before the area returns to a forest dominated by fir and hemlock trees. These changes are an example of

(1) humans degrading an ecosystem by removing wildflowers

(2) the loss of genetic variation in a plant species

(3) the growth of a forest through ecological succession

(4) the biological evolution of wildflowers, shrubs, and trees

12 The most likely result of completely removing carbon dioxide from the environment of a plant is that sugar production will

(1) continue at the same rate

(2) increase and oxygen production will also increase

(3) increase and oxygen production will stay the same

(4) decrease and eventually stop

13 Before a new shopping center can be built on previously undeveloped land, the builders must submit a proposal to the local government for approval. Which statement identifies an environmental concern associated with the development of the shopping center?

(1) Building the center would decrease resources needed by local organisms.

(2) The new shopping center would increase competition with already existing businesses.

(3) Building the center would decrease the amount of pollution in the area.

(4) The new shopping center would increase the biodiversity of the area.

14 Homeowners have been encouraged to learn how to identify invasive plants and to remove them if they find them. The most likely reason for removing invasive plants is to

(1) allow only one type of native plant to grow

(2) preserve biodiversity

(3) eliminate unfamiliar food sources

(4) increase the rate of ecological succession

15 Which row in the chart below correctly pairs a human activity with its impact on the environment?

Row	Human Activity	Impact
(1)	decrease in the use of pesticides	erosion of rock in the soil
(2)	increase in housing developments	improvement in air quality
(3)	increase in human population	reduction in water usage
(4)	decrease in recycling	reduction in amount of available resources

16 The diagram below represents some steps in a procedure used in the field of biotechnology.

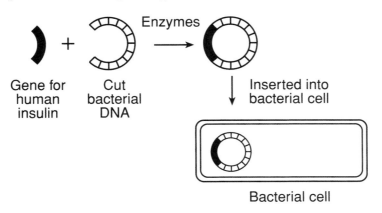

Gene for human insulin   Cut bacterial DNA   Inserted into bacterial cell

Bacterial cell

This bacterial cell can now be used to produce

(1) the bacterial gene for insulin that can be inserted into humans
(2) human genes for enzymes that can be inserted into humans
(3) insulin that can be used by humans
(4) enzymes necessary to treat human diseases

17 The graph below represents the number of brown and green beetles collected in a particular ecosystem.

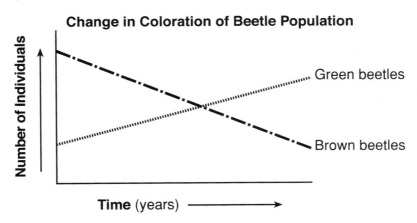

Change in Coloration of Beetle Population

Number of Individuals

Green beetles

Brown beetles

Time (years)

The change observed in the number of green and brown beetles in the population is most likely due to

(1) natural selection
(2) selective breeding
(3) gene manipulation
(4) a common ancestor

18 A reproductive system is represented in the diagram below.

Which structure is correctly paired with its reproductive function?

(1) *A* – pathway of gametes
(2) *B* – synthesis of progesterone
(3) *C* – production of sperm
(4) *D* – regulation of homeostasis

19 For centuries, humans have used resources from coastal areas and open ocean waters. An example of an activity that would promote the conservation of coastal areas and ocean resources is

(1) harvesting large numbers of different fish species
(2) allowing all-terrain vehicles access to beach areas
(3) creating protected zones of natural grasses and shrubs in beach areas
(4) encouraging the construction of factories along the ocean shoreline

20 Which activity would eventually result in a stable ecosystem?

(1) deforestation in an area to increase space for the species living there
(2) mowing a large field so it can be used for recreation
(3) allowing native plants to grow undisturbed in an abandoned field
(4) spraying pesticides on a field at the end of each growing season

21 Some states require shoppers to pay a deposit on certain beverage containers made of plastic and glass. When shoppers return the containers, their deposits are returned to them. How is this system intended to help the environment?

(1) It encourages people to buy products that do not have a deposit.
(2) It reduces the amount of money shoppers actually spend.
(3) It reduces the amount of plastics and glass put into landfills.
(4) It forces manufacturers to reduce air pollution when they are making the containers.

22 The diagram below represents a food web.

Which level contains organisms that carry out autotrophic nutrition?

(1) 1   (3) 3
(2) 2   (4) 4

23 Mad cow disease is a fatal disease that destroys brain tissue. Researchers have found that a prion protein, which is an abnormally constructed molecule, is responsible. Which statement best describes the characteristics a protein must have to function correctly?

(1) A protein is a long chain of amino acids folded into a specific shape.
(2) A protein is a long chain of simple sugars folded into a specific shape.
(3) A protein is made of amino acids synthesized into a short, circular chain.
(4) A protein is made of simple sugars synthesized into a short, circular chain.

24 The diagram below represents the results of the net movement of a specific kind of molecule across a living cell membrane.

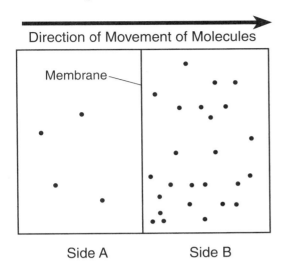

Direction of Movement of Molecules

The movement of molecules from side A to side B is an example of the process of

(1) active transport
(2) chromatography
(3) cellular respiration
(4) diffusion

25 Several companies now offer DNA "banking services," where DNA is extracted from a pet and is stored so that a "replacement pet" might be produced using cloning techniques when the original pet dies. Which statement best explains why the replacement pets that are produced in this way might *not* look or act like the original?

(1) The new animal must get the DNA from two different parents, not just one cell.
(2) Mutations could occur that change the cloned animal into a completely different species.
(3) Recombination of the cells as they are cloned will make the resulting pet act differently.
(4) The environment could influence how genes are expressed, changing how the animal looks and acts.

26 It is recommended that people avoid excessive use of tanning beds. Exposure to the radiation emitted by tanning beds can cause skin cancer. This cancer is the direct result of a

(1) change in a starch molecule
(2) mutation in the genetic material
(3) mutation in a protein
(4) change in a fat molecule

27 The diagram below represents a developing fetus in a human.

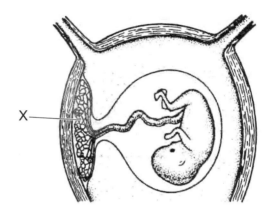

What would most likely happen if structure X were damaged in the early stages of pregnancy?

(1) The genes from the mother would not be turned on in the fetus.
(2) The nutrients necessary for development would not be able to reach the fetus.
(3) The fertilized egg would not be able to travel from the ovary to the uterus.
(4) Development would take longer since the fetus would have to synthesize nutrients.

28 The reproductive structure in a female mammal that produces sex cells is the

(1) ovary   (3) uterus
(2) testes   (4) placenta

29 Fungi are decomposers that play an important role in the maintenance of an ecosystem. The role of fungi i
important because they
   (1) synthesize energy-rich compounds that are directly used by producers
   (2) break down materials that can then be used by other organisms
   (3) limit the number of plants that can perform photosynthesis in an area
   (4) are competitors of other consumers such as herbivores

30 In 2011 and 2012, scientists working on the Banana River in Florida recorded a dramatic increase in th
number of manatee deaths. Over the past 50 years, this area has also seen the human population increas
by more than 500,000 people. It is believed that pollution from numerous sewage tanks leaked into th
water, eliminating the manatees' food source, replacing it with an alga that is toxic to the manatee. This is a
example of
   (1) a natural cycle in an ecosystem
   (2) the effect of increased biodiversity on an ecosystem
   (3) direct harvesting in an ecosystem
   (4) human actions altering ecosystems with serious consequences

GO ON TO THE NEXT PAGE ⇨

Part B–1

Answer all questions in this part. [13]

Directions (31–43): For *each* statement or question, record on the separate answer sheet the *number* of the word or expression that, of those given, best completes the statement or answers the question.

31 A student performed an experiment to see if water temperature affects the level of activity in aquatic snails. The student set up four tanks with five snails in each tank. All four of the setups were identical in every way, except for the temperature of the water. In order to make the conclusions more valid, the student could

(1) alter the pH of the water
(2) change the size of the tank
(3) carry out the experiment for a shorter period of time
(4) use a larger number of snails

32 The following events occur during sexual reproduction:

    A. mitosis
    B. meiosis
    C. fertilization
    D. birth

Which sequence represents the correct order of these events during sexual reproduction?

(1) $A \rightarrow C \rightarrow B \rightarrow D$
(2) $B \rightarrow C \rightarrow A \rightarrow D$
(3) $C \rightarrow B \rightarrow A \rightarrow D$
(4) $B \rightarrow A \rightarrow C \rightarrow D$

33 A broad body of evidence, subject to revisions, supported by different kinds of scientific investigations and often involving the contributions of scientists from different disciplines is necessary to develop

(1) an inference   (3) a theory
(2) a fact   (4) a prediction

34 The diagrams below represent portions of two genes that code for leaf structure in the same species of clover. Gene 1 was taken from the cells of a clover plant with 3 leaves and gene 2 was taken from the cells of a clover plant with 4 leaves.

The clover plant having gene 2 (4 leaves) was most likely the result of

(1) an insertion   (3) a substitution
(2) a deletion   (4) normal replication

35 Increased concern over the number of heat-related illnesses among football players has led to a possible change in uniform design. Shoulder pads were designed that constantly blew cool, dry air underneath the shoulder pads. Tests showed that the use of the device during rest and recovery periods resulted in a reduction of body temperature and heart rate. This new device would help the athlete to

(1) control the rate of muscle activity
(2) increase muscle strength
(3) maintain homeostasis
(4) eliminate the release of heat from the body

Base your answers to questions 36 and 37 on the information and data table below and on your knowledge of biology.

A student wanted to investigate the effect of light on the rate of ripening of tomatoes. She set up four pots of the same size with identical amounts of soil, water, and type of tomato plants. Each plant was exposed to a different intensity of light as shown in the table below.

Plant	Light Intensity (lumens)	
1	0	
2	1000	
3	5000	
4	10,000	

36 To report the final results, which label would be most appropriate for the third column of the data table?
(1) Height of Tomato Plants (cm)
(2) Average Ripening Time (days)
(3) Average Weight of Tomatoes per Plant (grams)
(4) Acidity of Tomatoes (pH)

37 The independent variable in this experiment is the
(1) type of tomato plant
(2) amount of soil provided
(3) color of tomatoes
(4) light intensity

GO ON TO THE NEXT PAGE ⟹

Base your answers to questions 38 and 39 on the diagram below and on your knowledge of biology. The diagram illustrates activities taking place in the body of a human.

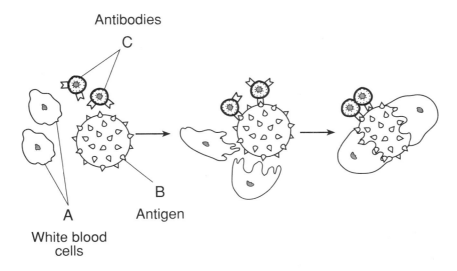

38 Vaccinations usually stimulate the body to produce more of

(1) structure A, only
(2) structure B, only
(3) structures A and C, only
(4) structures A, B, and C

39 Which structure normally stimulates an allergic response?

(1) A, only
(2) B, only
(3) C, only
(4) A, B, and C

40 Which population in the chart below has the best chance for survival in a rapidly changing environment?

Population	Type of Reproduction	Average Life Span of Individuals	Total Number of Offspring Produced
(1)	sexual	13 days	100
(2)	asexual	13 days	100
(3)	sexual	12 weeks	25
(4)	asexual	12 weeks	25

41 The table below represents a segment of a DNA molecule found in a stomach cell, both before and after undergoing replication.

DNA Segment Before and After Replication

Before replication	TGT	ATG	AAA	CAC	AAT	TAT
After replication	TGT	ATT	AAA	CAC	AAT	TTT

Which statement best describes a change that would most likely be observed in the cells formed as a result of this mitotic division?

(1) An enzyme the cell produces might no longer function.
(2) The cells would begin to form gametes to be released.
(3) Many new hormones would be synthesized by the cells.
(4) Chloroplasts would be produced by the ribosomes.

Base your answers to questions 42 and 43 on the information and diagram below and on your knowledge of biology.

The setup below shows four test tubes. Tube 1 contains water only. Tube 2 contains a live snail. Tube 3 contains a live green water plant. Tube 4 contains both a live green water plant and a live snail.

Tube1   Tube 2   Tube 3   Tube 4

42 In this setup, which tubes contain at least one organism carrying on cellular respiration?

(1) tubes 1 and 2, only   (3) tubes 3 and 4, only
(2) tubes 2 and 4, only   (4) tubes 2, 3, and 4, only

43 Which compound that directly provides energy in living cells is being produced in every tube where cellular respiration is occurring?

(1) oxygen   (3) DNA
(2) glucose   (4) ATP

Answer all questions in this part. [12]

Directions (44–55): For those questions that are multiple choice, record on the separate answer sheet the *number* of the choice that, of those given, best completes each statement or answers each question. For all other questions in this part, follow the directions given and record your answers in the spaces provided in this examination booklet.

Base your answers to questions 44 through 47 on the information and data table below and on your knowledge of biology.

The concentration of a specific antibody in the blood of an individual was measured at various times over a period of 50 days. The results obtained are shown in the data table below.

Antibody Concentration in an Individual

Day	Antibody Concentration in Arbitrary Units (arb. units)
5	0
10	110
16	120
25	10
35	200
45	390
50	200

Directions (44–45): Using the information in the data table, construct a line graph on the grid, following the directions below.

44 Mark an appropriate scale, without any breaks in the data, on each labeled axis. [1]

45 Plot the data on the grid. Connect the points and surround each point with a small circle. [1]

Example: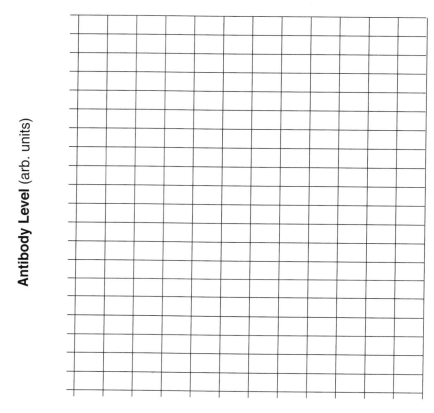

Antibody Concentration in an Individual

Antibody Level (arb. units)

Day

46 State *one* reason for the change in antibody production during the first 10 days. [1]

_____

_____

Note: The answer to question 47 should be recorded on your separate answer sheet.

47 The antibody level (in arb. units) of the individual on day 30 is closest to
   (1) 30   (3) 110
   (2) 70   (4) 160

August '17 Regents Examination

Base your answers to questions 48 and 49 on the information and diagram below and on your knowledge of iology.

If a Chihuahua with short hair has a hidden gene for long hair, it can produce both long-haired and short-haired puppies when bred to a Chihuahua with long hair.

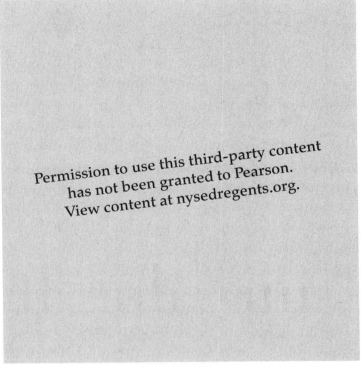

Permission to use this third-party content has not been granted to Pearson. View content at nysedregents.org.

48 A family decides that they want to produce Chihuahuas with long hair. Identify a procedure that could be used to make sure that the puppies all have long hair.   [1]

_____

Note: The answer to question 49 should be recorded on your separate answer sheet.

49 A Chihuahua is born having a trait that is different from either of its parents. A possible explanation for the difference is that the Chihuahua puppy

(1) was produced as a result of the recombination of genes during sexual reproduction
(2) was produced as a result of the process of asexual reproduction
(3) inherited a gene from one of its grandparents and not its parents
(4) had a mutation that occurred after it was born

August '17   Regents Examination

Base your answers to questions 50 and 51 on the diagram below and on your knowledge of biology. The diagram represents a technique used by scientists today to maintain the genetic makeup of an organism.

Original plant   Cell   Culture dish   Cluster of cells   New plant

Stage 1   Stage 2   Stage 3   Stage 4

Note: The answer to question 50 should be recorded on your separate answer sheet.

50 Which graph below best represents the DNA content found in each cell in each of the stages in the diagram above?

51 Describe *one* specific reason why scientists would want to maintain the genetic makeup of a particular plant. [1]

_____

_____

_____

Base your answers to questions 52 and 53 on the information below and on your knowledge of biology.

Breast Cancer Research

Most deaths that are a result of breast cancer occur because the cancer cells metastasize (spread) from the breast to other organs. As they metastasize, cancer cells travel through the bloodstream.

MicroRNA molecules are involved in both the movement and control of metastasized cells. One microRNA, known as miR-7, shuts down a protein that helps cancer cells travel through the blood.

Understanding how miR-7 interacts with cancer cells may lead to new treatments for certain types of cancer. Since certain levels of miR-7 expression can also stimulate the development of cancer cells, the use of miR-7 to treat cancer will have to be studied in more detail. Researchers are hoping that eventually levels of miR-7 will be used to diagnose, treat, and prevent the spread of cancer in an individual.

52 State *one negative* effect of using miR-7 as the only treatment for breast cancer. [1]

_____

_____

53 State *one* way cancer cells are different from normal body cells. [1]

_____

_____

[16]

Base your answers to questions 54 and 55 on the information and diagram below and on your knowledge of biology.

Each body cell contains the same genetic information, but can differ in appearance and size. The diagram below shows three different types of cells found in the human body.

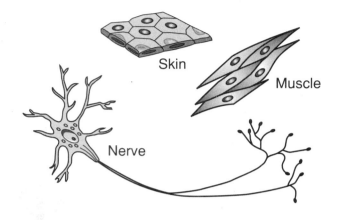

54 Identify *one* similarity, other than the genetic information, that these body cells have. [1]

_____

55 Explain why differences in these human body cells are a biological advantage. [1]

_____

_____

_____

August '17   Regents Examination

Part C

Answer all questions in this part. [17]

Directions (56–72): Record your answers in the spaces provided in this examination booklet.

Base your answers to questions 56 through 58 on the information below and on your knowledge of biology.

Owl vs. Owl

Barred owl

Spotted owl

Federal wildlife officials plan to dispatch armed bird specialists into forests of the Pacific Northwest starting this fall to shoot one species of owl to protect another that is threatened with extinction. …

…"If we don't manage barred owls, the probability of recovering the spotted owls goes down significantly," said Paul Henson, Oregon state supervisor for Fish and Wildlife. The agency's preferred course of action calls for killing 3,603 barred owls in four study areas in Oregon, Washington and northern California over the next four years. …

…Mr. Henson said unless barred owls are brought under control, the spotted owl in coming decades might disappear from Washington's northern Cascade Range and Oregon's Coast Range, where the barred owl incursion [takeover] has been greatest.

The northern spotted owl was listed as a threatened species in 1990. Barred owls are bigger, more aggressive and less picky about food. Barred owls now cover the spotted owl's range, in some places outnumbering them as much as 5-to-1.

Source: Associated Press, 7/26/13

56 Describe how the barred owl population is having a *negative* effect on the spotted owl population. [1]

_____

_____

57 Explain why it is important to protect the spotted owl from extinction. [1]

_____

_____

58 Certain groups oppose the plan to kill barred owls, in part because they feel it will not solve the problem. They recommend that the focus should be on protecting the habitat of the spotted owl. Describe the role that the habitat plays in the survival of an animal species such as the spotted owl. [1]

_____

_____

Base your answer to question 59 on the information below and on your knowledge of biology.

The 1990 Federal Clean Air Act requires New York State to conduct an emissions test on most gasoline-powered automobiles in order to help reduce harmful emissions. Vehicles that fail this test must be repaired and pass inspection before they can be driven on the road. Some people did not support this legislation.

59 State *one* advantage and *one* disadvantage of automobile emission testing. [1]

Advantage: _____

_____

Disadvantage: _____

_____

August '17   Regents Examination

Base your answers to questions 60 through 63 on the information below and on your knowledge of biology.

Enzyme Investigation

An enzyme was isolated from digestive juices taken from the small intestine. An experiment was set up to test the ability of the enzyme to break down protein. Two test tubes, labeled *A* and *B*, were placed in a hot water bath at 37°C, human body temperature.

Test tube *A* contained only protein and test tube *B* contained protein and the enzyme. The chart below shows the set-up.

Test Tube	Contents
A	protein
B	protein, enzyme

After two hours, the contents of both test tubes were analyzed. Test tube *A* showed only the presence of protein. Test tube *B* showed the presence of the end products of protein digestion, indicating the enzyme had successfully broken down the protein.

60 Identify the end products of protein digestion that made up the contents of test tube *B* after the two hours. [1]

_____

61 Explain the importance of temperature in the functioning of enzymes. [1]

_____

_____

62 State what the result would be if the same enzyme that was added to test tube *B* was added to a test tube containing starch. Support your answer. [1]

_____

_____

63 In the digestive system many large molecules, such as proteins, are broken down into much smaller molecules. State what happens to these smaller molecules following digestion. [1]

_____

_____

Base your answers to question 64–66 on the information below and on your knowledge of biology.

Secondhand Smoke and Estrogen

A fertility researcher conducted a study of pregnant women. The researcher's hypothesis was that the estrogen levels of pregnant women who were exposed to daily secondhand cigarette smoke would be higher than estrogen levels of pregnant women not exposed to daily secondhand smoke.

The researcher measured the estrogen levels of eight pregnant women each week throughout their pregnancy. Four of the women lived in houses with heavy smokers, the other four did not. The women's ages varied from 19 to 42 years old. Six of the women were pregnant with girls, one was pregnant with a boy, and one was pregnant with twin boys. The research was submitted for peer review.

64–66 Analyze this experiment. In your answer, be sure to:

- identify *one* error in the researcher's experimental design   [1]
- identify *one* way, other than affecting estrogen levels, that secondhand smoke could affect a developing embryo   [1]
- explain why the process of peer review is an important step in this research   [1]

_____

_____

_____

_____

_____

_____

_____

August '17   Regents Examination

Base your answers to questions 67 through 69 on the information and passage below and on your knowledge of biology.

Snowy Owls Move to the South

Snowy owls are large white birds that normally inhabit the cold northern regions of Canada. Recently, scientists and birdwatchers have sighted the snowy owls much farther south than usual.

When snowy owls are in northern areas, they feed on lemmings (small rodents). When lemmings are not available, as in the areas further south, the owls will seek out mice or rabbits as their food source.

Several snowy owls migrated into an area represented by the food web below.

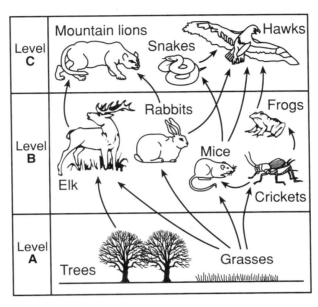

67 Identify *one* population of organisms shown in the food web, other than rabbits or mice, that would likely be affected by the introduction of the snowy owls and explain why their population would be affected. [1]

Population affected: _____

_____

_____

68 Identify *one* condition that might cause snowy owls to leave their usual habitat and move to another area. [1]

_____

69 State which level, *A*, *B*, or *C*, contains the *least* total available energy. Support your answer. [1]

Level: _____

_____

_____

Base your answers to questions 70 through 72 on the information below and on your knowledge of biology.

Pocket Mice

Pocket mice are small rodents that feed mainly at night and are preyed upon by owls, hawks, and snakes. Scientists studied pocket mice living on dark volcanic rock in both New Mexico and fifty miles away in Arizona. They recorded their data in the chart below.

	Number of Mice on Dark Volcanic Rock			
Year	**New Mexico**		**Arizona**	
	Light Fur	**Dark Fur**	**Light Fur**	**Dark Fur**
2000	120	122	16	125
2001	140	136	8	140
2002	134	130	6	135
2003	115	120	12	115
2004	122	126	8	129

70 State *one* possible hypothesis that would explain the differences in the observed data between the two locations. [1]

_____

_____

71 Dark fur color in pocket mice is the result of a mutation. Scientists analyzed the sequence of bases in the gene known to play a role in fur color and discovered that the mutation was identical in both the New Mexico and Arizona mouse populations. Explain how it is possible for these two different populations to have identical gene sequences for dark fur color. [1]

_____

_____

72 Explain what is meant by the statement: "While mutations are random, natural selection is not." [1]

_____

_____

_____

_____

August '17 Regents Examination

Part D

Answer all questions in this part. [13]

Directions (73–85): For those questions that are multiple choice, record on the separate answer sheet the *number* of the choice that, of those given, best completes each statement or answers each question. For all other questions in this part, follow the directions given and record your answers in the spaces provided in this examination booklet.

Note: The answer to question 73 should be recorded on your separate answer sheet.

73 The diagram below represents evolutionary pathways of seven groups of organisms alive today.

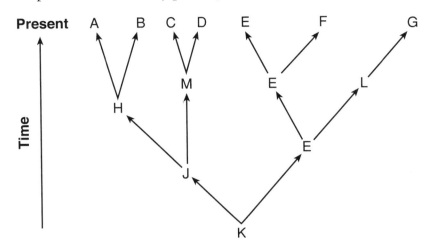

Which two living species would be expected to have the most similar proteins?

(1) *A* and *C*
(2) *B* and *C*

(3) *E* and *F*
(4) *H* and *M*

Note: The answer to question 74 should be recorded on your separate answer sheet.

74 Scientists recently discovered that three different types of squid, a marine animal, previously thought to be three different species, were actually all members of one species. Their earlier ideas were based on using squid carcasses (dead bodies). The new, more accepted classification is most probably based on an analysis of

(1) a greater number of squid carcasses
(2) the feeding habits of the three different species
(3) a number of newly found squid fossils
(4) the DNA present in the cells of squid

75 The diagram below represents a laboratory experiment involving sucrose and water molecules in a cellophane bag which functions in the same way as dialysis tubing.

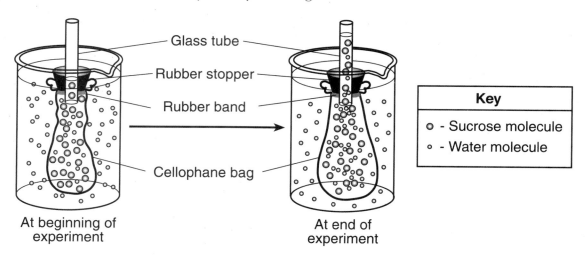

Which statement correctly explains the rise of liquid in the tube at the end of the experiment?

(1) The concentration of sucrose molecules increased as water molecules entered the bag. This concentration increase pushed the liquid up the tube.

(2) Water entered the bag due to the lower concentration of water inside. The extra water pushed the liquid up the tube as the bag filled.

(3) Sucrose indicator entered the bag and reacted with the sucrose molecules. The reaction made the bag increase in size and pushed the liquid up the tube.

(4) Sucrose molecules moved out of the bag and up the tube while water moved out, causing the rise of liquid in the tube.

Base your answers to questions 76 through 78 on the diagram below that shows variations in the beaks of finches in the Galapagos Islands and on your knowledge of biology.

Permission to use this third-party content has not been granted to Pearson. View content at nysedregents.org.

Note: The answer to question 76 should be recorded on your separate answer sheet.

76 Which row correctly pairs a finch species with its primary nutritional role and bill type?

Row	Finch	Bill Type	Nutritional Role
(1)	cactus finch	probing bill	carnivore
(2)	medium ground finch	grasping bill	herbivore
(3)	large tree finch	crushing bill	herbivore
(4)	warbler finch	probing bill	carnivore

77 In certain years, the Galapagos plants produce many tube-shaped flowers rich in nectar. Identify the finch that is best adapted to feed on the nectar within those flowers. Support your answer. [1]

_____

_____

August '17 Regents Examination

78 The number of small tree finches is increasing on an island inhabited by a large population of small ground finches. State *one* reason why the population of small ground finches has *not* been affected by the increasing number of small tree finches. [1]

_____

_____

_____

79 Explain why glucose molecules can cross a cell membrane and starch molecules can *not*. [1]

_____

_____

_____

Base your answers to questions 80 through 82 on the information below and on your knowledge of biology.

Progressive Resistance Exercise

Progressive resistance exercise (PRE) is a method of increasing the ability of muscles to generate force. The principles of PRE for increasing force production in muscles have remained unchanged for almost 60 years. These principles are (1) to perform a small number of repetitions until fatigued, (2) to allow sufficient rest between exercises for recovery, and (3) to increase the resistance as the ability to generate force increases. Traditionally, PRE has been used by young, healthy adults to improve athletic performance.

A student decided to incorporate PRE into his exercise program. He did not know how to determine when he had allowed sufficient rest between exercises for recovery. He hypothesized that waiting for his pulse to return to normal would probably be a good indication.

80 Explain why allowing his pulse rate to return to normal might be a good indication that he had waited long enough for recovery. [1]

_____

_____

Note: The answer to question 81 should be recorded on your separate answer sheet.

81 Students wanted to try PRE to increase their ability to rapidly squeeze a clothespin. They thought if they could do this, they could challenge another class to a clothespin squeezing competition and win. Which steps should the students take to follow the principles of PRE?

(1) Measure their pulse rate after squeezing the clothespin until fatigued. Then increase the resistance of the clothespin for the next trial.
(2) Squeeze a clothespin until fatigued, rest, and repeat. Over time, they should gradually increase the resistance of the clothespins they are squeezing.
(3) Measure their pulse rate, squeeze a clothespin for one minute, rest, and measure their pulse rate.
(4) Squeeze a clothespin for as long as they can, measure their pulse rate, rest, eat some candy. Increase the resistance of the clothespin for the next trial.

Note: The answer to question 82 should be recorded on your separate answer sheet.

82 Students following the principles of PRE monitored their ability to lift weights. Which observation would indicate that their exercise program was successful?

(1) They could eventually lift heavier weights than when they started.
(2) Their pulse rate increased more rapidly as they kept lifting weights.
(3) The number of weights their group could lift during competition decreased.
(4) Males and females could lift the same weight an equal number of times during competition.

83 Using the axes on the graph below, sketch a line graph showing the changes in heart rate of a person who is walking slowly, then begins running, and then sits down to rest for a few minutes.   [1]

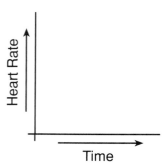

84 Identify *one* waste product that is released during exercise. Explain how this waste product leaves the body. [1]

Waste product: _____

_____

_____

85 State *one* way scientists could use the banding patterns produced by gel electrophoresis.   [1]

_____

_____

_____

Part A

Answer all questions in this part. [30]

Directions (1–30): For *each* statement or question, record on the separate answer sheet the *number* of the word or expression that, of those given, best completes the statement or answers the question.

1 An example of recycling is

(1) using a paper cup instead of a mug
(2) turning off the lights when leaving a room
(3) using plastic from a soda bottle to make a certain type of clothing
(4) using two paper towels rather than five to clean up a spill

2 One characteristic of a stable ecosystem is

(1) a high number of predators
(2) an interdependence of organisms
(3) a lack of biodiversity
(4) an increase in human interference

3 According to scientists, ocean waves could be a source of energy. Devices are being designed to capture the energy from waves and supply electricity to coastal areas. A direct benefit of utilizing this technology to produce energy would be the

(1) destruction of habitats near the devices
(2) decreased use of nonrenewable resources
(3) release of gases needed for photosynthesis
(4) increased use of finite resources

4 The emerald ash borer is an insect that is thought to have been accidentally brought to the United States from China in shipping containers. It attacks ash trees, eventually killing the trees, destroying an important part of the ecosystem. The presence of the emerald ash borer in the United States can be used as an example of how humans have

(1) purposely introduced an insect to correct a problem in an ecosystem
(2) used an insect to remove one insect species and replace it with another
(3) worked to increase the biodiversity in a particular area
(4) altered the equilibrium in an ecosystem by introducing a new species

5 Which graph best shows the changes in global human population and natural resource use over the past 500 years?

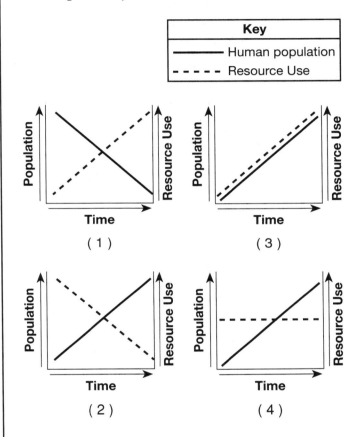

6 The burning of fossil fuels has harmed the environment by

(1) decreasing acid rain in the northeast United States
(2) adding carbon dioxide to the atmosphere
(3) increasing biodiversity in the lakes and ponds of the Adirondacks
(4) depleting the ozone shield directly over western New York State

7 Which method of collecting data would provide the most accurate information about how an ecosystem is being affected by human development?

(1) The people in the neighborhood record the number of birds they see in the area both before and after the construction of a new building.

(2) Deer in the area are identified before construction so that scientists can see where they go after the building is finished.

(3) More trees are planted in the area around the construction site to allow the animals a new place to live.

(4) The population size is recorded for each species present in the construction area before and after the building is completed.

8 Natural selection produces changes most quickly in

(1) species with short reproductive cycles
(2) individual pathogens killed by antibiotics
(3) complex multicellular organisms
(4) individuals that produce a small number of offspring

9 As a result of habitat destruction, the size of the Florida panther population has been drastically reduced. It is estimated that there are only 100 to 160 Florida panthers in the wild. Which statement best explains why the Florida panther population may *not* continue to evolve?

(1) There is no longer a chance of mutations occurring in the population.

(2) There is a lack of competition for limited environmental resources.

(3) There is no longer a chance of a trait providing a reproductive advantage to the population.

(4) There is a lack of genetic variation for selection to act upon.

10 Which level of the pyramid below is correctly paired with the type of organism that would most likely be found at that level in an ecosystem?

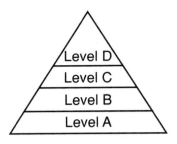

(1) Level A – producers
(2) Level B – carnivores
(3) Level C – herbivores
(4) Level D – decomposers

11 Which statement best describes what is most likely to occur if an animal population grows larger than the carrying capacity of its environment?

(1) The birth rate will increase.
(2) Both the birth rate and death rate will decrease.
(3) The death rate will increase.
(4) Neither the birth rate nor the death rate will decrease.

12 Many biotic factors affect individuals in a population. An example of an organism being directly affected by a biotic factor is

(1) a squirrel cannot find a mate
(2) a flood washes away a maple tree
(3) a plant is in a dark room
(4) a chipmunk finds a rock pile to use for a home

13 When people receive organ transplants, they often need to take medications that decrease immune responses because

(1) transplanted organs contain antigens that can trigger white blood cell activity

(2) hormones present in replacement organs prevent the synthesis of antibiotics

(3) transplanted organs produce their own antibiotics

(4) antigens present in these organs attack antibodies already present in the blood

14 Which structures regulate water loss and gas exchange in the leaves of plants?

(1) vacuoles
(3) guard cells
(2) chloroplasts
(4) mitochondria

15 Which life process carried out by a green plant is represented in the diagram below?

(1) respiration
(3) digestion
(2) photosynthesis
(4) replication

16 Scientists are developing a malaria vaccine that would most likely contain

(1) weakened drugs used to treat the symptoms of malaria
(2) white blood cells from the malaria-infected individuals
(3) a weakened form of the malaria-causing organism
(4) antibodies made from the malaria-causing organism

17 Proteins, starch, and DNA are similar in that they are all

(1) organic compounds
(2) parts of genes
(3) made of amino acids
(4) made of simple sugars

18 In response to an increasing blood glucose level, the human body will normally

(1) store the glucose in cell nuclei
(2) release a hormone that lowers the blood glucose
(3) produce a hormone that destroys the glucose
(4) use the excess glucose to make proteins

19 A kitten was born with black fur and green eyes. The fur and eye color of its parents are shown in the chart below.

Cat	Fur	Eye Color
Father	striped	green
Mother	black	yellow
Kitten	black	green

Which statement helps explain why the kitten has black fur?

(1) Chromosomes present on the genes code for the characteristics of its fur.
(2) Genetic mutations always cause the fur color and eye color to change.
(3) Offspring receive genetic information from both parents.
(4) Gene expression is changed in every generation, resulting in evolution.

20 Scientists have been investigating a way to recreate extinct species such as the saber-toothed cat illustrated below.

Source: https://IGS.Indiana.edu

Which technique would use DNA from an extinct species to recreate an organism of the species?

(1) natural selection
(3) cloning
(2) differentiation
(4) selective breeding

21 The sequence that best illustrates the flow of energy through an ecosystem is

(1) sunlight → plant → wolf → rabbit
(2) plant → sunlight → rabbit → wolf
(3) sunlight → plant → rabbit → wolf
(4) wolf → rabbit → plant → sunlight

22 Which cellular change in an organism could be inherited by the next generation?

(1) a change in the ribosomes in the pancreas of a squirrel

(2) the deletion of a single DNA base in a sperm cell of a trout

(3) a decrease in the size of a vacuole in a rose leaf cell

(4) the transfer of a piece of a chromosome in the skin cell of a raccoon

23 A chemical was added to hand sanitizers and dish detergents to kill bacteria. Certain species of bacteria are no longer killed by this chemical. One likely reason for the decreased effectiveness of this chemical is that these bacteria have

(1) slower metabolic rates

(2) a mutation for resistance

(3) been selectively bred for survival

(4) an adaptation to a different niche

24 The hemlock wooly adelgid is an invasive insect species that is destroying native hemlock trees in New York State. These insects can upset natural ecosystems because they

(1) provide food for native bird species

(2) can carry diseases that can be spread to pets

(3) increase biodiversity in New York State forests

(4) disrupt habitats that native species depend upon

25 A shark and a dolphin have similarly shaped bodies and fins. However, these two organisms are not closely related: The shark is a fish, and the dolphin is a mammal. Some species may have similar body structures even if they are not related because they evolved in

(1) similar environments and specific traits increased their chances of survival

(2) similar environments and were exposed to factors that caused exactly the same mutations

(3) different environments, but tried to adapt in the same ways so they could survive

(4) different environments, but ate similar foods that affected their growth and development

26 A dog gave birth to the three puppies shown in the photograph below. One of the puppies has darker fur on its face than the other two.

Which two biological processes account for this difference between the puppies?

(1) meiosis and recombination

(2) meiosis and cloning

(3) mitosis and differentiation

(4) mitosis and cloning

27 The diagram below represents a cell that produces digestive enzymes.

Which cellular structure would be the most likely location for the synthesis of these enzymes?

(1) 1   (3) 3

(2) 2   (4) 4

28 Energy drinks have become increasingly popular. Some of these drinks contain large amounts of caffeine, which is known to increase heart rates in most individuals. This effect on the heart rate can be dangerous because it can lead to

(1) a disruption in the absorption of starch
(2) an increase in blood volume
(3) a decrease in oxygen levels
(4) an imbalance in homeostasis

29 The kidney is an organ that collects wastes and excess water from the blood and sends them to the bladder where they are stored before being removed from the body. Which two systems work together to perform this function?

(1) immune and respiratory
(2) circulatory and excretory
(3) skeletal and nervous
(4) digestive and circulatory

30 Scientists have recently discovered a community of bacteria and clams living under an ice shelf in Antarctica. These organisms live under 600 feet of ice, in the absence of sunlight, and in temperatures considered too cold for most living organisms. The location where these organisms live is unusual because

(1) only biotic factors control the size of the populations
(2) bacteria and clams are found in the same area
(3) of the abiotic factors found in their environment
(4) green plants make energy-rich compounds available

Part B–1

Answer all questions in this part. [13]

Directions (31–43): For *each* statement or question, record on the separate answer sheet the *number* of the word or expression that, of those given, best completes the statement or answers the question.

31 The diagram below represents an important biological concept.

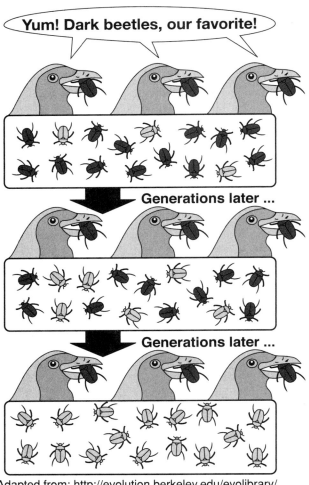

Adapted from: http://evolution.berkeley.edu/evolibrary/

The concept being represented is

(1) overproduction
(2) natural selection
(3) homeostasis
(4) ecological succession

32 The graph below shows levels of a form of ultraviolet radiation (UV-B) and ozone thickness in Australia during December 1987 and January 1988.

Adapted from: C. R. Roy, et. al., *Nature* 347:235, 1990

Which statement best describes the apparent relationship between ozone and UV-B?

(1) When ozone levels are at 2550 Dobson units, the UV-B levels are at 250 Dobson units.
(2) The increase in UV-B reduces the destruction of the ozone layer.
(3) When the ozone layer is thinner, more UV-B gets through it.
(4) If the ozone layer is thicker, UV-B levels on the ground increase.

33 In the diagram below, X represents a process that causes a protein to unfold and stop functioning.

Process X is most likely caused by

(1) the digestion of the amino acids that make up the proteins
(2) the synthesis of a protein with different simple sugars
(3) removal of the gene that codes for the production of the protein
(4) an internal factor in the body, such as a temperature increase

34 Which statement is an example of how the external environment can influence gene expression?

(1) Some flowering plants that inherit a gene for white flowers and a gene for red flowers will produce pink flowers.
(2) Some animals that inherit genes for brown fur will grow white fur if the outside temperature falls below a certain level.
(3) In some breeds of cat, certain fur-color genes are found only in females.
(4) A pea plant is short-stemmed only if it inherits the genes for the trait from both parents.

35 Which statement best illustrates a concept represented in the diagram below?

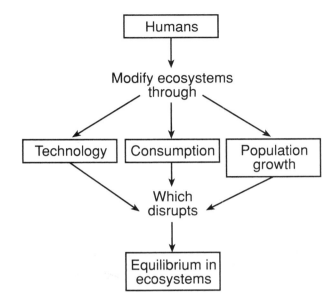

(1) Tsunamis triggered by oceanic earthquakes cause widespread flooding that can lead to large scale environmental destruction.
(2) Annual hunting laws determine the number of deer that can be hunted to ensure population stability.
(3) More individuals are purchasing hybrid cars that use less gasoline and produce less carbon dioxide.
(4) The increased use of electronics has led to increased mining for precious metals and minerals in developing countries.

36 The process shown below is used to

(1) determine if a person has a genetic disease
(2) produce human growth hormone
(3) identify the father of a newborn
(4) produce a hormone to regulate blood sugar

Base your answers to questions 37 through 39 on the diagrams below and on your knowledge of biology. The diagrams represent a single-celled organism and a multicellular organism.

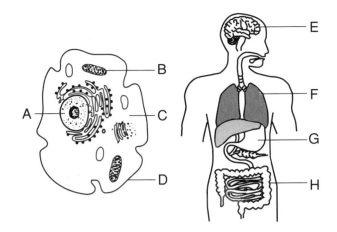

37 Which statement correctly identifies the levels of organization for the structures indicated?

(1) *A* and *B* are tissues; *E* and *G* are organs.
(2) *A* and *B* are organs; *E* and *G* are systems.
(3) *A* and *B* are tissues; *E* and *G* are organelles.
(4) *A* and *B* are organelles; *E* and *G* are organs.

38 Cells from structure *E* and cells from structure *G* are similar in that they

(1) have the same structure and function
(2) contain the same genetic material
(3) are identical in structure, but different in function
(4) contain only the genetic information needed for their specific job

39 Rotenone is an insecticide that is toxic to humans as well as to insects. Rotenone interferes with the process of ATP production in the cell. Which row in the chart below correctly identifies the structure where ATP is produced and the reason it is affected by rotenone?

Row	Structure	Reason Affected
(1)	A	It would be unable to store enzymes for ATP production.
(2)	B	Production of ATP would occur less efficiently.
(3)	C	The raw materials used for ATP production would be altered.
(4)	D	Absorption of the ATP would increase here.

Base your answers to questions 40 and 41 on the information and diagram below and on your knowledge of biology.

A student used a microscope like the one represented below to observe cell division in onion cells.

40 The part of the microscope that should be adjusted in order to better view the onion cells while using high power is

(1) *A*   (3) *C*
(2) *B*   (4) *D*

41 The student noticed that as the new cells formed, they contained rod-shaped chromosomes. It is necessary for onion cells to contain chromosomes because chromosomes

(1) are composed of genes that contain the instructions for an organism's traits
(2) are made of carbohydrates and are needed as an energy source
(3) direct the production of inorganic molecules within the cell
(4) are composed of lipids that contain stored nutrients for the new cell

42 The diagram below indicates a few of the many varieties of domestic dogs thought to have originated from wolves that were domesticated thousands of years ago.

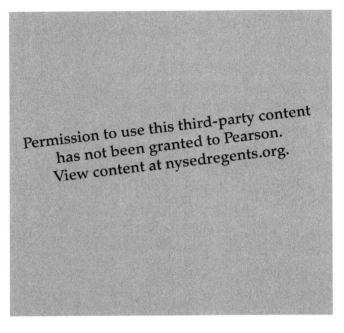

The many varieties of domesticated dogs were most likely produced as a result of

(1) mutating the body cells of the dogs
(2) selective breeding over many generations
(3) genetic engineering with specific enzymes
(4) cloning dogs with desirable traits

43 The graph below represents some changes in th number of individuals in a particular populatio in a stable ecosystem over a period of time.

Population Changes

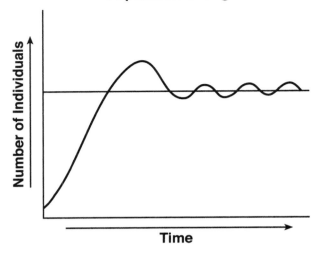

Which statement best describes the trend show in this graph?

(1) Ecosystem conditions will eventually cause population to become extinct.
(2) In a stable ecosystem, the number of inc viduals in a population is usually maintaine within a certain range.
(3) The interactions between a population ar various factors in an environment are alwa predictable.
(4) In order for any ecosystem to maintain a ba ance, populations must be reduced to h their original number.

Part B–2

Answer all questions in this part. [12]

Directions (44–55): For those questions that are multiple choice, record on the separate answer sheet ιe *number* of the choice that, of those given, best completes each statement or answers each question. For all her questions in this part, follow the directions given and record your answers in the spaces provided in this amination booklet.

Base your answers to questions 44 through 47 on the information and data table below and on your ınowledge of biology.

Illinois Greater Prairie Chicken on the Rise

As pioneers moved west in the mid-1800s, the greater prairie chicken population in Illinois was estimated to number in the millions. Since then, their population has drastically declined.

Evidence of the rapidly declining population was obtained from studying the number of eggs that hatched over several years. In Jasper County, Illinois, the number of prairie chickens fell from 2,000 to less than 50 in under 35 years. Researchers compared the DNA from feather samples from the living Illinois chickens to the DNA from feather samples dating from the year 1930 found in a museum. It was found that the living Illinois chicken population had a very low level of genetic diversity.

In 1992, researchers attempted to increase genetic variation by transporting more than 500 healthy prairie chickens into Illinois from the states of Minnesota, Kansas, and Nebraska. The data table below shows the changes in the percent of eggs that hatched from samples taken in different years. Researchers documented that this increase in the percent of eggs that hatched was not influenced by environmental events.

Prairie Chicken Egg Hatching

Years	Percent of Eggs Hatched
1970–1974	89
1975–1979	88
1980–1984	83
1985–1989	78
1990	38
1993–1996	94

Adapted from: http://www.sciencedaily.com/
releases/1998/11/981130045644.htm

Directions (44–46): Using the information given, construct a bar graph on the grid following the directions below.

44 Label the *y*-axis on the line provided. [1]

45 Mark an appropriate scale, without any breaks in the data, on the *y*-axis. [1]

46 Construct vertical bars to represent the data. Shade in *each* bar. [1]

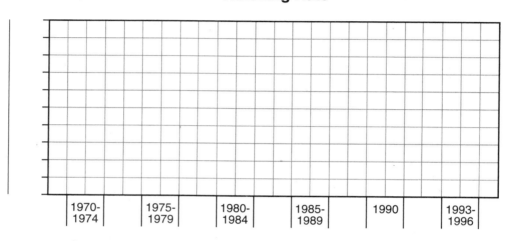

Hatching Rate

Years

Note: The answer to question 47 should be recorded on your separate answer sheet.

47 The scientists transported prairie chickens from three different states into the state of Illinois in order to
(1) decrease egg hatching rate
(2) increase genetic diversity
(3) increase egg fertilization
(4) develop different feather colors

Base your answers to questions 48 and 49 on the diagram below and on your knowledge of biology. The diagram shows the evolutionary history of several plant species.

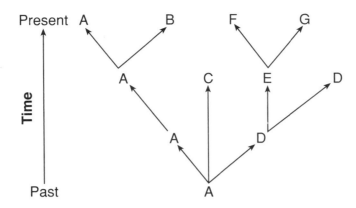

48 Identify *one* type of molecular evidence that could have been used to determine the evolutionary relationships illustrated in the diagram. [1]

_____

Note: The answer to question 49 should be recorded on your separate answer sheet.

49 Which biological technique could be used to obtain some structural evidence that species *A* and *B* are closely related?

(1) glucose testing
(2) cloning
(3) genetic engineering
(4) dissection

Base your answers to questions 50 and 51 on the diagram below and on your knowledge of biology. The diagram illustrates the steps in a process that occurs in the cells of many organisms.

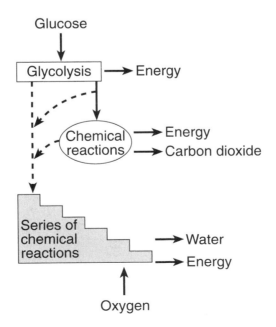

Adapted from: Biology: A Community Context,
W. H. Leonard and J. Penick, 1998

Note: The answer to question 50 should be recorded on your separate answer sheet.

50 Based on the diagram, the process of glycolysis most likely

    (1) begins the breakdown of glucose

    (2) produces oxygen for organisms to use

    (3) stores energy in molecules of water and carbon dioxide

    (4) recycles glucose within the cells of simple organisms

51 Identify *one* specific molecule used to store the energy being released during this process. [1]

    Molecule: _____

_____

52 The diagram below represents male gametes from different animals.

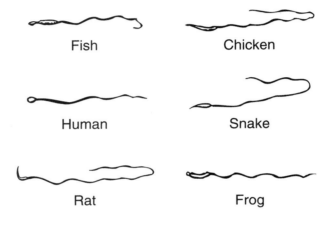

(Not drawn to scale)

State *one* way, other than the fact that they all contain DNA, the genetic content of these gametes is similar. [1]

_____

_____

53 Part of a food web is represented below. It includes organisms located in a stream near farm fields.

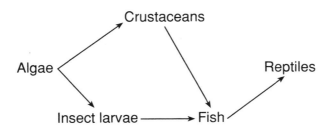

Select *one* type of organism, other than the crustaceans, from the food web. State how the population of organisms you selected might be affected if the population of crustaceans in this food web were reduced due to the use of chemicals harmful to crustaceans in the fields near the stream. Support your answer. [1]

Organism: _____

_____

_____

Base your answer to question 54–55 on the information below and on your knowledge of biology.

Indian blue peacocks live in dense forests and scrubland. Males use their colorful eye-spotted tail feathers and strutting display along with a loud mating call to attract females. This behavior, known as a hoot-dash, is made by the male before dashing toward a female to mate. Few species of other animals use loud courtship calls as the call attracts predators and uses energy.

54–55 Discuss the use of the hoot-dash by male peacocks. In your answer, be sure to:
- state *one* advantage of the hoot-dash [1]
- state *one disadvantage* of the hoot-dash [1]

_____

_____

_____

_____

Part C

Answer all questions in this part. [17]

Directions (56–72): Record your answers in the spaces provided in this examination booklet.

Base your answers to questions 56 and 57 on the information below and on your knowledge of biology.

The placenta secretes progesterone and estrogen during pregnancy.
Progesterone is responsible for the following functions:
- maintains the lining of the uterus
- inhibits (interferes with) contractions of the uterus
- inhibits the production and release of eggs

56 Describe *one* likely result if the placenta became damaged and could *not* maintain progesterone levels. Support your answer. [1]

_____

_____

57 Explain how the release of additional eggs is prevented during pregnancy. [1]

_____

_____

Base your answers to questions 58 and 59 on the information below and on your knowledge of biology.

"Cancer is a disease of genes gone wrong. When certain genes mutate, they make cells behave in odd ways. The cells divide swiftly, they hide from the immune system that could kill them and they gain the nourishment they need to develop into tumors...."

Source: Carl Zimmer, *NY Times*, February 6, 2014

58 Explain why the body of a person infected with HIV, the virus that causes AIDS, would have a different immune response to the presence of cancer cells than a person *not* infected with HIV. [1]

_____

_____

59 Explain why certain chemicals and radiation sources are risk factors for cancer. [1]

_____

_____

June '17   Regents Examination

60 Scientists have learned that when a pregnant woman smokes, one of the chemicals absorbed, nicotine, can narrow the diameter of her blood vessels that lead to the placenta. Explain why narrowing the diameter of these blood vessels can result in low birth weight babies. [1]

_____

_____

Base your answers to questions 61 through 63 on the information below and on your knowledge of biology.

In an experiment to test the effectiveness of a new vaccine, 50 rats received an injection of equal doses of the vaccine and 50 other rats received an injection of equal doses of a weak salt solution. Two months later, all of the rats received injections that contained equal doses of live, disease-causing organisms.

The experimental results are shown in the chart below.

Effectiveness of a New Vaccine

Injection: 50 Rats Received	Number of Rats That Developed the Disease	Number of Rats That Did Not Develop the Disease
vaccine	7	43
weak salt solution	48	2

61 Was the vaccine effective in preventing the disease? Use the information in the data table to support your answer. [1]

_____

_____

62 State *one* possible reason why two of the rats did *not* get sick even though they did *not* receive the vaccine. [1]

_____

_____

63 Do the results of this experiment indicate that the vaccine is ready for human testing? Support your answer with information from the table. [1]

_____

_____

Saving Florida Oranges

A disease that affects orange trees has led to the destruction of numerous orange trees in Florida. Orange growers have unsuccessfully tried to stop the spread of the disease by cutting down infected trees and using a variety of pesticides on the insects that spread the disease. The growers fear that if nothing further is done, entire crops could be wiped out in the near future. In hopes of saving Florida's orange industry, scientists are attempting to alter the DNA of orange trees by inserting DNA, that codes for disease resistance, from a different plant species.

64 State the name of the specific technique that is used to alter the DNA of orange trees. [1]

_____

65 Explain why growing oranges with disease resistance is better for the environment than using pesticides to control the spread of the disease. [1]

_____

_____

66 Identify a trait, other than disease resistance, that the orange trees could have that would be beneficial to the growers. [1]

_____

_____

67 The diagram below represents two energy pyramids. Each pyramid represents the productivity of one acre of land.

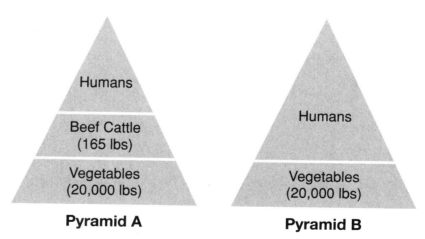

Based on the concept of energy transfer, explain why one acre of land can produce more vegetables for human consumption than beef for human consumption. [1]

_____

_____

June '17 Regents Examination

Base your answers to questions 68 through 72 on the information below and on your knowledge of biology.

Permission to use this third-party content has not been granted to Pearson. View content at nysedregents.org.

68 Explain how the molasses spill caused many of the animals to die off. [1]

_____

_____

69 State *one* reason why the die-off could attract sharks, barracuda, and eels to the harbor and lagoon. [1]

_____

_____

70 Identify *one* group of organisms responsible for the recycling of dead sea life that is *not* mentioned in the article. [1]

_____

71 Explain why it is important to preserve the biodiversity of the Honolulu Harbor ecosystem. [1]

_____

_____

72 Predict what will most likely happen to this ecosystem in 20 years if no other disasters occur. [1]

_____

_____

[20]

Part D

Answer all questions in this part. [13]

Directions (73–85): For those questions that are multiple choice, record on the separate answer sheet the *number* of the choice that, of those given, best completes each statement or answers each question. For all other questions in this part, follow the directions given and record your answers in the spaces provided in this examination booklet.

Note: The answer to question 73 should be recorded on your separate answer sheet.

73 On various Galapagos islands, finch species have different diets: seeds, insects, flowers, the blood of seabirds, and leaves. This is evidence that each species has a different

(1) mating behavior   (3) niche
(2) nesting material   (4) predator

Note: The answer to question 74 should be recorded on your separate answer sheet.

74 A person's pulse rate generally goes down while sleeping. One reason for this decrease is

(1) the body is producing more carbon dioxide when a person is sleeping
(2) a person is not using energy while sleeping
(3) a person requires less oxygen when sleeping
(4) the body is using more nutrients while asleep

GO ON TO THE NEXT PAGE ⇨

Base your answers to questions 75 through 77 on the information below and on your knowledge of biology.

Unique populations of giant tortoises live in the Galapagos Islands. This is the same group of islands where Darwin studied his famous finches. It is thought that the original ancestors of today's giant tortoises came from the mainland of South America. These animals left and drifted in the ocean to the islands where they began to live, reproduce, and evolve. Each of the islands has a different habitat. Each species varies in shell shape and body structure. Information about two of these species of giant tortoises and their habitats is found in the table below.

Giant Tortoises of the Galapagos Islands	
Tortoise Shell Type	**Habitat and Body Description**
Dome-shaped	• The island receives a lot of rain, and there is an abundant amount of available food (plant material). • The tortoises have shorter necks. They do not have to reach for food.
Saddle-backed Permission to use this third-party content has not been granted to Pearson. View content at nysedregents.org.	• The land on the island is dry, so there is limited available plant food. • The tortoises have long necks and legs, which allow them to reach for scarce food.

Adapted from: BenchPrep.com/blog/AP Biology-evolution-part-1/

Note: The answer to question 75 should be recorded on your separate answer sheet.

75 Which statement best explains the differences observed in the tortoises on each island?

(1) Each tortoise adapted to its environment during its lifetime.
(2) Sudden mutations changed the appearance of all of the tortoises.
(3) The tortoises grew different structures based on the available food.
(4) Different adaptations gave some tortoises a better chance of survival.

76 When the saddle-backed tortoises extend their long necks out of the shell, they are unprotected from attac
Scientists hypothesize that during the evolution of this tortoise, they had few predators. Which stateme
best supports this hypothesis?

  (1) Competition between the predators and the tortoises would have resulted in a greater number of lon
      necked tortoises.
  (2) The number of predators was greater than the number of tortoises.
  (3) Saddle-backed tortoises were not a part of the food chain.
  (4) Predators would have killed the tortoises with long necks, leaving more tortoises with shorter necks.

77 If a group of saddle-backed tortoises were brought to an island inhabited by dome-shaped tortoises, coul
both species survive? Circle yes *or* no and support your answer. [1]

Circle one: Yes *or* No

_____

_____

_____

78 During the laboratory activity *The Beaks of Finches*, you obtained food under two conditions: with competitio
and with no competition. State *one* way the results obtained from these two conditions differed when yo
did this activity. [1]

_____

_____

79 An investigation was carried out to determine the effects of exercise on the human body. Identify *one* body
system, other than the circulatory system, that becomes more active as a result of exercise. State *one* chang
the system you identified will undergo as a result of becoming more active. [1]

Body system: _____

Change: _____

_____

Base your answers to questions 80 through 82 on the information below and on your knowledge of biology.

A student designed an experiment to investigate a claim that athletes would have lower heart rates than nonathletes during exercise. After the students classified themselves as an athlete or a nonathlete, their resting pulses were determined. Then all the students performed the same exercise for four minutes and their heart rates were determined by recording the pulse rate in beats per minute. The students continued to measure their pulse rates for an additional four minutes. The average heart rate per minute for each group was determined. The data were recorded, as shown on the table below.

Average Heart Rate Response to Exercise (beats per minute)

	Time (minutes)	Athlete Students	Nonathlete Students
Resting Pulse	0	68	72
Exercising Period	1	76	78
	2	82	90
	3	95	115
	4	110	130
After Exercise	5	100	125
	6	95	120
	7	85	100
	8	68	95

80 State *one* appropriate hypothesis for this experiment. [1]

_____

_____

Note: The answer to question 81 should be recorded on your separate answer sheet.

81 Which statement is best supported by the data in the chart?
(1) After exercise, the nonathletic students had a lower heart rate than the athletic students.
(2) After exercise, the heart rates of the athletic students returned to resting pulse in four minutes.
(3) During exercise, both groups of students had the same increase above their resting pulse.
(4) During exercise, the athletic students had a higher heart rate than the nonathletic students.

Note: The answer to question 82 should be recorded on your separate answer sheet.

82 To improve the validity of the conclusion reached in this experiment, the students should repeat the experiment
(1) disregarding any data that don't fit the hypothesis
(2) with a larger number of athletes and nonathletes
(3) comparing the heart rates and breathing rates of males and females
(4) with the athletes doing different exercises than the nonathletes

Base your answer to question 83 on the information below and on your knowledge of biology.

A student added glucose indicator to a beaker of an unknown liquid. Starch indicator was added to a different beaker containing an equal amount of the same unknown liquid. The color of the indicator solutions before they were added to the beakers and the color of the contents of the beakers after adding the indicator solutions are recorded in the chart below.

Beaker	Solution	Color of Indicator Solution Before Adding to Beaker	Color of Contents of Beaker After Adding Indicator Solution
1	unknown liquid + glucose indicator	blue	blue (after heating)
2	unknown liquid + starch indicator	amber	blue-black

83 State *one* conclusion the student would make about the unknown liquid based on the results. Support your answer with information from the data table. [1]

_____

_____

_____

84 While getting ready to perform the *Making Connections* lab, a teacher did not have enough of the old wooden clothespins she was handing out to the students to squeeze in the lab. The teacher opened a bag of new plastic clothespins and handed them out to the students who had not received a wooden clothespin.

Explain why using new clothespins for some students and not others was an error in the experimental procedure. [1]

_____

_____

[25]

Base your answer to question 85 on the information and diagram below and on your knowledge of biology.

An unknown sample of DNA found at a crime scene was compared to DNA samples taken from three individuals. The results of the technique used to compare the samples are represented below.

85 What factor causes the DNA fragments to move in this technique? [1]

_____

_____

Part A

Answer all questions in this part. [30]

Directions (1–30): For *each* statement or question, record on the separate answer sheet the *number* of the word or expression that, of those given, best completes the statement or answers the question.

1 For a human zygote to become an embryo, it must undergo

(1) fertilization   (3) meiotic divisions

(2) recombination   (4) mitotic divisions

2 Many homeowners and businesses are installing solar electric systems. Greater use of solar electric systems benefits the environment because it

(1) depends on the greater use of fossil fuels

(2) conserves nonrenewable resources

(3) produces gases that cause global warming

(4) reduces the need for the ozone shield

3 A cell in the leaf of a corn plant contains more chloroplasts than a cell in the stem of a corn plant. Based on this observation, it can be inferred that, when compared to the cell in the stem, the cell in the leaf

(1) synthesizes more sugar

(2) has a higher chromosome count

(3) produces fewer proteins

(4) uses less carbon dioxide

4 When the human body is responding to stress, the hormone adrenaline is released. A short time later, the body returns to normal. This is an example of how a human

(1) reacts to an antibody

(2) develops genetic variation in body cells

(3) maintains cellular organization

(4) maintains dynamic equilibrium

5 A direct indication that the white blood cells of the body are functioning would be

(1) an increase in the number of oxygen molecules in the lungs

(2) a decrease in the number of pathogens in the body

(3) a decreased secretion of hormones by certain glands

(4) an increase of carbon dioxide in the cells of the body

6 A fully functioning enzyme molecule is arranged in a complex three-dimensional shape. This shape determines the

(1) specific type of molecule it interacts with during a reaction

(2) rate at which the enzyme breaks down during a reaction it regulates

(3) pH of all body systems

(4) temperature of the products of the reaction it regulates

7 A student received a flu shot in the fall. During the flu season, the student caught a cold. The most likely reason the vaccine he received did not prevent the cold was that

(1) his illness was not caused by a pathogen

(2) he did not get the vaccine at the right time of year

(3) his body produced antibiotics in response to the vaccine

(4) the vaccine he received contained only flu virus antigens

8 In August 2010, the Asian clam was discovered in Lake George. It is not native to that area. A single clam can reproduce and release hundreds of offspring in a day. Fish and crayfish eat the clams but cannot keep pace with the rate at which the clams reproduce. The introduction of the Asian clam into Lake George is

(1) positive, because it adds to the stability of the ecosystem

(2) positive, because the fish and crayfish would otherwise not have food

(3) negative, because it decreases water pollution in the lake

(4) negative, because it competes with native clam species and reduces stability

9 Like humans, animals including dogs and cats get goose bumps. On a cold day, these goose bumps cause their coats to expand creating a layer of insulation. If the animal is scared, the coat will also expand making the animal look larger to predators. These responses serve as examples of

(1) allergic reactions

(2) learned behaviors

(3) detection and response to stimuli

(4) reproductive and feeding success

10 Which factor is a major cause of the changes that occur during puberty, the years when the rate of human physical growth increases and reproductive maturity occurs?

(1) changes in some hormone levels

(2) an increase in meiosis in body cells

(3) a decrease in the rate of metabolism

(4) change in the gene sequences in reproductive cells

11 Which statement best describes how a new human trait develops and can be passed on to future generations?

(1) A mutation in a stomach cell results in the inability of a woman to produce a certain digestive enzyme.

(2) A mother consumes alcohol during pregnancy, causing the fetus to have a low birth weight.

(3) During meiosis, a new combination of DNA subunits is formed.

(4) During mitosis, DNA does not divide correctly and the cells die.

12 Survival of at least a few members of a population after a major environmental change is most dependent on

(1) the population having an individual that is adapted to the original environment

(2) the population having an individual that is adapted to great changes in the temperature in its environment

(3) variations in many different traits in many individuals in the population

(4) no variations in the color of the fur, skin, or feathers of the individuals in the population

13 A characteristic common to both diffusion and active transport is that

(1) enzymes are required

(2) oxygen is moved across a membrane

(3) ATP is needed

(4) the movement of molecules occurs

14 The theory of evolution states that

(1) species that are extinct have no biological relationship to living species

(2) different animal species always interbreed to form new and different species

(3) species change over time, sometimes developing into new species

(4) the environment of Earth is constant over time

15 Scientists in Brazil have developed specific fertilizers and special breeds of soybeans and corn so crops can grow on large areas of tropical lands. This is valuable because farmers can help to feed the growing human population and strengthen the economy. However, trade-offs must be considered because farming on tropical lands can also

(1) add helpful microorganisms to the soil

(2) remove oxygen from the atmosphere

(3) reduce populations of native species

(4) reduce mutations and disease in wildlife populations

The photograph below shows two color variations of Himalayan rabbits. In the winter, the rabbits resemble the one on the left. In the summer, the rabbits resemble the one on the right.

Himalayan Rabbits

Winter   Summer

The changes in fur color are most likely due to

(1) a virus that affected genes in specific areas of the body
(2) the sorting and recombination of genes
(3) gene expression due to the differences in abiotic conditions
(4) the molecular arrangement of sugars

7 The diagram represents a process used to modify bacterial cells.

In the diagram, arrows labeled *X* and *Y* represent the use of

(1) clones   (3) genes
(2) receptors   (4) enzymes

18 The diagram below represents the changes over time in an area.

Which example is *not* a natural process that could return a hardwood forest to the grass stage once again?

(1) a forest fire caused by a lightning strike   (3) clearing the land for agriculture
(2) the aging and falling of trees   (4) a hurricane or tornado

19 The Mississippi River Delta wetlands ecosystem is home to a large number of fish, birds, and other aquatic organisms. During the last century, this ecosystem has seen a decrease in wetland areas and species diversity due to land development, agriculture, and flooding. Conservation groups have been working to reconnect the Mississippi River with its flood plain and restore lost wetlands. One result of restoring wetland areas in this ecosystem would be

(1) an increase in abiotic factors that would cause organisms to develop new adaptations
(2) the development of an ecosystem that will prevent invasive species from settling there
(3) an increase in the carrying capacity of the ecosystem for wetland organisms
(4) to prevent the organisms that live in this ecosystem from competing for food and shelter

20 The diagram below represents a form of cellular reproduction.

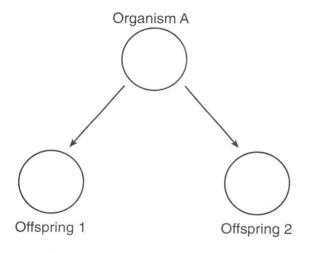

As a result of this process, offspring 1 and offspring 2 will have

(1) the same number of genes but different traits
(2) a different number of genes but the same traits
(3) the same number of genes and the same traits
(4) a different number of genes and different traits

21 The instructions for the genetic traits of an organism are directly determined by the

(1) numbers of A, T, C, and G units in a sugar molecule
(2) sequence of bases in DNA molecules
(3) length of a DNA molecule
(4) way the bases are paired in the two strands of a DNA molecule

22 Which statement best describes some protein molecules in a cell?

(1) Proteins are long, folded chains that can form various cell parts.
(2) Proteins are composed of four different starches that direct cell activity.
(3) Proteins are long, twisted strands of glucose that regulate cells.
(4) Proteins are genetically diverse substances that are synthesized in the nucleus.

23 *Rafflesia arnoldii* is a bright red and yellow flowering plant that has no leaves, roots, or stems. Rafflesia do not carry out photosynthesis. They take nutrients from the cells of grapevines. *Rafflesia arnoldii* is an example of a

(1) producer   (3) carnivore
(2) omnivore   (4) parasite

24 Female hammerhead sharks sometimes produce offspring by a type of asexual reproduction. These offspring

(1) are a result of the uniting of a male and a female gamete
(2) have cells that contain DNA found only in the female shark
(3) are considered to be a different species from the male parent
(4) have cells that contain genetic information from both parents

January '17   Regents Examination

25 A tomato gene, known as the SIKLUH gene, has recently been discovered. The gene leads to the production of larger tomatoes. The gene affects fruit size by increasing cell layers and promoting extra cell divisions. In order to produce large fruit in other commercial plant species, scientists might

(1) clone the genes of other types of plants until they develop larger fruits
(2) breed the tomatoes with other fruits such as apples
(3) insert the gene into other types of plants
(4) stimulate the process of meiosis in the other plants

26 During the last century, human impacts on our planet have led to an increasing and alarming loss of biodiversity in rainforest ecosystems. Scientists estimate that current extinction rates exceed those of some prehistoric mass extinctions. This loss of biodiversity also means loss of genetic diversity and loss of ecosystems. What could be done to minimize this loss of biodiversity?

(1) Introduce new species to rainforest ecosystems.
(2) Write and pass new environmental protection laws specific to rainforest ecosystems.
(3) Build barriers around rainforest ecosystems to keep animals and plants contained.
(4) Move all rainforest animals to new ecosystems where they will be safe.

27 Molecules in a certain medication attach to receptors on nerve cells. This prevents the normal chemical signal from binding to the receptor. One immediate result of taking this medication might be a disruption in the ability of

(1) the body to produce reproductive cells
(2) cells to communicate with each other
(3) cells to synthesize proteins
(4) the body to convert inorganic material into organic nutrients

28 The chart below contains information about some structures found in single-celled organisms

Cell Structures

Structure	Function
contractile vacuole	maintains water balance
flagellum	movement
chloroplast	food production

The information in this chart best illustrates the biological concept that

(1) all single-celled organisms contain contractile vacuoles, a flagellum, and chloroplasts
(2) single-celled organisms contain structures that function in maintaining homeostasis
(3) the organs found in complex organisms evolved from these three structures
(4) multicellular organisms do not contain any cell structures

29 The diagram below represents a process that occurs in human systems.

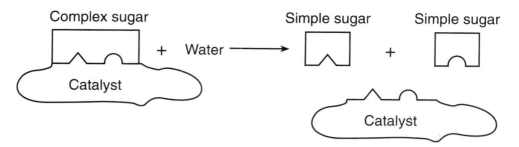

This process is known as

(1) excretion

(2) respiration

(3) circulation

(4) digestion

30 The diagram below represents levels of glucose and insulin found within the bloodstream of a healthy person throughout the course of the day.

The increase in insulin levels following an increase in glucose levels in the blood can best be explained by

(1) insulin being released into the blood to digest glucose

(2) a feedback mechanism that regulates blood glucose levels

(3) an excess of glucose-stimulating guard cells

(4) a response of the immune system to lower excess blood glucose levels

January '17   Regents Examination

Directions (31–43): For *each* statement or question, record on the separate answer sheet the *number* of the word or expression that, of those given, best completes the statement or answers the question.

31 The number of white-tailed deer in certain areas of Long Island, NY has increased significantly. Homeowners and farmers have put up tall fencing to protect their gardens and crops from the deer. One reason why the white tailed-deer might have increased significantly in certain areas of Long Island is

(1) the lack of natural predators
(2) an increase in deer pathogens
(3) a shortage of biotic resources needed by the deer
(4) that carrying capacity has no effect on deer populations

32 Researchers have discovered a chemical that sterilizes soil by killing all of the bacteria that are normally present. If this chemical were released in a forest ecosystem, the most likely result would be that

(1) the food web would be disrupted because there would be little recycling of nutrients
(2) fewer animals would suffer from disease such as cancer
(3) there would be more energy available for insects and worms that live in the soil
(4) the diversity of plants and animals present would increase

33 In order to be accepted, a scientific theory must be

(1) widely tested and supported by extensive data
(2) based on the results of a single experiment
(3) controversial and cause debate
(4) in line with all previous historical ideas

34 Anoles are a group of lizards consisting of approximately 400 species. A scientist studying them on an island observed two species that live in different habitats and display different behaviors. His observations are listed in the table below.

Observations of Two Species of Anoles

Characteristics	Species A	Species B
length	130 – 191 mm	55 – 79 mm
toepad size	large	intermediate
color	usually green	brown
tail length	long	long

Based on the scientist's observations, which statement best describes these two species of anoles?

(1) Both species evolved through the process of ecological succession.
(2) Each species is adapted to a different niche.
(3) The two species can interbreed.
(4) Species *A* is an herbivore and species *B* is a decomposer.

35 In an appropriately designed experiment, a scientist is able to test the effect of

(1) a single variable
(2) multiple variables
(3) the hypothesis
(4) scientific observations

Base your answers to questions 36 through 38 on the information and diagram below and on your knowledge of biology. The diagram represents a plant leaf cell and two different molecules used in the process of glucose synthesis.

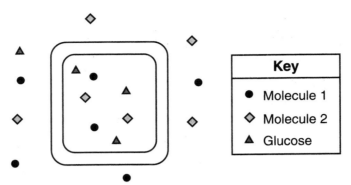

36 Molecules 1 and 2 are most likely
(1) carbon dioxide and oxygen
(2) carbon dioxide and water
(3) nitrogen and oxygen
(4) nitrogen and water

37 Molecules 1 and 2 enter the cell and glucose leaves the cell through the process of
(1) respiration
(2) digestion
(3) active transport
(4) diffusion

38 Which statement best describes a function of glucose in plant cells?
(1) It is converted into solar energy in the chloroplasts.
(2) It can be used directly as a building block in protein synthesis.
(3) It can be used during the digestion of fats.
(4) It is used during cellular respiration in the mitochondria.

39 Students collected data about the capacities of their lungs by inflating balloons with a single breath. They measured the circumference of the balloons in centimeters. Each student completed three trials and calculated the average.

Balloon Circumference (cm)

Student	Trial 1	Trial 2	Trial 3	Average
1	66.0	66.5	68.5	67.0
2	67.5	64.0	70.5	67.3
3	60.3	60.5	60.5	61.0
4	55.0	58.0	59.0	57.3

Which student miscalculated her average?
(1) student 1
(2) student 2
(3) student 3
(4) student 4

Base your answers to questions 40 and 41 on the information and chart below and on your knowledge of biology.

In recent years, biologists have noticed that honeybees responsible for pollinating food crops across the United States are dying at an alarming rate. Farmers, economists, and biologists are very worried about the impact that the loss of honeybees might have on the food supply.

Relying on Bees

Some of the most valuable fruits, vegetables, nuts and field crops depend on insect pollinators, particularly honeybees. Besides insects, other means of pollination include birds, wind and rainwater.

	Crop value in billions 2006	Percentage pollinated by honeybees	Percentage of crop pollinated by...
Soybeans	$19.70	5%	
Cotton	5.20	16	
Grapes	3.20	1	
Almonds	2.20	100	
Apples	2.10	90	
Oranges	1.80	27	
Strawberries	1.52	2	
Peanuts	.06	2	
Peaches	.05	48	
Blueberries cultivated	.05	90	

Adapted from: United States Department of Agriculture:
Roger A. Morse and Nicholas W. Calderone, Cornell University

40 Based on this information and the graph provided, which crops are most at risk if honeybees continue to decline?

(1) strawberries, peanuts, and grapes
(2) almonds, apples, and blueberries
(3) almonds, oranges, and soybeans
(4) peaches, cotton, and grapes

41 Peach blossom pollinations could be at risk if there is a total loss of honeybee populations in areas where peaches are grown. Which action would be most likely to help peach growers stay in business and be able to produce good-sized crops of peaches?

(1) Hire scientists to find a way to kill other pollinating insects in the area so there are more peach blossoms for the honeybees to pollinate.
(2) Hire researchers to identify which other native insects are able to pollinate peach blossoms and find a way to increase their populations.
(3) Encourage the peach growers to plant other kinds of fruit instead of peaches.
(4) Genetically engineer peach trees to be able to reproduce without producing any fruit (peaches) or seeds.

Base your answers to questions 42 and 43 on the information and diagram below and on your knowledge of biology. The diagram represents a cell.

42 Which structure is responsible for the passage of materials into and out of the cell?

(1) A   (3) C
(2) B   (4) D

43 Which structure is responsible for the synthesis of ATP?

(1) A   (3) C
(2) B   (4) D

January '17   Regents Examination

Directions (44–55): For those questions that are multiple choice, record on the separate answer sheet the *number* of the choice that, of those given, best completes each statement or answers each question. For all other questions in this part, follow the directions given and record your answers in the spaces provided in this examination booklet.

Base your answers to questions 44 through 47 on the information and data table below and on your knowledge of biology.

Hydrogen peroxide (H_2O_2), a byproduct of cellular metabolism, is broken down by the enzyme catalase which is produced by nearly all organisms. When catalase is added to hydrogen peroxide, a reaction occurs that produces bubbles of oxygen gas (O_2) and water (H_2O).

$$2H_2O_2 \rightarrow 2H_2O + O_2$$

The laboratory setup represented below was used to investigate the effect of pH on the breakdown of H_2O_2. Five setups were made with H_2O_2 solutions, each at a different pH level.

Catalase was added to the solution in the first setup and the reaction proceeded for one minute and the amount of gas produced by the reaction was recorded on the data table. This exact procedure was repeated with the other four setups containing different H_2O_2 solutions.

Gas Collected in Reactions at Different pH Levels	
pH	Gas Collected in One Minute (mL)
3	2
5	5
7	11
9	9
11	6

Directions (44–45): Using the information in the data table, construct a bar graph on the grid provided, following the directions below.

44 Mark an appropriate scale, without any breaks in the data, on the axis labeled "Amount of Gas Collected in One Minute (mL)." [1]

45 Construct vertical bars to represent the data. Shade in each bar. [1]

Gas Collected at Different pH Levels

46 This investigation was performed again with identical conditions except with a hydrogen peroxide solution at pH 8. Predict the number of mL of gas that was collected in one minute. [1]

_____ mL

Note: The answer to question 47 should be recorded on your separate answer sheet.

47 Based on the investigation, the student should conclude that enzymes
    (1) function best within a specific range of conditions
    (2) function best when observed in living cells
    (3) are not affected by changes in environmental factors
    (4) are easily broken down by hydrogen peroxide

January '17   Regents Examination

Base your answers to questions 48 and 49 on the information below and on your knowledge of biology.

Mutations cause many disorders in humans. Cystic fibrosis (CF) is a disorder that can be passed on from generation to generation. Skin cancer is a disorder that sometimes originates in skin cells as a result of overexposure to the Sun.

48 Explain why some disorders, such as CF, can be passed on from generation to generation, whereas some other disorders, such as skin cancer, cannot. [1]

_____

_____

Note: The answer to question 49 should be recorded on your separate answer sheet.

49 Which statement best explains the formation of the mutations that cause both cystic fibrosis and skin cancer?

(1) These mutations are a direct result of a change in the amino acid molecule that controls the formation of genetic codes in gametes.
(2) These mutations are caused by a change in the sugars that make up the genetic codes in all cells.
(3) Both of these mutations involve a change in the makeup of genes.
(4) Both of these mutations are a result of the incorrect synthesis of the proteins that make up DNA.

Base your answers to questions 50 and 51 on the information and table below and on your knowledge of biology.

Prey selection in a species of California garter snake depends upon where the snake lives. Snakes living inland feed on frogs, leeches, and fish while coastal snakes have added banana slugs to their diet. Banana slugs are found only in coastal areas. Researchers performed an experiment to determine what prey newly born snakes preferred. The table below summarizes the findings.

Prey Preference in Newborn Garter Snakes

	Newborn Coastal Snakes	Newborn Inland Snakes
Percentage of Snakes Eating Banana Slugs	60%	20%

Note: The answer to question 50 should be recorded on your separate answer sheet.

50 Which inference best explains these differences?
(1) The coastal snakes have been selectively bred for slug-eating behavior.
(2) Genetic manipulation has enabled the coastal snakes to recognize slugs as prey.
(3) The coastal snakes evolved a new organ so that they could recognize and feed on slugs.
(4) An adaptation enabled coastal snakes to use slugs as food source.

51 State how the feeding habits of this population of inland snakes would most likely change over many generations if they were relocated to a coastal region where frogs, leeches, and fish were rare. [1]

_____

_____

_____

52 Estrogen is one of the hormones produced by human females. Identify *one* organ that produces estrogen and state *one* specific function of estrogen in a human female. [1]

Organ: _____

Function: _____

Base your answer to question 53–54 on the information below and on your knowledge of biology.

   Both food chains and food webs can be used to illustrate relationships between organisms in an ecosystem.

–54 Discuss these methods of representing relationships. In your answer, be sure to:
- state *one* similarity in the way relationships between organisms are shown in food chains and food webs [1]
- explain why using a food chain is more limiting than using a food web to show relationships between organisms in an ecosystem   [1]

_____

_____

_____

_____

Base your answer to question 55 on the information below and on your knowledge of biology.

   A student measured oxygen and carbon dioxide concentration levels in an aquatic ecosystem during a 24 hour period. The data are represented in the graph below.

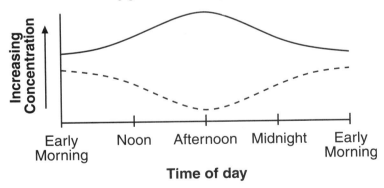

Daily Concentrations of Carbon Dioxide and Oxygen in an Aquatic Ecosystem

Key	
——	Oxygen
- - -	Carbon dioxide

55 Identify *two* biological processes that are responsible for the production of varying amounts of carbon dioxide and oxygen within the aquatic ecosystem.   [1]

   Processes: _____ and _____

_____

Part C

Answer all questions in this part. [17]

Directions (56–72): Record your answers in the spaces provided in this examination booklet.

Base your answer to question 56–58 on the information below and on your knowledge of biology.

Super-Size It?

The American Academy of Pediatrics has noted an increase in the population of children with disorders that are usually associated with older adults, such as diabetes. Observers of American culture point to the trend to "super-size" food servings as a possible cause. Larger servings might encourage children of today to eat more fats and sugars than children ate a generation ago.

In an attempt to determine if there is a relationship between diet and the development of diabetes in children, a study was done which surveyed a group of children regarding their eating habits and whether or not they were diabetic. When the survey results were collected, the data were used to organize the children into two groups based on their responses, and then the data were analyzed.

56–58 Discuss this investigation. In your answer, be sure to:

- state the hypothesis being tested in this investigation [1]
- identify *one* survey response that was most likely used for organizing the children into two groups [1]
- state what survey results would support the hypothesis stated above [1]

_____

_____

_____

_____

_____

_____

_____

_____

_____

January '17 Regents Examination

Base your answer to question 59 on the expression below and on your knowledge of biology.

Think globally, act locally!

59 This expression has been applied to many ecological problems, such as global warming [global climate change], and air pollution. Choose *one* of these ecological problems and write the name of the problem on your answer sheet. For the problem chosen, state *one* specific "local action" that could be taken. [1]

Problem: _____

Local action: _____

_____

Base your answer to question 60 on the information below and on your knowledge of biology.

Increased food production is essential to feed the growing human population. Some experts suggest that technology will be the answer. One application of technology is to clone a single plant to produce large numbers of it to grow as a single crop.

60 Explain how using cloning to produce a single crop could actually lead to a loss of the entire crop. [1]

_____

_____

Base your answers to questions 61 through 64 on the information below and on your knowledge of biology

61 Biofuels are produced from resources that can be grown, such as algae. Explain *one* specific benefit o using biofuels in place of the fossil fuels in wide use today. [1]

_____

_____

62 State *one* specific way that radioactive wastes from nuclear fuels can be harmful to humans. [1]

_____

_____

63 State *one* way the scientists may "have been able to manipulate the algae's process to be more strontium-selective." [1]

_____

_____

64 These algae are adapted to live in fresh water. State *one* way their cells would likely be affected if the scientists tried to use them in a saltwater environment. [1]

_____

_____

January '17   Regents Examination

Base your answers to questions 65 through 67 on the information below and on your knowledge of biology.

Gray Wolves in the Rocky Mountains

Reintroduction of gray wolves in the northern Rocky Mountains has increased the ecological health of Yellowstone National Park in Wyoming. When all wolves in Yellowstone National Park were killed in 1920, elk soon ate trees and shrubs down to short stubs. Now that wolves are reducing elk numbers, many aspens and willow trees are taller and fuller and birds are returning to the trees to nest. The beaver population has grown from one colony to 12 colonies in 13 years. Spreading these benefits across the Rocky Mountain region would require increasing the present wolf population of 1,770 to 17,000.

In September 2012, wolves lost federal protection in Wyoming. In 2014, Wyoming closed its hunting season after meeting its quota of 26 wolves around Yellowstone and Grand Teton parks. The sizes of traps to catch wolves have been regulated to reduce the chance of trapping endangered species such as lynx and wolverines and the hunting season was shortened. Some ecologists wonder if removing the wolves from federal protection and allowing them to be hunted is a good ecological decision.

65 Explain how increasing the wolf population caused an increase in birds and beavers. [1]

_____

_____

_____

66 Explain why some ecologists are concerned about removing wolves from federal protection. [1]

_____

_____

_____

67 In the space below, construct a food chain using *three* organisms identified in the above passage. [1]

_____

Base your answers to questions 68 and 69 on the information below and on your knowledge of biology.

Some viruses can enter cells by first attaching to the cell membrane. The flu virus targets and attaches to the cells of the nose and mouth. The hepatitis virus targets only specific cells of the liver.

68 State *one* way the immune system reacts when one of these viruses enters the body.   [1]

_____

_____

69 Most people who get vaccinated develop immunity to the disease. Explain why the contents of the vaccine usually do *not* cause people to get sick.   [1]

_____

_____

_____

Base your answers to questions 70 through 72 on the information below and on your knowledge of biology.

Mitochondrial Replacement Therapy

Mutations in mitochondrial DNA (mtDNA) are associated with some severe human diseases and are inherited through the cytoplasm in the egg cell. These diseases vary, but often affect organs and tissues with the highest energy requirements, including the brain, heart, muscle, pancreas, and kidney.

Scientists have successfully used mitochondrial replacement therapy with monkeys. Scientists are considering using this technique to reduce the incidence of mitochondrial disease in children. The proposed treatment would involve removing the nucleus from an egg donated by a healthy woman and replacing it with an egg nucleus from a patient (mother) with mitochondrial disease. This would place the patient's egg nucleus into the cytoplasm of the donor's egg containing healthy mitochondria. The egg is then fertilized with the father's sperm externally using *in vitro* fertilization (IVF) to produce a zygote. The zygote is cultured for a few days to produce an embryo.

70 Explain what must be done with the embryo after *in vitro* fertilization (IVF) has been completed so the embryo can complete development. [1]

_____

_____

71 Explain why the scientists used the cytoplasm from the donor's egg. [1]

_____

_____

72 State *one* reason why muscle tissues are likely to be affected by mitochondrial diseases. [1]

_____

_____

_____

Part D

Answer all questions in this part. [13]

Directions (73–85): For those questions that are multiple choice, record on the separate answer sheet the *number* of the choice that, of those given, best completes each statement or answers each question. For other questions in this part, follow the directions given and record your answers in the spaces provided in the examination booklet.

Note: The answer to question 73 should be recorded on your separate answer sheet.

73 A student collected data from an experiment on muscle fatigue. In order to interpret these data, the student should

(1) ignore the data because they do not support their hypothesis
(2) recalculate the data so that the numbers are easier to work with
(3) share the data with a student who has none
(4) organize the data into a table or graph

Note: The answer to question 74 should be recorded on your separate answer sheet.

74 Paper chromatography is a method used in

(1) comparing the shapes of plant leaves
(2) separating mixtures of plant pigments
(3) comparing habitats of different plants
(4) separating individual DNA fragments of plants

The diagram below represents the relationship between beak structure and food in several species of finches found on the Galapagos Islands.

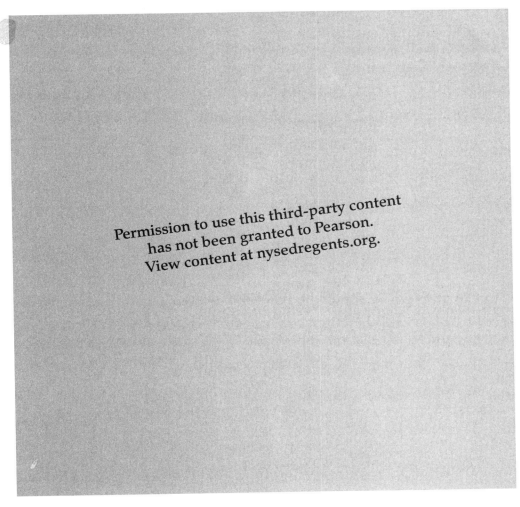

Permission to use this third-party content has not been granted to Pearson. View content at nysedregents.org.

Note: The answer to question 75 should be recorded on your separate answer sheet.

The different beak structures observed in the diagram are evidence of

(1) different species of finches adapting to different environments over many generations
(2) finches changing their beak characteristics so that they could feed efficiently
(3) finch species with different beak structures coming to the Galapagos Islands from the mainland
(4) finches mating with birds of other species and acquiring some of their traits

Base your answers to questions 76 through 78 on the information below and on your knowledge of biology

Permission to use this third-party content
has not been granted to Pearson.
View content at nysedregents.org.

Note: The answer to question 76 should be recorded on your separate answer sheet.

76 If a sudden genetic mutation in the birds that feed on these frogs made them able to consume any amount of the poison with no harm to them, it is most likely that

(1) the frogs that are least poisonous and less conspicuous now would survive better than those that have more poison

(2) the frogs that are most poisonous would continue to survive and be protected by the poison they contain

(3) without the protection of the poison, all of the frogs would need to change color to become less conspicuous

(4) the birds would find another source of food that does not contain any poison

77 Researcher Austin Penner of the University of Alberta has noted that climate change and deforestation in the habitat of the strawberry poison dart frog could have "drastic effects" as the habitat required for the development of the tadpoles [young] of these frogs is extremely specific. Explain why it is important to protect these poisonous frog species and the habitat that supports them. [1]

_____

_____

78 Frogs come in "more than a dozen different color patterns." State *one* method the scientists could have used to determine that they are all the same species. [1]

_____

_____

January '17   Regents Examination

Pulse rate is measured in beats per minute (bpm). Individual *A* has a resting pulse rate of 64 bpm. Individual *B* has a resting pulse rate of 82 bpm. Identify *two* reasons why the pulse rates of both of these individuals could be considered "normal." [1]

Reason 1: _____

Reason 2: _____

Base your answers to questions 80 and 81 on the information below and on your knowledge of biology.

An athlete bought a sport gel food and wanted to test it to see if it contained fats, starches, and glucose. The tests that the student used are shown in the table below.

	Test for Fat	Test for Starch	Test for Glucose
Positive Result	paper that is greasy	blue black color	brick red/orange color
Negative Result	paper that is not greasy	amber color	blue color

) The athlete received the following results from the tests.

	Test for Fat	Test for Starch	Test for Glucose
Student's Result	paper not greasy	blue black color	brick red/orange color

Identify the contents of the sports gel. [1]

_____

Note: The answer to question 81 should be recorded on your separate answer sheet.

1 If a starch-digesting enzyme were added to a sports gel that lists starch as an ingredient, which substance would increase in concentration?

(1) fat

(2) glucose

(3) amino acids

(4) water

Base your answers to questions 82 through 84 on the information below and on your knowledge of biology

Students in a high school biology class conducted an investigation on pulse rates. The thirty students performed three different activities and determined their pulse rates. Each activity was done three times. The average is shown in the graph below.

Note: The answer to question 82 should be recorded on your separate answer sheet.

82 The students want to improve the validity of their conclusion. The best way to accomplish this is to
(1) change the hypothesis
(2) repeat the investigation several times
(3) increase the number of variables
(4) increase the height of participants in each group

83 Some biology students concluded that classmates over 6 feet tall always have higher pulse rates than shorte classmates. Does the information from the investigation support this conclusion? Support your answer. [1

_____

_____

84 State the relationship between intensity of physical activity and pulse rate. [1]

_____

_____

85 Identify *one* adaptation, other than beak size and shape, a finch species might possess and state how tha would aid in its survival. [1]

_____

_____

January '17 Regents Examination

Part A

Answer all questions in this part. [30]

Directions (1–30): For *each* statement or question, record on the separate answer sheet the *number* of the [w]ord or expression that, of those given, best completes the statement or answers the question.

1 Which sequence represents structures organized from most complex to least complex?

(1) chloroplast → guard cell → leaf → oak tree
(2) guard cell → chloroplast → leaf → oak tree
(3) oak tree → guard cell → leaf → chloroplast
(4) oak tree → leaf → guard cell → chloroplast

2 Autotrophs differ from heterotrophs in that only autotrophs

(1) require carbon dioxide for cellular respiration
(2) release oxygen as a product of cellular respiration
(3) synthesize nutrients using carbon dioxide and water
(4) break down sugars to assemble other molecules

3 Burmese pythons are large snakes that have been introduced into the Florida Everglades ecosystem. Burmese pythons and alligators hunt the same prey. One likely effect of the introduction of the pythons is that

(1) alligators will have more prey available
(2) pythons will become native to the Everglades
(3) alligator populations will decline
(4) pythons will become an endangered species

4 Which activity enables humans to produce new genetic combinations in other organisms?

(1) selecting and breeding the organisms for specific traits
(2) increasing the number of enzymes available to the organisms
(3) growing organisms that reproduce asexually
(4) decreasing the amount of DNA in the diet of the organisms

5 Before a cell divides, an exact copy of each chromosome is made by the process of

(1) genetic engineering   (3) mutation
(2) replication   (4) recombination

6 Some time ago, there were thousands of California condors in North America. Large numbers were poisoned from lead in bullets that were used to kill the animals the condors fed on. An effort was made to help save this large scavenger. There are now more than 350 California condors in North America. The condors most likely increased in number because humans decided to

(1) produce lead-resistant condors through asexual reproduction
(2) pass laws against using lead bullets to kill animals used by condors for food
(3) introduce plants that didn't absorb the lead from discharged bullets
(4) produce lead-resistant prey for the condors through genetic engineering

7 In humans, the maintenance of a stable internal temperature is a direct result of

(1) detection of and reaction to stimuli in the environment
(2) digestion of starches and absorption of protein from the internal environment
(3) diffusion of water and excretion of glucose to the external environment
(4) transport of ATP and locomotion through the environment

8 Which molecules are needed to cut and copy segments of DNA?

(1) reproductive hormones
(2) carbohydrates
(3) antibodies
(4) biological catalysts

9 Evolution can occur at different rates; however, for evolution to occur, there must be

(1) variations within a species
(2) extinction of the species
(3) asexual reproduction
(4) no change in the genes of an organism

10 The two reactions illustrated in the diagrams below often occur when a foreign substance enters the boc

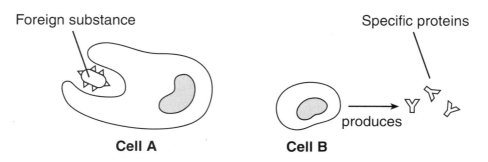

Cell A   Cell B

The cells labeled *A* and *B* are examples of cells known as

(1) guard cells
(2) reproductive cells
(3) white blood cells
(4) specialized skin cells

11 The diagram below represents a protein molecule present in some living things.

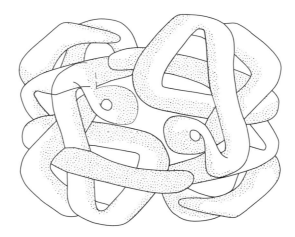

This type of molecule is composed of a sequence of

(1) amino acids arranged in a specific order
(2) simple sugars alternating with starches arranged in a folded pattern
(3) large inorganic subunits that form chains that interlock with each other
(4) four bases that make up the folded structure

12 Three human actions that have been made possible in recent times are:

• Doctors are able to diagnose and treat some fetal problems prior to the birth of a child.
• Cloning can produce large numbers of plants that are resistant to drought.
• Male insects can be sterilized with radiation to prevent them from mating successfully.

Which statement summarizes these three actions?

(1) Reproductive technology has medical, agricultural, and ecological applications.
(2) Development is a highly regulated process involving mitosis and differentiation.
(3) Reproduction and development are subject to environmental effects.
(4) Human development, birth, and aging should be viewed as a predictable pattern of events.

August '16 Regents Examination

3 Natural selection is best described as

(1) a change in an organism in response to a need of that organism
(2) a process of nearly constant improvement that leads to an organism that is nearly perfect
(3) differences in survival rates as a result of different inherited characteristics
(4) inheritance of characteristics acquired during the life of an organism

14 Which statement best describes a situation where competition occurs in an ecosystem?

(1) A deer outruns an attacking wolf.
(2) A deer, during the winter, consumes tree bark.
(3) A deer and a rabbit consume grass in a field.
(4) A deer and a rabbit are both startled by a hawk flying overhead.

15 A woman changes her hair color to red; however, her children will not inherit this red hair color because the woman does not have

(1) genes for red hair in her skin
(2) genes for red hair in her sex cells
(3) proteins for red hair in the placenta
(4) proteins for red hair in her egg cells

16 Fossils provide evidence that

(1) life on Earth millions of years ago was more complex than life is today
(2) the changes that will occur in species in the future are easy to predict
(3) many species of organisms that lived long ago are now extinct
(4) most species of organisms that lived long ago are exactly the same today

17 A male frigatebird displays to the female by inflating its large red throat sac, throwing its head back, vibrating its wings, and producing a "drumming" sound with its throat sac. For the frigatebird, this behavior has most likely resulted in

(1) hiding from predators
(2) greater reproductive success
(3) locating new sources of food
(4) reduced population growth

18 Plant species X lives in a hot, dry environment. Slowly, over hundreds of years, the climate becomes wetter. Fungi attack species X and cause the population of species X to decrease. However, plant species X could survive if the plants

(1) try to mutate quickly and synthesize new proteins
(2) are watered often and fertilized with extra nutrients
(3) can adapt to the new conditions by mating with the fungus
(4) have a few members of the population that are fungus-resistant

19 The diagram below represents reproduction in a yeast cell. The genes in the bud are identical to the genes in the parent.

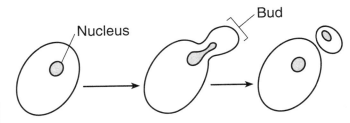

This type of production of offspring is a form of

(1) sexual reproduction
(2) asexual reproduction
(3) gene manipulation
(4) genetic engineering

20 A human cell that contains all of the information necessary for the growth and development of a complete organism is

(1) a sperm cell   (3) a zygote
(2) a gamete   (4) an egg cell

21 When would exposure to a potentially harmful substance be most likely to damage many organs in a developing embryo?

(1) during the last three months of pregnancy
(2) during the early stages of pregnancy
(3) during the formation of the zygote
(4) during meiosis in both males and females

22 The human female reproductive system is represented below.

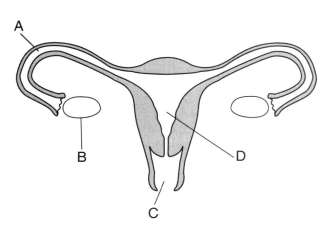

Within which structure does the placenta normally develop?

(1) *A*   (3) *C*
(2) *B*   (4) *D*

23 An energy-rich organic compound needed by organisms is

(1) water   (3) oxygen
(2) salt   (4) glucose

24 SCIDS (Severe Combined Immunodeficiency Syndrome) is a disorder where a genetic mutation inhibits the production and functioning of T-cells. T-cells are special types of white blood cells that play a role in the body's immune response. A possible symptom of SCIDS would be an increase in the

(1) number of antigens produced
(2) red blood cell count
(3) number of infections by pathogens
(4) ability to maintain homeostasis

25 An organ, such as a kidney, used for transplant needs to be tested for compatibility with the person who is to receive the organ. If this is not done, the

(1) donated organ might attack the body
(2) donated organ might attack the immune system
(3) immune system might attack its own body cells
(4) immune system might attack the donated organ

26 A researcher concludes from a 10-year stu that the biodiversity of an ecosystem h increased. Which set of observations represer evidence for this claim?

(1) There were more niches and greater stabili in the ecosystem.
(2) There were more niches and less energy lc as heat in the ecosystem.
(3) There were fewer niches for decompose and less stability.
(4) There were fewer niches for consumers a greater cycling of materials.

27 The final consumers in many food webs are

(1) autotrophs   (3) herbivores
(2) hosts   (4) carnivores

28 Abandoned farmland that once grew corn is nc covered with bushes and small trees. The observed changes resulted directly from

(1) evolutionary change
(2) ecological succession
(3) loss of biodiversity
(4) selective breeding

29 The overuse of chemical fertilizers has resulte in the growth of some lawns in whic decomposers cannot live. This would interfe most directly with the ability of the law ecosystem to

(1) recycle energy
(2) recycle nutrients
(3) maintain atmospheric pH
(4) reduce biodiversity

30 On Long Island, several businesses us geothermal technology. This involves taking he; from within Earth and using it to heat building One benefit of this technology is that it

(1) contributes to global warming
(2) reduces the ozone shield
(3) reduces dependence on fossil fuels
(4) decreases resources for many species

Answer all questions in this part. [13]

Directions (31–43): For *each* statement or question, record on the separate answer sheet the *number* of the word or expression that, of those given, best completes the statement or answers the question.

31 Recently, researchers from Stanford University have changed mouse skin cells into mouse nerve cells. This was accomplished by inserting genes that control the synthesis of certain proteins into the skin cells. This type of research is often successful in advancing knowledge regarding the functioning of human cells because

(1) cells present in humans often function in similar ways to cells present in other organisms
(2) cells from different types of organisms function differently when transplanted into humans
(3) the cells in all complex organisms contain the same genes and function in similar ways
(4) cellular research using mice can always be applied to human cells since all complex organisms produce the same proteins

32 In the experimental setup below, which substance would be used to prove that the gas produced by the yeast in the vacuum bottle could change the pH of the liquid in the flask?

(1) an indicator
(2) a chemical messenger
(3) an enzyme
(4) a salt solution

33 Which statement best expresses a basic scientific assumption?

(1) Interpretation of experimental results has provided explanations for all natural phenomena.
(2) If a conclusion is valid, similar investigations by other scientists should result in the same conclusion.
(3) For any conclusion to be valid, the design of the experiment requires that only two groups be compared.
(4) After a scientist formulates a conclusion based on an experiment, no further investigation is necessary.

34 The diagram below represents a cycle that occurs in nature.

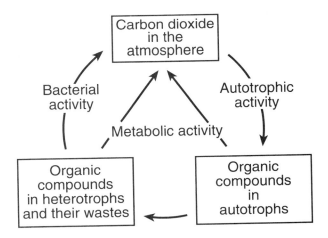

Which phrase describes a human activity that could have a *negative* effect on this cycle?

(1) a decrease in the amount of sulfates given off by motor vehicles
(2) an increase in recycling programs for plastics and metals
(3) the continued deforestation and removal of forest resources
(4) development of programs to conserve wildlife

August '16   Regents Examination

Base your answers to questions 35 through 37 on the information and graph below and on your knowledge of biology.

A farmer growing potatoes notices aphids, a type of insect, feeding on the plants. An insecticide was sprayed on the plants several times over a two-year period. The graph represents samples of three different generations of insecticide-resistant and nonresistant aphids over this time period.

Generations of Aphids

35 The resistance gene was present in the aphid population as a result of
(1) the need of the potatoes to become resistant to the insecticide
(2) changes in the aphids' local habitat by the insecticide
(3) a recombination of the proteins in the potato cells
(4) a random change in the aphids' DNA sequence

36 In year three, the farmer discontinued the use of the insecticide. Which statement would best predict th population in generation 4?
(1) The nonresistant aphid would become extinct.
(2) The nonresistant aphid population would likely increase.
(3) The resistant aphid would mutate to a nonresistant aphid.
(4) The plants would be free of insect populations.

37 One *negative* consequence of using an insecticide is that it
(1) selects for insecticide-resistant organisms
(2) keeps a balance of organic compounds
(3) encourages biodiversity in plants
(4) gives the nonresistant aphids a survival advantage

8 The activity of a single-celled organism is represented in the diagram below.

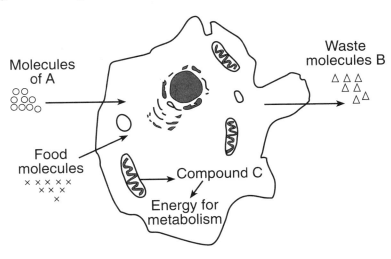

Which concept is best illustrated by this diagram?

(1) The life functions performed by single-celled organisms are different from the life functions performed by complex organisms.
(2) Single-celled organisms carry out life functions that are essential for survival.
(3) Since single-celled organisms lack organs, they can survive only in moist environments.
(4) Single-celled organisms contain one organelle that performs all the life functions.

39 The chart below provides information about two scientific discoveries in the field of biology.

Early Discovery	Later Discovery
People living near swamps are more likely to get malaria than people who do not live near swamps. Burning swamps early in the summer reduces the amount of malaria.	Mosquitoes breed and lay their eggs in swamps and other pools of still water. Mosquitoes are the carriers of the organisms that cause malaria.
Dark-staining bodies called chromosomes can be seen only in dividing cells. The number of chromosomes doubles during cell division.	Chromosomes contain DNA, which is able to copy itself. DNA carries the genetic code, which is passed from a parent cell to two or more daughter cells.

Which statement is the best interpretation of the material presented in the chart?

(1) Scientific explanations are built by combining evidence that can be observed with what people already know.
(2) Inquiry involves making judgments about the reliability of the source and relevance of the information.
(3) Science provides information, but values are also essential to making ethical decisions.
(4) Hypotheses are valuable even if they turn out not to be true, because they may lead to further investigation.

Base your answers to questions 40 through 43 on the diagram below and on your knowledge of biology. This diagram represents the roles of different parts of the human body in keeping blood sugar at a balanced normal level over time.

Homeostasis of Blood Sugar Level

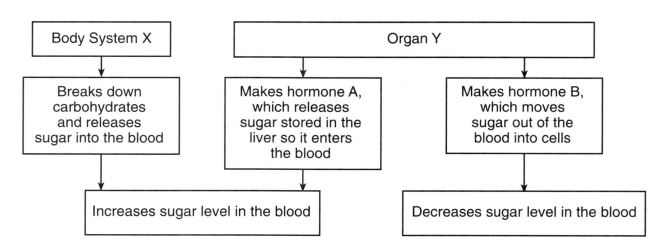

40 The diagram shows human body structures that are coordinated to maintain homeostasis. Which row correctly identifies the functions of these structures?

Row	Body System X	Organ Y
(1)	Digestion	Regulation
(2)	Circulation	Synthesis
(3)	Excretion	Transport
(4)	Locomotion	Nutrition

41 When body system *X* releases too much sugar into the blood, the body can maintain homeostasis by making

(1) more hormone *A*, only
(2) more hormone *B*, only
(3) more hormone *A* and more hormone *B*
(4) no hormone *A* and no hormone *B*

42 If organ *Y* becomes unable to produce enough hormone *B*, then homeostasis would be disrupted. To restore homeostasis and compensate for the lack of hormone *B*, one useful action would be to

(1) increase the production of hormone *A*
(2) remove organ *Y* from the body surgically
(3) reduce the carbohydrates in body system *X*
(4) reduce the synthesis of enzymes in organ *Y*

43 If body system *X* temporarily stops releasing sugar into the blood, a likely response of the body would be to

(1) stop using enzymes in body system *X*
(2) stop organ *Y* from producing hormone *A*
(3) start to increase synthesis of hormone *B*
(4) start to increase synthesis of hormone *A*

Part B–2

Answer all questions in this part. [12]

Directions (44–55): For those questions that are multiple choice, record on the separate answer sheet e *number* of the choice that, of those given, best completes each statement or answers each question. For all her questions in this part, follow the directions given and record your answers in the spaces provided in this amination booklet.

Base your answers to questions 44 through 47 on the information, diagram, and table below and on your howledge of biology.

A concentrated starch solution was placed in a thistle tube with a semi-permeable membrane covering the wide opening. It was then placed in a beaker of water. The height of the solution in the tube was measured every 5 minutes for 25 minutes. The setup and the data collected are shown below.

Height of Liquid in Thistle Tube

Time (min)	Height (cm)
0	2
5	3
10	6
15	8
20	10
25	11

Directions (44–45): Using the information in the data table, construct a line graph on the grid below following the directions below.

44 Mark an appropriate scale, without any breaks in the data, on each labeled axis. [1]

45 Plot the data for height on the grid. Connect the points and surround each point with a small circle. [1]

Example:

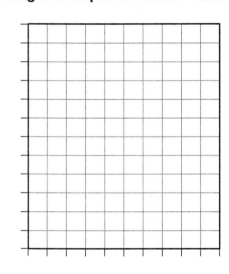

Height of Liquid in Thistle Tube

Height (cm)

Time (min)

46 Explain why the height of the solution in the thistle tube increased during the 25-minute period. [1]

_____

_____

Note: The answer to question 47 should be recorded on your separate answer sheet.

47 The experiment was repeated, and an amber-colored solution was added to the water in the beaker. After 10 minutes, the water in the beaker remained amber-colored and the starch solution had turned blue-black. The most likely reason for this observation is that

(1) starch molecules moved out of the thistle tube
(2) water molecules moved into the thistle tube
(3) amber-colored solution moved into the thistle tube
(4) water molecules moved out of the thistle tube

August '16   Regents Examination

Base your answer to question 48 on the information and diagrams below and on your knowledge of biology.

When fish of certain species are injured, a chemical substance stored in skin cells of the fish is released into the water. This chemical causes an alarm response among other fish of the same species in the area. Nearby fish of this species become more alert and group together near the bottom.

No Alarm Response

Alarm Response

48 Explain why the chemical released from the injured fish may *not* cause an alarm response in other fish species. [1]

_____

_____

_____

Base your answers to questions 49 through 51 on the diagram below and on your knowledge of biology.

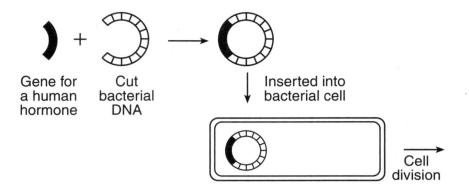

Note: The answer to question 49 should be recorded on your separate answer sheet.

49 The process represented in the diagram is

(1) DNA replication   (3) gel electrophoresis

(2) natural selection   (4) genetic engineering

Note: The answer to question 50 should be recorded on your separate answer sheet.

50 The original gene for the production of a human hormone was most likely removed from a

(1) chromosome   (3) mitochondrion

(2) ribosome   (4) cell membrane

51 State *one* possible reason why a gene for the production of a human hormone would be placed in bacterial DNA. [1]

_____

_____

_____

Base your answers to questions 52 through 55 on the passage below and on your knowledge of biology.

The lake sturgeon is a fish that often grows over six feet long and can weigh close to two hundred pounds. It is currently an endangered species in the Great Lakes area, although the species has lived in those lakes and rivers for millions of years. Now, there is a program to increase the sturgeon population by reintroducing lake sturgeon to areas where they have disappeared.

Like the lake sturgeon, bloater fish are also found in the Great Lakes. Both find their food on or near the bottoms of lakes. They eat a variety of small organisms, including insect larvae, worms, and clams. These small organisms feed on algae.

52 Identify *one* population that will *decrease* in size after the lake sturgeon are added to the new ecosystems. Support your answer. [1]

_____

_____

53 Part of the food web of a lake ecosystem is represented in the diagram below. Indicate the position in the food web where each organism listed below would be placed, by writing the name of each in the appropriate box. [1]

algae
bloater fish
clams

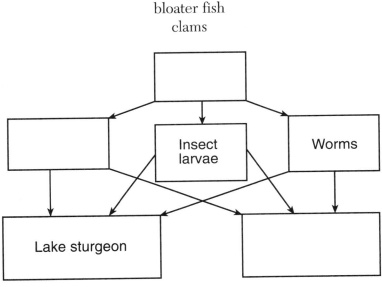

54 Identify which population, other than lake sturgeon, will increase in size after the lake sturgeon are added to the new ecosystems. Support your answer. [1]

_____

_____

55 State what the arrows in the food web represent. [1]

_____

_____

Part C

Answer all questions in this part. [17]

Directions (56–72): Record your answers in the spaces provided in this examination booklet.

Base your answers to questions 56 and 57 on the information and drawing below and on your knowledge of biology. The drawing represents a salamander. Salamanders are small amphibians that live in a variety of environments.

Two species of salamander inhabit an island. The habitat on each side of the island is different. One side tends to be wet; the other side tends to be dry. Researchers want to know if the salamanders will survive equally well on either side of the island. Species *A* lives on the wet side of the island, while Species *B* lives on the dry side of the island. Researchers develop two artificial habitats, one that simulates conditions on the wet side and one that simulates conditions on the dry side.

56 Explain why researchers would put the salamanders in an artificial environment, as opposed to conducting the experiment in their natural habitat. [1]

_____

_____

57 Researchers put three salamanders of each species in each of the two different artificial environments. Why would other scientists question the validity of the conclusions based on this setup? [1]

_____

_____

August '16   Regents Examination

Base your answers to questions 58 through 61 on the information and diagram below and on your knowledge biology.

Green Roofs

People in Albany and New York City are using "green roofs" to improve the environment. A green roof can be added to many buildings that have large, flat roofs. Green roofs have three parts: a protective layer to separate plant roots from the roof of the building, an absorptive layer to catch and hold rainwater, and a layer of plants. Often, green roofs use *Sedum*, a short, desert plant, because it is efficient at storing water in its leaves and can withstand the colder climate.

A green roof saves energy, reduces carbon dioxide in the atmosphere, and prevents rainwater and melting snow from overloading sewer systems. It can also protect the roof of a building from damage. However, green roofs can be expensive to install, and require care and maintenance.

58 Most varieties of *Sedum* are not native plants in Albany or New York City. State *one* reason why it may be dangerous to introduce a new species to an established ecosystem. [1]

_____

_____

59 State *one* reason why a green roof reduces the amount of carbon dioxide in the atmosphere. [1]

_____

_____

60 State *one* reason why it is important to reduce the amount of carbon dioxide in the atmosphere. [1]

_____

_____

61 State *one disadvantage* of a green roof. [1]

_____

_____

62 A scientist took samples from a culture of *E. coli* bacteria and placed them in each of 100 petri dishes. Once the bacteria began to grow in the dishes, she exposed 50 of the dishes to x-ray radiation and 50 to natural light. After five days, she examined samples of DNA from the bacteria and recorded any differences she found between the DNA of the two groups. State *one* hypothesis the experiment would test. [1]

_____

_____

Base your answers to questions 63 and 64 on the passage below and on your knowledge of biology.

63 Identify *one* specific difference, other than it is a two-step vaccination, between Nabel's vaccination and a traditional flu vaccine. [1]

_____

_____

64 Explain how injecting dead or weakened viruses into a person can help to fight against future infection from that virus. [1]

_____

_____

August '16   Regents Examination

Base your answers to questions 65 through 68 on the information below and on your knowledge of biology.

Bald Eagle Facts

- Bald eagles eat primarily fish, carrion (dead animals), smaller birds, and rodents. Their most important non-carrion food is fish, which they catch by swooping down and grabbing fish that are near the surface of the water.
- The number of nesting pairs in the lower 48 United States increased from fewer than 450 in the early 1960s to more than 4,500 adult bald eagle nesting pairs in the 1990s. Today, there are an estimated 9,789 nesting pairs of bald eagles.
- Bald eagles are found in large numbers in certain areas during the winter (known as roosts). These winter roosts are located in areas where prey are plentiful. Winter roosts are protected under federal law, and managed with a buffer zone to reduce human disturbance. As winter ends, the eagles return to their summer nesting/hunting areas.

Bald Eagle Research

In the winter of 2009, volunteers from an Audubon group conducted a survey of roosting bald eagles at four locations in an area in the lower Hudson River Valley. The data below show the average number of eagles sighted and the number of visits made by the volunteers each month. Among the other data collected were percent ice cover and percent cloud cover on the surface of the water. The eagles fly freely between these four sites, depending on a variety of conditions.

Some of the data are shown in the table below.

Bald Eagles Sighted at Four Hudson Valley Locations in 2009

Location	January		February		March	
	Average Number of Eagles	Number of Visits	Average Number of Eagles	Number of Visits	Average Number of Eagles	Number of Visits
Croton Reservoir	22.86	7	47.88	8	9.17	6
George's Island Park	27.00	7	18.38	8	5.00	4
George's Island North	12.29	7	4.43	7	2.20	5
Stony Point	3.57	7	3.63	8	0.00	5

65 State *one* reason why the percent ice cover is important to the ability of eagles to obtain food. [1]

_____

_____

66 What inference can be made about the percent ice cover at Croton Reservoir between January and February 2009? Support your answer. [1]

_____

_____

67 State *one* reason why the number of eagles sighted showed a change at all four sites between February and March. [1]

_____

_____

68 State *one* possible reason why a popular hiking trail in this area is closed during eagle roosting seasons. [1]

_____

_____

Base your answers to questions 69 through 72 on the information below and on your knowledge of biology.

Coral Reef Ecosystems

There are many ecological interactions that maintain the biodiversity present in coral reefs. In addition to coral, microscopic algae, seaweed, sea grasses, sponges and worms, and a variety of fish are among the organisms that live in reef ecosystems. Ocean currents often link different reef systems and move organisms from one reef area to another. This movement is a factor in repopulating a reef that has been damaged by environmental changes.

One environmental change involves an increased growth of seaweed. When the population of seaweed increases, the reef shifts from a coral-dominated ecosystem to a seaweed-dominated ecosystem. This change disrupts the relationships between the organisms that live there.

Studies have shown that, as the density of seaweed in a reef area increases, the number of fish that eat the seaweed in that area decreases. This may be due to the presence of more predators, or the taste of the more mature plants. The fish move to areas where there is less seaweed growth. As this trend continues, the reef areas are taken over by the seaweed. Once this happens, it is very hard to remove the seaweed and restore the reef to a healthy ecosystem.

In addition to this problem, temperature changes are threatening the ocean currents that connect the reef systems. A change in the currents would reduce the movement of fish larvae from one area to another. This contributes to the seaweed problem.

69 State the role of the sea grasses in the reef ecosystem. [1]

_____

_____

70 Identify *one* abiotic factor that is affecting the stability of the coral reef ecosystems and state how the factor identified is important to the coral reef ecosystems. [1]

Abiotic factor: _____

Effect: _____

_____

71 State *one* reason why it is important to maintain the stability of the coral reefs. [1]

_____

_____

72 State *one* advantage of the fish larvae moving by ocean currents into a damaged reef ecosystem. [1]

_____

_____

Part D

Answer all questions in this part. [13]

Directions (73–85): For those questions that are multiple choice, record on the separate answer sheet th[e] *number* of the choice that, of those given, best completes the statement or answers the question. For all oth[er] questions in this part, follow the directions given and record your answers in the spaces provided in th[e] examination booklet.

Base your answers to questions 73 and 74 on the diagram below, which represents a process that occurs [in] living cells, and on your knowledge of biology.

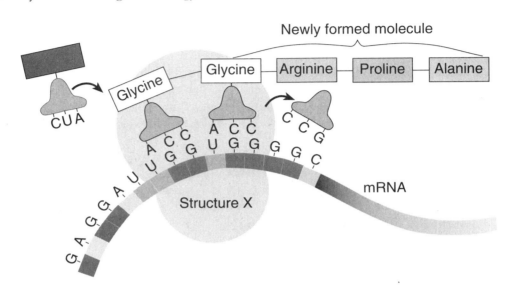

Note: The answer to question 73 should be recorded on your separate answer sheet.

73 The process shown in the diagram is

   (1) cellular respiration   (3) gene recombination
   (2) cellular reorganization   (4) protein synthesis

Note: The answer to question 74 should be recorded on your separate answer sheet.

74 Structure *X* is a

   (1) mitochondrion   (3) nucleus
   (2) vacuole   (4) ribosome

Base your answers to questions 75 through 77 on the diagram below and on your knowledge of biology.

Variations in Beaks of Galapagos Islands Finches

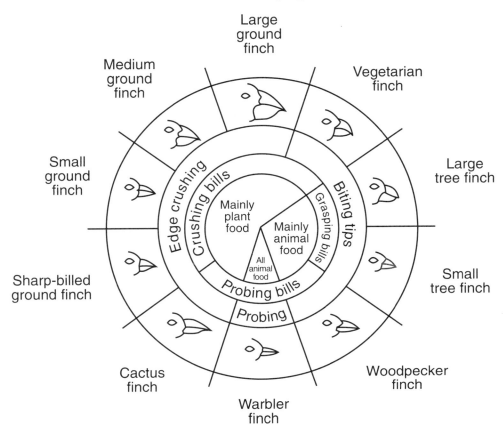

from: *Galapagos: A Natural History Guide*

Note: The answer to question 75 should be recorded on your separate answer sheet.

75 A finch that picks small insects out from cracks in the bark of trees would most likely have a beak that is

(1) sharp and thin
(2) sharp and thick
(3) rounded and thin
(4) rounded and thick

Note: The answer to question 76 should be recorded on your separate answer sheet.

76 Which statement is a basic assumption from *The Beaks of Finches* lab?

(1) The type of beak indicates the type of food the finch eats.
(2) Different birds have different songs.
(3) Birds with larger beaks can find mates more easily.
(4) Nesting behavior of finches is an inherited trait.

77 State *two* reasons why the large ground finch and sharp-billed ground finch could live on the same island but not compete for food, even though they both eat mainly plant food. [1]

Reason 1: _____

Reason 2: _____

August '16   Regents Examination

Base your answer to question 78 on the table below and on your knowledge of biology. The table sho
which of four enzymes are present in three related plant species.

Comparison of Four Enzymes

Plant Species	Enzyme W	Enzyme X	Enzyme Y	Enzyme Z
Species A	present	present	absent	present
Species B	absent	absent	present	absent
Species C	present	present	absent	present

The tree diagrams below show two possible evolutionary relationships between the three species.

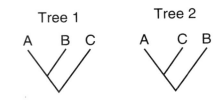

Tree 1
A B C

Tree 2
A   C B

78 In the space below, write the number of the tree diagram that shows the most probable evolution
relationship between the three species. Support your answer. [1]

Tree diagram: _____

_____

_____

_____

Base your answers to questions 79 and 80 on the diagram below, which represents the shrinking of a cell in response to an increase in the concentration of a substance outside of the cell.

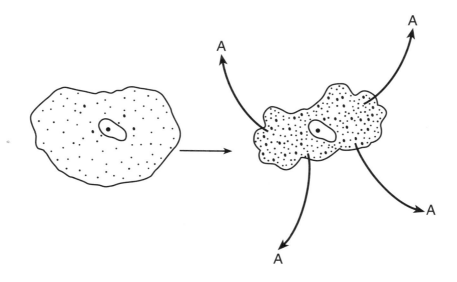

Identify substance A. [1]

_____

Identify *one* likely substance in the environment of the cell that caused this response. [1]

_____

_____

Note: The answer to question 81 should be recorded on your separate answer sheet.

A student lifted weights after school and found that his muscles started to burn. He couldn't continue to lift the weights after prolonged exercising. This muscle fatigue is most likely due to
(1) the heart beating too fast and tiring out
(2) the lungs accumulating oxygen
(3) lack of oxygen and build up of waste in the muscles
(4) lack of carbon dioxide in the muscles

Base your answers to questions 82 and 83 on the diagram below and on your knowledge of biology. The diagram represents three sections of a cell membrane showing three different methods involved in the transport of various molecules across the membrane.

Method A **Method B** **Method C**

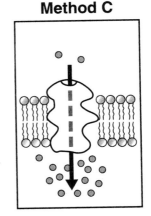

Note: The answer to question 82 should be recorded on your separate answer sheet.

82 Methods *A* and *B* are classified as methods of passive transport because they do not require

(1) ATP
(2) carbon dioxide

(3) light
(4) DNA

83 Using information from the diagram, state *one* reason why the movement of molecules in method *C* represents active transport. [1]

_____

_____

_____

34 State *one* reason why some species might have similar body structures even if they are *not* closely related. [1]

_____

_____

35 A student went out to the school track and walked two laps, ran two laps, and then walked two more laps. On the grid below, draw a line that shows what most likely happened to the pulse rate of the student during these activities. [1]

Effect of Activity on Pulse Rate

Pulse Rate

Time

_____

Part A

Answer all questions in this part. [30]

Directions (1–30): For *each* statement or question, record on the separate answer sheet the *number* of the word or expression that, of those given, best completes the statement or answers the question.

1 Which statement is an example of the interdependence of organisms?

(1) Owls hunt at night.
(2) Ants get food from insects and protect insects from predators.
(3) Ticks feed on the blood of animals and the ticks grow larger.
(4) Crows feed on dead mice.

2 Residents of a town are concerned that a recently built factory could pose health risks. Scientists were asked to investigate the effects of the factory on the health of local residents. The most relevant information they reported was that

(1) in a survey, residents felt that the air in town looks dirtier now
(2) there have been reports that other types of factories have been linked with health issues
(3) residents have occasionally seen smoke coming from the factory
(4) local medical facilities have recently reported a 15% increase in the number of patients treated for asthma

3 Farmers may someday clone their best milk-producing cow into a whole herd. What potential disadvantage might be important to consider in having such a large group of clones on one farm?

(1) It may be difficult to tell the animals apart.
(2) Lack of variation may limit survival in the herd.
(3) The cows could be fertilized by only one type of bull.
(4) The cows could be mated only with each other.

4 DNA replication occurs in preparation for

(1) mitosis, only
(2) meiosis, only
(3) both mitosis and meiosis
(4) neither mitosis nor meiosis

5 An individual eats a hamburger. Which two systems must interact to transfer the nutrients in the hamburger to human muscle tissue?

(1) respiratory and excretory
(2) digestive and immune
(3) digestive and circulatory
(4) circulatory and respiratory

6 The diagram below shows cell *A* completing a life process.

Cell *A*

Cell *A* performs functions similar to the tissues and systems in complex, multicellular organisms. This process results in

(1) increased genetic variation
(2) the maintenance of homeostasis
(3) a reduction in competition
(4) increased autotrophic nutrition

7 The shape of a protein molecule directly determines its

(1) movements through the cytoplasm
(2) functions inside and outside of cells
(3) roles in building water molecules
(4) circulation throughout the body

8 The diagram below represents a cell and some molecules in its environment.

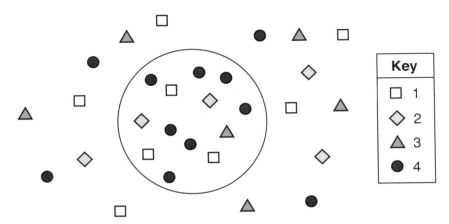

Which molecule would require the use of energy in order to be brought into the cell?

(1) 1

(3) 3

(2) 2

(4) 4

9 Many domestic plants that are currently used for food by humans share a wild plant ancestor. The chang
that have occurred in four common plants and the results are shown in the chart below.

Wild Plant Ancestor	Change That Occurred	Resulting Modern Plant
wild mustard	reduced flower development	broccoli
wild mustard	sterile flowers	cauliflower
wild mustard	enlargement of leaves	kale
wild mustard	shortened stem length	cabbage

What event most likely produced the changes that occurred in the wild plant ancestor?

(1) Mutations in wild mustard sex cells were passed on to offspring.
(2) Humans did not like to eat wild mustard.
(3) Competition for survival occurred in all ecosystems of the world.
(4) Ancient herbivores overgrazed wild mustard.

10 A strand of DNA in a skin cell contains the bases:

A-T-G-C-C-A-T-C-G-G-T-A

After the cell is exposed to ultraviolet light, the strand contains the bases:

A-T-G-G-C-C-A-T-C-G-G-T-A

Which statement describes the result of this exposure?

(1) A new base has been inserted.
(2) A base has been deleted.
(3) One base has been substituted for another.
(4) There have been no changes in the bases.

11 An ameba, a one-celled organism, can move, ingest, and transport materials within the cell, because it has

(1) organs   (3) tissues
(2) organelles   (4) systems

12 In humans, the placenta is essential to the embryo for

(1) nutrition, excretion, and reproduction
(2) respiration, nutrition, and excretion
(3) movement, reproduction, and nutrition
(4) coordination, movement, and growth

13 A student infected by a common cold virus ran a low-grade fever. After a few days, the student's temperature returned to normal and the student was free of cold symptoms. The fever served as

(1) an antigen in the circulatory system
(2) an immune response to a pathogen
(3) a biological catalyst
(4) a weakened pathogen

14 Many animals have developed courtship behaviors. Males will often dance, swim, or sing in a particular way to attract a female. Males who are more successful at the courtship behavior will have a greater chance of having more offspring. This behavior is a result of

(1) natural selection
(2) genetic engineering
(3) asexual reproduction
(4) gene manipulation

15 After a zygote is formed, specialization of cells occurs. Through which process do the cells of a zygote become specialized?

(1) sexual reproduction   (3) fertilization
(2) meiosis   (4) differentiation

16 A farmer wanted to rid his apple trees of a particular leaf-eating insect. He sprayed his trees with an insecticide that killed 98% of the insects. The survival of 2% of this population of insects is most likely due to

(1) genes obtained from another species
(2) certain chemicals that stimulated over-production
(3) variations that resulted from sexual repro-duction
(4) their ability to produce food from the pesticide

17 Which occurrence represents an example of evolution?

(1) Exposure to radiation reduces the rate of mutation in leaf cells.
(2) A mutation in a liver cell causes a person to produce an enzyme that is less efficient.
(3) Cells in a zygote eventually change into bone cells or skin cells.
(4) Some antibiotics are almost useless, because pathogens have developed a resistance to these antibiotics.

18 Populations of aspen trees in the western United States are being destroyed by an unexplained illness. The altered landscape is affecting the animals that live there. Populations of deer mice are increasing greatly in these areas. Unfortunately, these mice often carry a virus that is deadly to humans. This scenario best illustrates that

(1) a change in the environment always results in disease
(2) humans are the cause of the breakdown of this ecosystem
(3) the stability of this ecosystem is limited by the amount of water available
(4) every population in an ecosystem is linked with other populations

19 The paramecium is a single-celled organism that reproduces asexually. The offspring of a paramecium usually contain

(1) only half of the genes of the parent cells
(2) more DNA than the parent cell
(3) genetic material identical to that of the parent cell
(4) fewer mutations than the parent cell

20 A dead or weakened pathogen used to establish immunity would most likely be found in

(1) a pesticide   (3) a vaccine
(2) an antibiotic   (4) a toxin

21 Which statement is true for all of the organisms in the ecosystem represented in the diagram below?

(1) They use energy to combine the inorganic molecules carbon dioxide and water into energy-rich organic compounds.
(2) Stored energy cannot be used by these organisms as a source of energy for life processes.
(3) Energy stored in inorganic molecules is released during cellular respiration in these organisms.
(4) Energy is used by the organisms to obtain and transport materials, and to eliminate wastes.

22 When a natural disaster destroys a stable ecosystem, the area is temporarily less stable than before. This is most likely due to

(1) a decrease in biodiversity
(2) an increase in the number of food chains
(3) an increase in the number of species
(4) a decrease in the rate of mutation

23 An individual walks out of his air-conditioned (75°F) home into the hot outside environment (85°F). His ability to adjust to this changing environment involves a mechanism similar to

(1) the regulation of water loss by guard cells in plant leaves
(2) the digestion of carbohydrates by enzymes
(3) using ATP for the diffusion of water
(4) glucose production in the pancreas

24 Nonrenewable resources are

(1) not finite and are not depleted over time
(2) not finite and are depleted over time
(3) finite and are not depleted over time
(4) finite and are depleted over time

25 Dodder, a plant with no chlorophyll, grows on a living plant of a different species from which it obtains nutrients. Which pair of terms describes this relationship?

(1) parasite and host
(2) predator and prey
(3) producer and decomposer
(4) consumer and scavenger

26 Three human hormones most directly involved in sexual reproduction are

(1) estrogen, insulin, and progesterone
(2) testosterone, estrogen, and insulin
(3) progesterone, ATP, and testosterone
(4) estrogen, progesterone, and testosterone

27 At one point, scientists observed that the ozone shield was getting thinner. They warned that the loss of the effectiveness of this shield may lead to an increase in

(1) allergies to ozone
(2) mutations that lead to cancer
(3) viral diseases, such as AIDS
(4) ice formation at the poles

28 As it grows from a seed to a mature plant, a plant will grow taller and thicker. Which are abiotic factors most responsible for the increase in the mass of the plant?

(1) water, minerals, bacteria
(2) sunlight, oxygen, plant receptors
(3) minerals, water, plant enzymes
(4) water, sunlight, carbon dioxide

29 Structures in an animal cell are represented in the diagram below.

Which row in the chart correctly identifies the functions of structures *A*, *B*, and *C*?

Row	Structure A	Structure B	Structure C
(1)	waste removal	extract energy from nutrients	protein synthesis
(2)	information storage	transport of materials	storage of liquids
(3)	protein synthesis	storage of wastes	reproduction
(4)	cell communication	transport of materials	waste removal

30 The diagram below represents how air pollution may move across the eastern United States.

Movement of Air Pollution

In order to reduce the amount of air pollution in Pennsylvania, which change is necessary?

(1) Laws must be passed to protect endangered species.
(2) The use of natural resources must be increased.
(3) More coal-burning power plants must be built.
(4) The cooperation between the different states must be improved.

Part B–1

Answer all questions in this part. [13]

Directions (31–43): For *each* statement or question, record on the separate answer sheet the *number* of the word or expression that, of those given, best completes the statement or answers the question.

Base your answers to questions 31 and 32 on the diagram below and on your knowledge of biology. The diagram represents part of a food web.

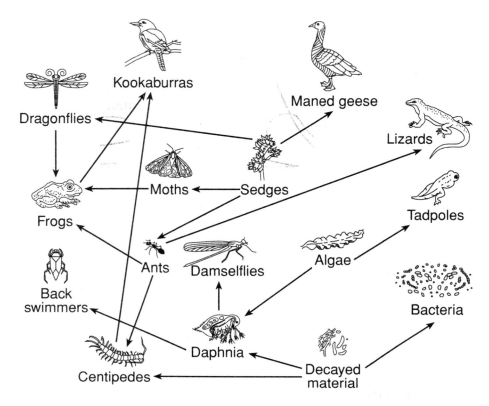

31 Which sequence of organisms represents a food chain within this food web?

(1) tadpoles → algae → daphnia → back swimmers
(2) sedges → ants → frogs → kookaburras
(3) algae → daphnia → decayed material → bacteria
(4) dragonflies → sedges → ants →centipedes

32 Which population would be most immediately affected by the removal of the lizard population?

(1) sedges   (3) ants
(2) algae   (4) centipedes

33 During an investigation, a student measures out 15 grams of salt. Then, he measures 15 milliliters of water and adds the salt to it. Next, he measures a 1 centimeter wide by 4 centimeters long section of plant leaf. Which list of tools is arranged in the order that the student used them?

(1) graduated cylinder, ruler, balance
(2) balance, ruler, graduated cylinder
(3) graduated cylinder, balance, ruler
(4) balance, graduated cylinder, ruler

Base your answers to questions 34 through 36 on the graph below and on your knowledge of biology. The graph shows the masses of different types of plants found in an area of the Adirondack Mountains after a forest fire occurred.

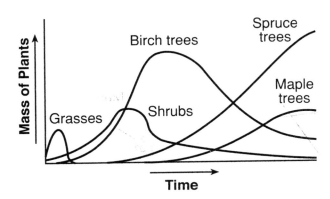

34 Based on the information provided in the graph, the process that is occurring is

(1) ecological succession
(2) biological evolution
(3) selective breeding
(4) genetic engineering

35 The time shown in the graph is most likely measured in

(1) days
(2) weeks
(3) months
(4) years

36 The mass of plants shown in the graph refers to the mass of a number of

(1) populations
(2) decomposers
(3) ecosystems
(4) communities

June '16   Regents Examination

Base your answers to questions 37 and 38 on the diagram below and on your knowledge of biology. The diagram represents a portion of a starch molecule.

37 The building blocks for this molecule are
(1) amino acids
(2) simple sugars
(3) fats
(4) molecular bases

38 The energy in this molecule is stored
(1) in the bonds between atoms
(2) in the oxygen found in the molecule
(3) when the carbon atoms break off
(4) when water breaks this molecule apart

Base your answer to question 39 on the information below and on your knowledge of biology.

A genetically modified pig, nicknamed the "enviropig," has the ability to produce a bacterial enzyme in its saliva that helps reduce the amount of phosphorus in its wastes. Phosphorus pollution is a serious environmental concern. Enviropigs are expensive, but the cost is balanced against the benefit to the environment. There is also a concern that the US Department of Agriculture still has not cleared enviropig meat for human consumption.

39 Government agencies and citizens should propose the use of enviropig in the future only after
(1) developing ways to remove the bacterial enzyme
(2) assessing risks, costs, and benefits
(3) people have eaten lots of enviropig meat and determined the effects
(4) a different, cheaper pig can be produced regardless of the output of phosphorus

Base your answers to questions 40 and 41 on the information below and on your knowledge of biology.

Researchers have produced rice plants that can withstand being completely submerged for up to two weeks. This is good news for farmers in the flood regions of Southeast Asia. The farmers in this region rely heavily on this crop. The diagram below illustrates the process used to genetically modify plants, such as rice.

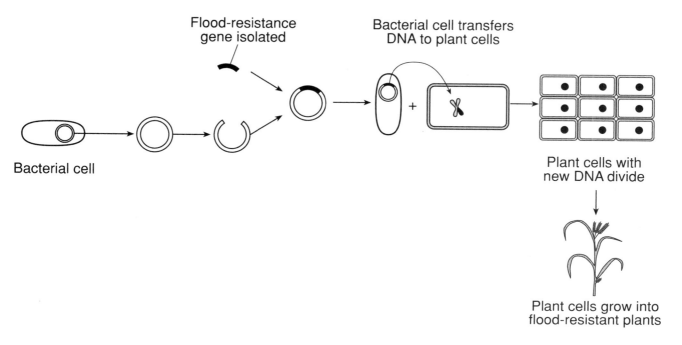

40 The molecules used to cut, copy, and connect the DNA segments used in this process are
(1) sugars
(2) enzymes
(3) indicators
(4) antigens

41 The best explanation for these modified rice plants being flood resistant is that
(1) the gene for flood resistance was inserted into plant cells, which grew into plants whose cells are expressing this gene
(2) they were produced by fertilization, using gametes from two flood-resistant bacterial cells
(3) there was a mutation in the bacterial DNA after it was inserted into the plant that caused it to be flood resistant
(4) the researchers used selective breeding for the flood-resistance trait

42 The diagram below represents two cells viewed using the same magnification with the same microscope.

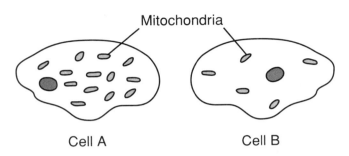

Mitochondria

Cell A   Cell B

One possible conclusion that can be drawn about the activity of these two cells is that

(1) more active transport occurs in cell B than in cell A
(2) more active transport occurs in cell A than in cell B
(3) cell B uses some of the extra mitochondria to make food
(4) cell A is a plant cell since it has a cell wall

43 The diagram below represents the processes leading to the formation of a human embryo.

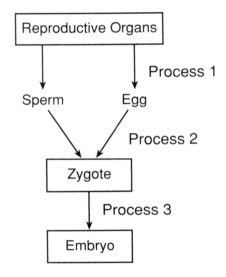

The correct sequence for processes 1, 2, and 3 represented in the diagram is

Row	Process 1	Process 2	Process 3
(1)	gamete formation	cell division	fertilization
(2)	cell division	gamete formation	fertilization
(3)	gamete formation	fertilization	cell division
(4)	fertilization	gamete formation	cell division

June '16   Regents Examination

Part B–2

Answer all questions in this part. [12]

Directions (44–55): For those questions that are multiple choice, record on the separate answer sheet the *number* of the choice that, of those given, best completes each statement or answers each question. For all other questions in this part, follow the directions given and record your answers in the spaces provided in this examination booklet.

Base your answers to questions 44 through 47 on the information and data table below and on your knowledge of biology.

For most animals, the sex of the offspring is determined by sex chromosomes. In some species of reptiles, such as the painted turtle, there are no sex chromosomes. It has been discovered that the sex of the offspring is determined by the temperature of the nest in which the egg develops.

Sex of Painted Turtle Offspring at Various Nest Temperatures

Temperature (°C)	Sex of Offspring	
	Males (%)	Females (%)
19	0	100
20	5	95
21	20	80
22	25	75
23	0	100
24	0	100
25	0	100

Directions (44–46): Using the information in the data table, construct a line graph on the grid below following the directions below.

44 Mark an appropriate scale, without any breaks in the data, on each axis. [1]

45 Plot the data for percent males on the grid. Connect the points and surround each point with a small circle. [1]

Example: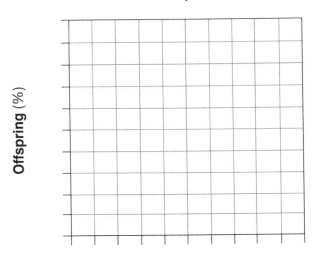

46 Plot the data for percent females on the grid. Connect the points and surround each point with a small triangle. [1]

Example:

Sex of Painted Turtles at Various Nest Temperatures

Offspring (%)

Temperature (°C)

Key	
⊙	Males
△	Females

Note: The answer to question 47 should be recorded on your separate answer sheet.

47 The fact that the sex of the painted turtle offspring is controlled by the temperature of the nest is an example of

(1) natural selection causing a new species to form
(2) a predator-prey interaction

(3) habitat destruction decreasing biodiversity
(4) environment modifying gene expression

Base your answers to questions 48 through 50 on the information and graphs below and on your knowledge biology. The graphs represent the results of two investigations using leaf disks from spinach plants.

Small disks were cut from spinach leaves that had been treated to remove any air from inside the leaf. The disks were placed in a solution that allowed them to carry out photosynthesis. At first, all the disks sank to the bottom of the container. These disks were then used for two different investigations.

Investigation 1

The disks were divided into five groups. Each group was exposed to light of a different intensity, measured in watts per meter squared (W/m^2). Some of the disks began to float. The results of the first investigation are shown in the graph below.

State the relationship between increasing light intensity and the percentage of disks floating at the conclusion of Investigation 1. [1]

_____

_____

Note: The answer to question 49 should be recorded on your separate answer sheet.

The substance produced inside the leaf disks that caused them to float to the surface of the solution is

(1) ozone
(2) oxygen

(3) water
(4) nitrogen

Investigation 2

A number of freshly prepared disks were placed in five containers. These containers were then each exposed to light of a different color. The results of the second investigation are shown in the graph below.

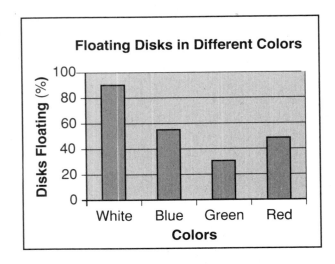

Floating Disks in Different Colors

Disks Floating (%) vs *Colors* (White, Blue, Green, Red)

Note: The answer to question 50 should be recorded on your separate answer sheet.

50 Which color of light appears to be *least* effective for photosynthesis in spinach leaves?
    (1) white
    (2) blue
    (3) green
    (4) red

Base your answer to question 51 on the information and photograph below and on your knowledge of biology. The photograph shows an oriental hornet.

Oriental hornets are unique insects. A yellow pigment in the body of the insect converts solar energy to electrical energy. Plants also convert energy from the Sun.

— Yellow pigment

51 Identify the organelle present in plants where this conversion takes place.   [1]

_____

_____

June '16   Regents Examination

Base your answer to question 52 on the information below and on your knowledge of biology.

The SUNY Solar Car Model Racing Team's Sunhawk: Car of the Future?

The Sunhawk, a car built by students at SUNY New Paltz, prompted Forbes Magazine to ask "Is The $250,000 Sunhawk the Solar Car of the Future?" These cars show the most advanced solar technology and vehicle construction.

52 There are trade-offs involved in the use of solar-powered cars. Provide *one* advantage and *one* disadvantage of owning a solar car. [1]

Advantage: _____

Disadvantage: _____

Base your answer to question 53 on the information below and on your knowledge of biology.

Ten years ago, scientists discovered a well-preserved set of dinosaur remains in China. This dinosaur, which walked on Earth about 125 million years ago, had feathers and was about the same size as a turkey — but don't be fooled. This dino's bite was a lot worse than a turkey's gobble. After a close (and careful!) examination of the dino's teeth, scientists recently concluded that this dinosaur was probably poisonous. The study was led by David Burnham, who works and teaches at the University of Kansas in Lawrence.

Source: www.sciencenewsforkids.org

53 State *one* inference that could be made based on the fact that this dinosaur had feathers. [1]

_____

_____

Base your answers to questions 54 and 55 on the photograph and information below and on your knowledge of biology.

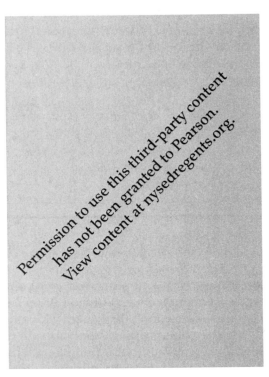

A Great Larvae Meal

New Caledonian crows consume a wide range of foods. These crows require tools to extract the larvae of wood boring beetles from their burrows. A bird pokes a larva with a stick until the larva is disturbed enough to bite the stick and hang on to it. The bird is then able to pull the larva out of its burrow. These larvae, with their unusual diet, have a distinct chemical that can be found in the feathers and blood of crows—allowing scientists to determine the percentage of the crows' diet that is made up of beetle larvae. Scientists found that the beetle larvae are so energy-rich that just a few could satisfy the daily energy requirement for a crow. The crows with the greatest skill in using a twig as a tool benefit most in terms of nutrition.

54 State *one* reason why the offspring of crows skilled at using twigs as tools would have the greatest chance of survival. [1]

_____

_____

55 State *one* reason why some members of a population of crows equally skilled in the use of twigs have different rates of survival. [1]

_____

_____

June '16 Regents Examination

Part C

Answer all questions in this part. [17]

Directions (56–72): Record your answers in the spaces provided in this examination booklet.

Base your answer to question 56–57 on the information below and on your knowledge of biology.

African violet plants are grown for their delicate, colorful flowers and furry, soft leaves. People often want to touch the leaves and brush the hairy leaves with their fingers. Growers and plant owners were concerned that this could negatively affect the plant. Of particular concern was the presence of body lotion or other skin products on the hands of persons touching the leaves.

A student thought this might be the basis of a science project. He selected two African violet plants. Ten leaves on each of the two plants were brushed with a gloved hand for 30 seconds, once a day, for a period of five days. The difference was that leaves of the second plant were brushed with a gloved hand that had hand lotion applied to the glove.

56–57 As part of the peer review process, evaluate the student's experiment. As part of your evaluation, be sure to:

- state *one* possible hypothesis for the experiment proposed by the student [1]
- describe the type of data that should be collected to determine if the brushing with lotion was having a *negative* effect on the African violet plant [1]

_____

_____

_____

_____

_____

Base your answers to questions 58 and 59 on the information and chart below and on your knowledge of biology.

Scientists studied the distribution of a species of pocket mouse that lived in the sandy desert regions of the southwestern United States. They are eaten by a variety of predators. Pocket mice are active at night, and feed on seeds and grasses. A single female mouse can reproduce several times each year, producing a litter of 3 to 13 offspring each time. Each new litter is considered a generation.

A volcanic eruption that resulted in lava flows changed the color of the area that the mice inhabit from light brown to black. Data from the scientist's research of the population are shown in the chart below.

Changes in Pocket Mouse Fur Color after a Volcanic Eruption

Number of Generations	Percentage of Pocket Mice with Light Brown Fur	Percentage of Pocket Mice with Black Fur
10	95%	5%
25	90%	10%
50	75%	25%
100	5%	95%

58 State the role of mutation *or* recombination in the appearance of the trait for black fur color in the pocket mouse population. [1]

_____

_____

59 Explain why the percentage of black pocket mice changed so much after the volcanic eruption. [1]

_____

_____

Base your answers to questions 60 and 61 on the information below and on your knowledge of biology.

In 2003, as a result of the Human Genome Project, the complete sequence of all the bases in human DNA was released to the public. Although knowing the entire sequence of bases has proven valuable, scientists are currently working to map genes. Mapping genes involves determining the exact location of each gene. Since much of human DNA does not code for a protein, it is challenging to figure out which segments are actual genes. Often, scientists look at the percent composition of bases in a segment of DNA. If the segment of DNA has a large percentage of C and G bases (together over 50%), it is likely that it is a gene and codes for a protein.

60 A scientist analyzes the bases in a segment of DNA from a human skin cell to determine if it codes for a protein. The base A is 12% of the bases in this segment of DNA. Calculate the percentage of bases that would be C. [1]

_____ %

61 Is it likely this segment of DNA codes for a protein? Circle yes or no and support your answer. [1]

Circle one: Yes   or   No

_____

_____

_____

Base your answers to questions 62 through 64 on the illustration and information below and on your knowledge of biology. The illustration is of a Tasmanian devil.

Source: http://www.statelibrary.tas.gov.au

The Tasmanian devil is the largest surviving carnivorous marsupial in Australia. It is in danger of extinction due to an unusual type of cancer called Devil Facial Tumor Disease (DFTD). It can be passed from one individual to another through wounds that occur when they fight over food. Tumor cells in the mouth of an infected animal break off and enter the wound on an uninfected animal. The tumor cells multiply in the body of the newly infected devil, forming new tumors that eventually kill the animal.

Recent research has shown that the immune system of a Tasmanian devil accepts tumor cells from another devil as if they were cells from its own body. The tumor cells are ignored by the immune system. No immune response develops against them, and the cancerous cells multiply. Scientists predict that DFTD could wipe out all the remaining Tasmanian devils in 25 years, unless a treatment is developed.

62 Using the terms antigens and antibodies, explain why the tumor cells are ignored by the immune system in Tasmanian devils. [1]

_____

_____

63 Explain how cancer cells differ from normal cells. [1]

_____

_____

64 Describe *one* possible way to maintain a population of healthy, uninfected Tasmanian devils until treatment or cure can be found. [1]

_____

_____

Base your answers to questions 65 through 67 on the information below and on your knowledge of biology.
The photograph below shows a Canada lynx, a mammal native to North America.

Source: http://www.allposters.com

Lynx are found in areas where there is deep, soft snow cover during the winter months. The body design of the Canada lynx helps keep the animal on top of the soft snow. Several unique characteristics, such as the design of its feet and its weight, enable the cat to successfully chase and catch snowshoe hares, its primary source of food. Snowshoe hares are also able to remain on top of the snow.

Increased winter recreation has created packed snow trails in lynx habitat. This allows coyotes and cougars to compete with lynx.

65 Explain why coyotes were *not* in competition with the lynx prior to the presence of packed snow trails. [1]

_____

_____

66 Describe the niche that the lynx, coyote, and cougar are competing to fill. [1]

_____

_____

67 Explain how the carrying capacity affects the number of predators in an area. [1]

_____

_____

Base your answers to questions 68 and 69 on the information below and on your knowledge of biology.

68 State *one* way that the use of pesticides to kill ticks could lead to the decline of the oxpecker population [1]

_____

_____

69 State *one* ecological advantage of using oxpeckers to solve the problem with these ticks. [1]

_____

_____

Base your answers to questions 70 through 72 on the information below and on your knowledge of biology.

Over the past few decades, researchers have observed declining numbers in two species of penguins native to the West Antarctic peninsula. New evidence is pointing to a decline in their food supply as the primary cause for the recent drops in their numbers. These penguins feed on krill, small animals that grow and develop under ice masses. The graphs below show data related to two factors: atmospheric carbon dioxide (CO_2) levels and Antarctic ice mass. The diagram of a generalized Antarctic food web illustrates the role of the penguins.

Direct CO_2 Measurements: 2005-2011

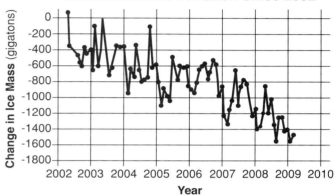

Antarctica Mass Variation Since 2002

Source: http://www.nasa.gov

Permission to use this third-party content has not been granted to Pearson. View content at nysedregents.org.

70 State *one* possible relationship between CO_2 levels and the change in Antarctic ice mass.   [1]

_____

_____

71 Explain why the change in ice mass is resulting in a decline in the penguin populations.   [1]

_____

_____

72 State *one* specific way in which humans might have caused the changes in atmospheric CO_2 levels.   [1

_____

_____

June '16   Regents Examination

Part D

Answer all questions in this part. [13]

Directions (73–85): For those questions that are multiple choice, record on the separate answer sheet the *number* of the choice that, of those given, best completes the statement or answers the question. For all other questions in this part, follow the directions given and record your answers in the spaces provided in this examination booklet.

Base your answers to questions 73 through 75 on the diagram below and on your knowledge of biology. The diagram represents an experimental setup.

Note: The answer to question 73 should be recorded on your separate answer sheet.

73 Which statement best describes what would most likely be observed after 20 minutes?

(1) The contents of the dialysis tube would turn blue-black.
(2) The liquid in the beaker would turn blue-black.
(3) The dialysis tube would burst.
(4) There would be no change visible.

Note: The answer to question 74 should be recorded on your separate answer sheet.

74 Which term correctly identifies the process by which molecules move through the dialysis tube membrane?

(1) paper chromatography
(2) active transport
(3) diffusion
(4) digestion

Note: The answer to question 75 should be recorded on your separate answer sheet.

75 A student filled a dialysis tube with 97% water solution and sealed the ends. The tube and its contents had a mass of 55 grams. The student placed the tube in a solution, and the mass of the tube and its contents increased to 60 grams. Into which solution was the dialysis tube placed?

(1) 0% water
(2) 95% water
(3) 97% water
(4) 99% water

[26]

Base your answers to questions 76 and 77 on the information and diagram below and on your knowledge of biology.

Scientists attempted to determine the evolutionary relationships between three different finch species, A, B, and C. In order to do this, they examined the physical characteristics and DNA of these species. DNA was extracted from all three species and analyzed using gel electrophoresis. The results are shown in the diagram.

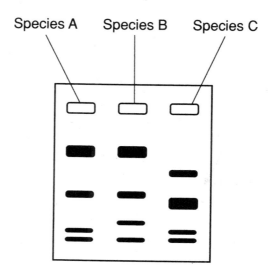

Note: The answer to question 76 should be recorded on your separate answer sheet.

76 Which statement best describes the method used above to determine the evolutionary relationships between three species of finches?

(1) Examine the structure of the beaks and compare them.
(2) Observe behavioral and physical characteristics of all the finches and group them by similarities.
(3) Obtain molecular evidence from all three species and identify similarities.
(4) Compare common ancestors of all three of the species to see if they are the same.

77 Based on the data they collected using gel electrophoresis, label the branching tree diagram below. Write the letters A, B, and C, to represent the possible evolutionary relationships between species A, B, and C. [1]

June '16   Regents Examination

Base your answers to questions 78 through 80 on the information and diagram below and on your knowledge of biology.

Two species of finches found on a particular Galapagos island eat the seeds of a certain variety of plant. The relative strength of their beaks is shown in the graph below.

Beak Strength of Two Finch Species

Key
——— Species 1
- - - - Species 2

Relative Number of Individuals

Increasing Beak Strength

78 One of the finch species has a slightly smaller, weaker beak. Is this species 1 or species 2? Support your answer with information from the graph. [1]

Species: _____

_____

_____

79 Select the point on the graph where beak strength of the two bird species is equal. Support your answer. [1]

Point: _____

_____

_____

80 If the environment on the island changed and the seeds of more of the plants became harder to crack open, describe what the graph might look like after many years have passed. [1]

_____

_____

_____

Base your answers to questions 81 and 82 on the information and diagram below and on your knowledge of biology.

Using a microscope and a wet-mount slide, a student observed a pond water sample containing paramecia, which are single-celled freshwater organisms. He noticed that there was a structure within each living paramecium that contracted regularly—about four times each minute. He researched the organism in his science textbook and found that the structure was a contractile vacuole and its function was to remove excess water from the paramecium.

In the diagram below, a paramecium is represented as seen through a microscope. The function of the contractile vacuole is described.

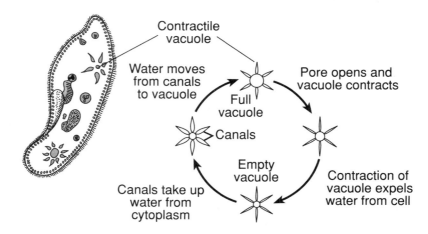

He decided to determine if the concentration of salt in the environment of the paramecium would affect the rate at which the contractile vacuole would contract.

Note: The answer to question 81 should be recorded on your separate answer sheet.

81 The process used to remove excess water from the paramecium by the contractile vacuole is

(1) synthesis
(2) digestion
(3) active transport
(4) passive transport

Note: The answer to question 82 should be recorded on your separate answer sheet.

82 The student predicted that the contractile vacuole would contract fewer times in one minute in a solution that had a higher concentration of salt than that found in typical pond water. This prediction is most likely

(1) correct, because a high concentration of salt in the environment will force water into the cell, causing the contractile vacuole to pump
(2) incorrect, because salt would be entering the cell, and the contractile vacuole would have to pump it out
(3) incorrect, because the concentration of salt in the environment should not affect a cell
(4) correct, because water would be moving out of the cell into the salt solution

June '16   Regents Examination

Base your answers to questions 83 through 85 on the information below and on your knowledge of biology.

Five individuals had their pulses taken in beats per minute (bpm) before and after exercise. The data are shown in the chart below.

Pulse Rates

Individual	Pulse before Exercise (bpm)	Pulse after Exercise (bpm)
A	68	100
B	70	120
C	54	130
D	64	122
E	75	115

83 State *one* reason why an individual's pulse rate increased during exercise. [1]

_____

_____

84 Calculate the average pulse rate *before* exercise for this group, to the *nearest tenth*. [1]

_____ **bpm**

85 State why the individuals in this group have different pulse rates before exercise. [1]

_____

_____

_____